"This book may change your life"

Lord Cullen

# Total
# Safety Culture

## Organisational Risk Literacy

Dr. Tim Marsh

RYDERMARSH

i

Published by
Ryder Marsh Safety Limited
21 York Road
Chorlton
MANCHESTER
M21 9HP

www.rydermarsh.co.uk

A CIP catalogue record for this book is available from the British Library

ISBN 978-0-9570912-1-4

Cover design, Illustrations and Layout by AZZZA Limited

Printed and Published in the UK

# Dedication:

For Debbie - whose father would be proud of her

# Acknowledgements:

I would like to thank the former editor of the Safety and Health Practitioner, Tina Weadick, for her patient proofreading and many constructive observations. I'd also like to thank my business partner Paul Bizzell and the rest of the Ryder Marsh team whose hard work taking care of business allowed me the time and space to write. Finally, I must thank the management of the Jumerei hotel chain who kindly allowed me to stay on in one of their gorgeous hotels after working with them so that I could finish the book.

I must also thank Lord Cullen for his extremely kind comment. Looked at closely it's clear that the wily old legal eagle left himself some wriggle room here based as it is on previous work (and presentations) not the (new) book in question. However, that doesn't matter as it works as an excellent illustration of what much of this book is about – namely the power and resonance of words and gestures. It's positive, it's Lord Cullen so it's bloody well on the cover!

# Chief Executive's Introduction

IIRSM has worked closely with Tim since producing Affective Safety Management (ASM) together in 2008. ASM had an overwhelmingly positive response to the launch event and the book has recently had it's sixth print run.

We tagged that book 'The next step in safety leadership'; Over the intervening five years Tim has built developed some new models to complement the principles in ASM which broaden the scope and offer some additional tools to the practitioner. We hope then that this book will give you a lift.

Therefore, as Chief Executive of IIRSM, I am pleased to endorse this latest book. I trust that you find the style accessible and the content a stimulus to new thinking about how you manage your risks.

**Phillip Pearson**
**Chief Executive IIRSM**
**May 2014**

# About the Author:

Tim Marsh was one of the team leaders of the original UK research into behavioural safety in the early 1990s and is a Chartered Psychologist and a Chartered Fellow of IOSH.

He has worked with more than 400 organisations around the world since including the European Space Agency and the BBC. He now specialises in safety leadership and organisational culture assessment & change.

Tim developed and ran open courses on Behavioural Safety and Safety Culture for IOSH, was awarded a 'President's Commendation' in 2008 by the International Institute of Risk and Safety Management and was selected to be their first ever 'Specialist Fellow' in 2010.

The author of several bestselling books Tim is a regular contributor to magazines including the Safety and Health Practitioner and Health and Safety at Work.

Tim has a reputation as a lively and engaging speaker and has presented at dozens of conferences around the world as well as regularly chairing them.

In 2014 he was invited to give the key note address at the Campell Institute symposium in Florida.

Ryder Marsh Safety Limited can be contacted via their website:

www.rydermarsh.co.uk

or by email at

info@rydermarsh.co.uk

The book seeks broadly to follow the simple 3 x 3 model outlined in the introduction. First, we'll look at the various well-known models of organisational safety culture to set the scene. We'll see that culture is really all about 'norms' of behaviour – 'what people do around here' – so the first interlink with the individual is explicit.

The next chapter addresses seven topics that allow us to increase our risk literacy. It covers the **Safety Triangle**; the **Safety Hierarchy** and Reason's **Cheese Model**; Reason's **Just Culture,** ABC analysis, Dekker's '**New View'** of human error, and specifically the **fundamental attribution error**. Finally, some notes on the **Limitations of Training** and **Lead** and Lagging Measures.

A chapter on the **business** case for safety is followed by a chapter looking more closely at the strengths and weaknesses **individuals** bring to the party. There follows a chapter looking at the **interaction of perception and behaviour** then one looking at the use of **NLP** and other **person centred approaches** to safety. A chapter on **leadership** skills is followed by an explicit look at the **management 'walk and talk'** and finally there is a chapter summarising the practical **methodologies** of culture change – an attempt to draw all the arguments together with an overview of what an organisation needs to do to strive for world class.

# Contents

## Chapter 9
## **The Management 'Walk and Talk'** *p. 233*

## Chapter 10
## **Applying these Principles via a Robust Holistic Methodological Framework** *p. 247*

## **References** *p. 261*

# List of Illustrations

# Introduction

The past few decades have been something of a golden age for safety management. Here in the UK we have reached a level where, despite a population of around 60 million, deaths from accidents at work are currently running at fewer than 200 a year, (In 1974, when the Health and Safety at Work, etc. Act was introduced it was around 650, while back in 1910 it was around 12,000). This is an achievement to be proud of and must, by definition, represent a huge amount of excellent work by hundreds of major corporations that many would normally assume are run by fat cats 'grinding their workers into the dirt', with scant regard for safety. Even better, many researchers and academics have been able to articulate clearly how we can push on significantly from here to even higher standards and come closer to the fabled 'zero'; several case studies mentioned in this book reference companies that have had zero-incident months – or years – for the first time ever.

I must add a few caveats to these positive words, however. The first, of course, is that 'fewer than 200' still means around 300 children will spend next Christmas without a parent who was with them the Christmas just past. Then there are the thousands of workers who will suffer 'life changing injuries', which, in plain English, means the likes of the loss of a limb, brain damage, or paralysis. Inspirational speakers, like the late Ian Whittingham, Jason Anker and Ken Woodward, articulate, with real power, exactly what that can mean to families.

We also need to consider the individuals who die on the roads on their way to work as, rather shamefully, they're not counted in official figures in the UK. Next, we must consider the workers who die driving to the shops on the weekend. While this is nothing to do with their employer – unless they are being worked to exhaustion, or are travelling in a badly maintained company car – we can still agree they're not likely to be much use to 'UK plc' on Monday morning, so employers have a vested interest in reducing this figure, too.

All combined, that's another 2000 deaths or so.

When we add 'life-changing injuries' on the roads to the figures above we get into decent-sized, football-crowd numbers. That's a lot of blood and tears, and no one is going to be closing any UK accident and emergency facilities any time soon for lack of work. Thankfully, the UK is near the top of the table in terms of the lowest number of work-related deaths and major injuries – qualifying for the Champions League year after year, if not winning it. In most of the countries in which this book might be read, you'll need to extrapolate up.

Then, of course, we need to tackle the real 'elephant in the room': occupational illness. The 2012 Rushton report has calculated (not at all controversially) that around **12,000** people a year die in the UK from an occupational illness. Many times that figure will be suffering what is referred to as a 'meaningfully reduced quality of life' – again, in plain English, that means something like wheezing into a portable ventilator for half the day. This means that the number of people unable to join in that game of touch rugby, or cricket at a picnic in the park is now pushingin *six figures* the UK alone.

Finally, we need to add in the individuals who didn't make the picnic because they are still in bed nursing a 'self-medicated' hangover, or *are* at the picnic but who are staring into the distance with their stress levels through the roof because of the way they're treated at work.

The good news is that, as above, there is a lot we can do about this, and the mindset and methodologies that will enable an organisation to contribute to a further step change in safety and health are nearly all *generic*. Good for the individuals. Good for their families. Good for profits.

To move from very good to world class will require, among other things:

> resource use being led by hard data and objective analysis;

> excellent communication and 'soft' skills (or 'non-technical') as standard throughout the company – especially in front-line management;

> enhanced understanding of the human factor at work and why errors (of any sort) occur;

> maximal workforce empowerment and involvement in job design and planning; and frequent empathic 'brother's keeper' behaviours.

It's not just about good systems; you simply can't get to a high level of performance in these areas without addressing 'soft issues', and these skills won't just be applied to safety – or even to safety and health and well-being. This is just *general* excellence – and that's good for everyone.

In very many companies the commitment is there to back up the words "We want to make a profit but, genuinely, without hurting anyone". Although many companies have pockets of excellence what is often missing is the practical understanding of what needs to be done *holistically* – top to bottom and on a day-to-day basis, as an on-going process, so that it embeds as "the way we do things around here" not as the way we'd *like* to do things around here.

## The Simplicity of Safety and Health

One of the UK's most respected safety presenters, Ian Whittingham MBE, used to say in all his talks that safety is simple, really; and I honestly think that safety *is* a simple concept. There hasn't yet been an accident in history that we can't find a simple way of preventing, with the benefit of hindsight. Even with 'catastrophic' acts of nature, it is often clear that obvious opportunities to minimise the impact of them were missed. For example, there has been criticism of the Japanese authorities' failure to apply the extremely basic 'what if?' question prior to the earthquake and the nuclear events at Fukushima in 2011. It's also clear that the choice not to commission an effective early warning system before the Boxing Day *tsunami* of 2004 was the very definition of a false economy. Even on the day itself the half decent use of the communication systems that *were* available would have saved countless lives.

Two *simple* truisms:-

> "You get the level of safety standards that your actions show you really want – not what you say you want. All else is just detail and case study."

And:

> "Your organisation is, by definition, perfectly tailored, funded and resourced to deliver the safety standards that you are getting right **now**. If you want to change that output you are going to have to change something about the input."

Another simple saying is "past; present; future", which reminds us that while we must learn from our mistakes we also need to be proactive. We must have a clearly defined vision of the future towards which we are working day by day. Having an overall target of 'zero harm', or halving the accident injury rate to 0.5 is certainly necessary but it's certainly not sufficient. We will achieve little with the goal alone unless today's *plans* and *actions* aren't driving us inexorably *towards* that goal, behaviour by behaviour.

I need to acknowledge at this early stage that while writing a book describing what needs to be done to achieve a world-class safety culture is relatively straightforward, actually going out and *doing* it as an organisation is rather harder. A simple framework is a good start.

# A Suggested Holistic Framework

All organisations should adopt an explicitly holistic approach, and a robust definition of holistic for me is to make sure we tackle any problem from at least two angles: "tough on crime but also tough on the causes of crime", as the former UK Prime Minister Tony Blair used to say. Mind you he used to say a lot of things! However, in safety and health I'd argue it shouldn't be 'top down' *or* 'bottom up' but 'top down' and *also* 'bottom up'.

A holistic approach can help avoid some of the more obvious pitfalls of a one-sided approach. For example, I once worked with an organisation with excellent systems that were well embedded. The '80:20 principle' tipping point had long been passed and diminishing returns had most definitely set in. However, most of their efforts were geared towards enhancing these systems further, and they were happily working with generalist consultants who were being paid a small fortune to identify improvement opportunities in their *already excellent* systems.

The safety department itself was also excellent in technical knowledge but was a huge problem for *political* reasons. Worried about internal politics they fought desperately to control the agenda and were very uncomfortable rolling out the soft skills training that was an obvious need, as that would have meant ceding some control to HR. For similar reasons they also sought control of the 'train the trainer' methodology we'd agreed but without anyone in their department having the time to be trained by us, let alone to then cascade the learning. They were genuinely very busy 'doing safety' for the organisation, which isn't an entirely positive thing – as we'll see.

The point is, however, that they were hopelessly myopic. Overly concerned with the detail (and how the detail would look politically) they had completely lost sight of the bigger goal. They agreed with us in meetings, of course (nobody wants to be the one who causes the consultants to walk away in this blame culture) but we could get nothing done at all once we left these meetings. They said they wanted to empower the workforce but really only if they could do that *for* the workforce. Likewise, they desperately needed to move beyond a systems obsession but sought to achieve this through endless meetings and the production of even more paperwork and procedures. If I had any business nous at all I'd have simply sat one of our consultants in an office, reviewing paperwork and writing endless reports (and invoices!).

You can't move forward from broad compliance by being even better at compliance.

A problem from the other side of the fence is that we've seen organisations where the management team has been reduced to tears by an inspirational speaker, a piece of safety theatre, or even some leading-edge social psychology. The call is made loudly that "**this is great** - **everyone must see this!**" and a roll-out to all staff is planned immediately. Unfortunately, there are no simple 'magic bullets' and although such individually focused sessions can have a dramatic effect in the short-term, in the medium to long-term nothing will change if the environment stays the same and slowly, *or not so slowly*, the organisation will return to traditional standards.

This simple framework suggested below aims at ensuring that the cultural improvement plan is neither too systems nor politics-focused and not too person-focused either. It aims to blend the best research on general leadership (for example, Thaler and Sunstein's 'nudge' theory and Cialdini's research on influencing skills) with the best of 'Just Culture' and human factors writing from James Reason, Sidney Dekker, Andrew Hopkins, and others). It is cross-referenced with Azjen's classic theory of planned behaviour, which explains why individuals do what they do.

Its aim is a very simple one: to help stop organisations investing time and effort in a safety initiative that, for whatever reason, takes them off at a tangent in one direction only. To use a rugby analogy, it is no use whatsoever charging off on a brilliant run sideways with the ball tucked under your arm and making it 40 yards across the field only to be felled by the opposition well away from any support from your team mates. The opposition now has the ball (and in plenty of space, too) and my team is on the defensive.

Individual brilliance is of little use if it's not part of an overall strategy. The very best teams use all 15 players – they don't just keep the ball in the pack of forwards and let the fleet-footed backs stand in the cold, watching. You might well grind out a winning result, just as a tight systems focus might keep you out of court, but it's boring and uninspiring. You won't score as many points as you could have done and it's no fun to be around. World-class culture as 'total rugby', perhaps?!

# A Holistic Culture Model

An organisation's level of risk can be determined by three things:

Its **systems** and procedures (selection, induction training, monitoring, auditing, risk assessments and job safety audits);

The quality of its **learning** from a Just Culture perspective, i.e. how objective, analytical and (as often as feasible) *proactive* it is in identifying the weaknesses that are *inevitably* present in even good systems and procedures); and

The quality of its **leadership**, which can be broken down into the following sub elements:

Communicating a genuinely desired vision;

Leading by example;

Coaching rather than telling (most specifically, using praise whenever feasible and drawing out 'discovered' learning);

Maximising workforce involvement and empowerment;

Challenging when required (as in the truism 'walking past is condoning'); and

Measuring what matters and making those measures matter (as in 'what gets measured gets done' and 'if we can measure, it we can manage it').

As well as traditional audits we can measure all of these things with checksheets, observations and simple behaviourally-anchored 360 degree feedback scales.

This is great, as far as it goes, and allows us to identify where we are weak. However, this book is all about helping organisations improve and, ideally, we need something more sophisticated than 'let's do more of that, then and/or do it better' (though that's a decent place to start!).

## A Wider View

As a psychologist it's in my DNA to look everything from at from at least *two* angles and, so far, we've talked very much about the organisation but organisations are simply a collection of *individuals*. The really obvious second angle of view, therefore,

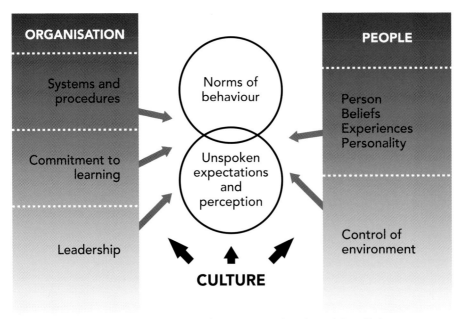

**Figure 1. A Holistic Culture Model** With acknowledgement to Azjen's classic theory of planned behaviour

is to talk about the *individual's* view of all this. The simple model that pulls them together is Ajzen's model of 'planned behaviour'. This version of the classic academic model says that in order to understand why a person has done what they have done, we simply need to know about three things:

The individual person;
The general and local norms; and
The control the person has over their environment.

You'll note that in my model the norms are in the middle reflecting the fact that they are influenced by both the individual and the organisation.

First, what about the **individual?** What is their attitude generally and to the situation at hand specifically? For example:

Are they health conscious?
Are they fatalistic?
Are they trained?
Are they naturally conscientious?
What past experiences have they been through?

The second factor considers **norms**.

What are the universal norms and/or in this particular society generally?
What are the norms among this specific person's peers?

In particular, what are the unspoken assumptions and subconscious perceptions that determine so much of day-to-day behaviour?

For example, norms regarding smoking, racism and homophobia have changed hugely among the general UK population over the past 20 years or so, but among specific sub-groups they can still vary a great deal. The general societal shift in relation to these issues might not be reflected among a group in the smoke shack outside the clubhouse of the right wing British National Party.

The final factor is **control**, or **perceived control**.

This is the most obvious linking bridge to the organisational issues above and is where many of the problems occur. It is where our safety aware employees know *what* to do but can't realistically do it under the environmental circumstances in which they find themselves. This book is heavily anchored around James Reason's principles of 'Just Culture', which addresses this link directly. What I also want to address, however, is the grey area that surrounds not the 'I physically can't' aspect (utterly vital though that is) but also the issues of perception and social psychology. Specifically where an individual technically *could* act safely but doesn't because of more nebulous factors.

I've often found myself saying to investigative teams that, OK, they could have done

X or not done Y, but in their shoes on that day we would have done exactly the same. As Prof Sidney Dekker has stressed, the proactive removal of hindsight bias is utterly central to understanding objectively why individuals act the way they do on a given day and also to allow us to predict in advance how they are likely to act.

Even more interesting to me is the mindset about *regaining* control to put the world back in balance that affects more proactive, or 'above the line' behaviours (sometimes called 'citizenship behaviour'). This is where: "I *could* choose to do it but you have no chance of that happening because the way you treat me really ticks me off".

To illustrate this simple framework I need some heavyweight support, so I'd like to call in 'The Godfather' and reference the world's (second) most performed playwright, Henrik Ibsen.

**Michael Corleone.** In the film 'The Godfather' the decision of the character Michael Corleone to shoot his father's rival and a corrupt policemen illustrates how these factors interplay.

Initially, though a trained and skilled killer from his WW2 army experiences, Michael is influenced by society's norms in general and is considered the 'war-hero *civilian*'. His brother Sonny is very much the prince in waiting, as far as the family business is concerned. However, Michael finds himself in a situation where he realises that action needs to be taken to protect his father, that he personally is capable of taking that action, and, moreover, that *only* he has the opportunity to take this action. He dramatically shifts to operating from *societal* norms to the *local* norms of the Corleone family – and it makes for an Oscar winning film.

In particular, Michael first suggests the plan of action Sonny dismisses the idea as ridiculous, chuckling: "You? Ha!" and exchanges smirks with the others in the room. Aristotle said that humour is merely common sense speeded up and this simple dismissal is a succinct articulation of the unspoken and often subconscious perceptions that so often rule our behaviour. However, when Sonny thinks about Michael's proposal in more depth, he stops laughing and realises his brother is making sense.

This is just a film, of course, but when the BP employee articulated concerns about a 'bladder effect' explanation for the worrying pressure readings on Macondo (Deepwater Horizon) he was silenced when his colleagues from other companies chuckled and teased him for his 'overcaution'. Reports comment that his concerns were met with 'robust humour'.

Smirks and scoffs and raised eyebrows have led to countless fatalities over the years around the world and a key argument of this book is that subtle assumptions and perceptions that lead us to these sorts of mindset are largely unarticulated but are utterly central to any culture.

**Ibsen's 'A Doll's House'.** In one of the most performed plays of all time (Ibsen's 'A Doll's House') the female lead kicks against the norms of society by wanting to be her own woman and not just the chattel of her husband. In the final dramatic scene she walks out on the uncomprehending husband *and* her children to start a new life alone and on her own terms. As you can imagine, this was a very controversial piece at the time (Denmark in 1878), as it went very much against existing norms. What's most interesting to me, however, is what happened to the *actual* person (a friend of Ibsen), whose need to 'find herself' inspired the play. In *reality*, although her actions weren't illegal they simply weren't accepted at all and she was promptly locked in a psychiatric hospital for a couple of years.

Similarly, two recent infamous suicides in the UK illustrate the point that violating *norms* can have more serious consequences than violating rules. The nurse who committed suicide after the infamous Kate Windsor hoax phone call from the Australian disc jockeys wasn't reprimanded, as she hadn't broken any rules. But she was devastated because she felt she had 'let people down'.

Similarly, in 2013, the UK press reported the suicide of a Royal Society for the Prevention of Cruelty to Animals charity worker. People who work for low pay in charity organisations tend to take the psychological contract even more seriously than most. In her case, she very much resented the fact that her charity occasionally put down healthy dogs if homes could not be found for them (some charities, like the 'Dogs Trust', make it a point that they never do) so she went to the press. The organisation reacted angrily and a press release from them in response to her story referred to her as nothing but a "disgruntled former employee" and alluded darkly to an outstanding charge of theft. (She'd taken a sickly tortoise home to nurse it, but without permission). It is, of course, too simplistic to conclude that this rather spiteful press release directly *caused* the suicide but it certainly didn't help her state of mind at all.

The point is that whether on the shop floor, in the mafia, or even in a charity organisation we take 'not telling' as a golden unwritten rule, and breaking *these* 'rules' often elicits more disapproval and opprobrium than breaking *actual* rules. If we want to understand why people do what they do, we don't just want to know how they are *supposed* to perceive things according to the book – we need to understand how they *actually* perceive things because, often, the two may be very different.

There are examples of this principle everywhere. In the 2013 Trent Bridge Test cricket match between England and Australia, Stuart Broad stood his ground when the umpire missed that he'd *very* clearly hit the ball and was caught out. He didn't say "I didn't hit it" – he just stood there and left it to the umpire. Some months earlier, the West Indies wicket-keeper Ramadin failed to catch a ball that everyone assumed he had caught – until replays showed what had happened. Again, he didn't say anything when he realised that no one had spotted that he'd fumbled it. Neither of these men lied – they simply didn't speak up and tell the mistaken umpire the truth.

The vastly different reaction to the two events gives a perfect example of the core of the hugely influential book by the Nobel Prize winning Daniel Kahneman, *Thinking, Fast and Slow*. The response to Broad was widespread shrugging and chuckling at the irony (Australia virtually invented and perfected this professional, hard-nosed attitude to cricket and many jokes were made about the 'biter being bit' and chickens coming home to roost). Ramadin's act, on the other hand, was met with worldwide disgust and he was banned from all forms of cricket for some months.

Indeed, illustrating the point, the esteemed West Indian commentator Michael Holding pointed out that, logically, the two acts were the same and the in public response was hugely inconsistent. The response to him from other commentators on the day (and the media) was, effectively: "I can't argue with your logic, Michael" but then they shrugged and moved on. Because in cricket, batsmen who don't confess are fine but fielders who don't are despised. *That's just the way it is.* (Simon Barnes, writing in the *Sunday Times*, suggested this has its basis firmly in the English class system, with batsmen the 'toffs' and fielders the 'serfs' – but that's a different book.)

Basically, in an attempt to defend a compatriot, Michael Holding attempted to apply 'slow' (logical) thinking to a situation that was dominated by 'fast' (instinctive) thinking. For me, the key point is that everyone politely acknowledged his *logic* as correct – then ignored him. The best organisations look for situations where logic doesn't apply.

Sometimes, however, instinctive reactions are very *helpful* to a safety culture.

## Rosa Parks and Civil Rights

Rosa Parks' role in the civil rights movement in the US is an excellent example of people behaving in an unexpectedly *positive* way. Again, this was driven by largely subconscious psychology. I'm very much hoping you'll think at the end of the example: "I didn't know that but it makes perfect sense now I think about it. I'd have acted that way, too."

Most people will know that Rosa Parks was the black woman who refused to give up seat on a bus in Montgomery, Alabama in 1955, thereby effectively starting the US Civil Rights movement. Indeed, I live in a politically aware part of Manchester and one of my daughter's friends is named after her.

What is perhaps less well known is that that Rosa was far from the first person to make such a stand and get arrested. Her arrest was different because it was the first one to spark mass protest in a population that even Martin Luther King had described at the time as "frustratingly accepting and fatalistic" of the status quo.

What was different about Rosa wasn't just that she was a nice woman who was widely liked by all that met her – it was that she met a lot people and these people came from all elements of Montgomery life. Malcolm Gladwell, in his hugely influential book *The Tipping Point*, would call her a 'connector'. As well as being on any number of committees she made dresses for the children of many of the rich and powerful, for example. In simple terms, when the first phone calls were made saying "Rosa has been arrested" and "can you help?", nearly everyone said "yes" and *acted*.

This is because when you meet someone, they go from being a stranger to a *casual acquaintance* and, as described by Charels Duhigg in *The Power of Habit*, that can make all the difference in the world because studies have shown that we often respond behaviourally to casual acquaintances as strongly as we respond to friends – e.g., when we're asked to endorse someone on a networking site like 'LinkedIn'. In fact, we can be even 'better behaved' for acquaintances in some cases, as we know well this is an early 'critical incident' in our burgeoning relationship! We will return to this issue when talking about the importance of management walking the worksite.

## Applying this Model – Risk Literacy

This brings us to the concept of 'Risk Literacy'. It's said that all risk assessments should boil down to: "I'm worried that X might happen because of Y, and that Z will result so therefore, and allowing for the likelihood of it happening, I've decided to do (or not do) ABC." It's the quality and thoroughness of *thinking* that counts. Certainly, when things go wrong lawyers are on the lookout for surprises that suggest a lack of thought. Reflecting this, risk assessment gurus often chant the mantra: "Our ultimate aim – no surprises!" whether we're talking about financial risk, public-relations risk, or technical issues, such as fire.

There are many excellent books on these topics and this is an attempt squarely to address *cultural and behavioural* risks. Our ability to manage risk has an upper limit set by the objectivity of our analysis as to what's happened, what's likely to happen, and why.

Most people are aware that the HSE and others would suggest that "95 per cent of incidents are caused by behaviour" and that it is 100 per cent if we include management decisions and design issues (see Collins and Keeley's 2003 study of offshore incidents, for example). This book will, I hope add to the number of books that have shown that culture is all pervasive and influences everything, as so many infamous disasters have shown. Perhaps the main aim of this book, therefore, is to leave the reader broadly risk literate about the interaction and overlap between individual behaviour, organisations and culture.

It's an area that is infinitely complex and contradictory, of course, but it's not entirely impossible to make predictions because though people are hugely complex and unpredictable they are often so in a very predictable way (as Thaler and Sunstien, authors of 'Nudge', observed). And often, as the Rosa Parks example shows, these influences are so obvious we can't see them – like the proverbial wood obscured by the leafy trees.

## The Importance of Considering the Obvious When Predicting Behaviour

As a young psychology undergraduate my first-ever psychology experiment caused a bit of controversy in the department and a punch-up on the road side but I think it illustrates a robust approach to the subject of woods and trees.

In an early tutorial, we were discussing the 'positive helping model' and how, if people have seen an example of someone helping and are then presented with an opportunity to help soon afterwards, they are statistically more likely to take that chance to help. The classic experiment (run by Hornstein and others in 1968) was to have someone appear to have pulled up to help a woman change a car tyre on the side of the road and then have a similar woman a mile further along also needing help – spare wheel and jack out and the woman staring at the tools as if uncertain what to do.

It was suggested by one of the men "that whether she's attractive or not must be more important, you'd think". Adjudicating the heated debate that followed between the male and female students the tutor suggested that instead of arguing about it why not put this view to the test?

Consequently, Hull Police were informed and the experiment was set up. In the first run, a friend of mine at the time was dressed in jeans and trainers, hair in a ponytail and no make-up. Twelve out of 600 cars stopped. In the second run, we placed the positive helping model a mile down the straight road with no turn offs and this increased to 19 out of 600 cars, which is indeed a statistically significant increase, replicating Hornstein's research. In the third run, however, my friend Alison gamely got herself dressed up in a mini dress with heels, make-up and the 'big hair' style popular in the 1980s (do you remember Bucks Fizz or Bonnie Tyler?)

We never got to the 600-car sample as we stopped the experiment after around 450, when a punch-up developed between 'stopees' 50 and 51. This was because 50 was reversing back when 51 cheekily and rather dangerously pulled in front of him and gestured: "Ha, too slow my friend!" at him. After we sorted that out and as we packed away, one of the drivers that had stopped earlier came back with his wife – having implored her to verify that he was always a helpful type and not a 'dirty old man'. I'm sure he wasn't a dirty old man (though maybe he 'protesteth too much'?) but *something* was making a big difference to people's behaviour!

Such early experiences left me with the view that we need to step back, take a broad view and *never* ignore the 'bleeding obvious'. Later on, when I came across models of Just Culture, ABC analysis, the safety hierarchy and 'nudge' theory my response was: "Of course! This makes perfect sense". I'd like to think that several important arguments in this book (for example, about ensuring training efficacy in the medium to long-term) are like the Rosa Parks example – both 'very obvious when you think about it' and also not automatically thought about! (Incidentally, Alison is now a very senior psychologist and responsible for the mental health of a large part of England).

Similarly, good **ergonomics** includes the systematic application of this principle and is increasingly taking account of 'bleeding obvious' psychosocial factors, as well as physical ones. For example, the UK ergonomist David Hitchcock gives the example of young wheelchair users not wanting anything to do with the best designed and most stable wheelchairs because an alternative version had a back rest that could be detached and put through a laser printer so that it can be *personalised*. This makes perfect sense when you know that a huge frustration for wheelchair users is the public 'seeing the chair not the person'. Apparently, a funky chrome-wheel finish is much appreciated, too!

The very specific aim of this book is to try to distil the essence of all the main areas of safety culture assessment, measurement and enhancement and then be quite prescriptive about what the research, writing and experience means and what organisations and individuals need to **do** with it. This book is for the director of safety, the safety professional, the line manager and the company union rep who are reading it in the hope that there are some things in it they can take away and **use**.

I'd also hope there are enough ideas and suggestions that, because they are mostly based on experience and observation rather than formal research, would make for some excellent MSc & PhD theses. Please do copy me in on the findings if it does.

# Returning to the Obvious Elephants in the Room – Health and Driving

Most organisations are determined to drive down accident rates, or have had a serious accident and want to ensure they don't have another, and much of the genuine excellence in the field of HSE has been targeted specifically at safety issues.

At a recent oil and gas event in Denmark, for example, Maersk drilling described how it has recently invested some €11 million in a simulator via which non-technical skills training can be given to drill teams, as the company has quite rightly identified (following Macondo) that the ability to react effectively to issues as a team on site is crucial. Dong Energy has an advanced 11-day leadership training course, during which tablet devices are given out containing all the course material, along with a pack of tailored playing cards to use as toolbox talks. Maersk also described the use of professional actors to finely adjust the nuance of interpersonal interactions in team decisions. (In my mind's eye I can see "let's redo that exchange but this time a little more anger and defensiveness please, Hans *darling*…")

This is very high-level preparation and training and no one would say that the oil and gas industry isn't taking safety genuinely seriously – especially following Macondo. There are still many weaknesses but huge efforts have been made and continue to be made, with the industry looking outside of itself to see if there is learning they can incorporate, or advanced technologies they can harness.

However, most of us work in '***health*** and safety' within a SHE team, or under a director of health, safety and environment. Tragically, 11 people were killed when the Macondo (Deepwater Horizon) well exploded but on the *same day* in the USA around 100 people died of occupational illness. According to the World Health Organisation the number of working days lost to occupational illness around the world annually is estimated to be several *billion*. To say that this is the elephant in the room is an understatement of colossal proportions. These are illnesses caused, or made worse by exposure to any of:

Biological agents

- Chemical
- Dusts
- Fumes

Ergonomics

- Noise
- Temperature
- Vibration

Traditionally, ergonomists tackle the latter list and hygienists the former but there is an overlap. Most if not *all* of the techniques and principles covered in this book are as applicable to the management of health and the environment as they are to safety. They are also applicable to productivity. Indeed, with reference to quality gurus like Deming and others, most of the techniques described in the methodology section (in the same way that nearly all Internet advances are driven by pornography!) were developed very explicitly with *productivity* in mind!

Having been invited to give the opening Warner Lecture to the 60th Annual International Conference for the British Occupational Hygiene Society I attended their presentation at that year's Wellness event at the NEC Birmingham in preparation. To my surprise, only 10 other people attended, though there were *thousands* at the event. Health really is a huge elephant in the room with which even the SHE profession itself seems unable to fully engage.

Although the challenge dwarfs that of anything that has gone before, health management encompasses many tools that have yet to be systemically applied. For example, at the above-mentioned conference only a minority of delegates were familiar with the principles of ABC (or temptation) analysis, which, more than any other factor, explains why an individual would fail to wear personal protective equipment in the presence of pathogens.

Everything described in this book is designed to increase the amount of *leeway* an individual or organisation has. More objective learning increases leeway. Better leadership increases leeway. A more empowered and risk literate workforce increases leeway. The more holes in your defences and the bigger those holes, the *less* leeway you have. And so on.

The most dangerous thing most of us do is drive but driving at speed isn't the most dangerous thing we do. Driving *too close* to the car in front, at whatever speed, is. Studies based on on-board computer feedback (known as 'telematics') show that what correlates best with incidents is not speed *per se* but sharp braking. Of course it does, when you think about it: sharp braking is often caused solely by excessive speed but *also* at least as often by lack of attention and/or not leaving enough space. Unless there has been an accident and someone's been hurt (too late) we don't prosecute people for driving too close, or for braking sharply because it's logistically more difficult than prosecuting for speed. We should.

Having to break sharply means we've run out of leeway and leeway is, in many ways, a metaphor for life. It's also a simple way of understanding every model and principle discussed in the book because risk literate thinking that increases leeway is always a good thing. An explicit aim is to suggest a mindset that treats health and safety as an infinitely complicated *art* form, as much as a science. Putting on a hard hat isn't necessarily the best way to make you safe, and insisting that someone puts a hard hat on doesn't necessarily make for the most effective safety leadership. At least as often it's all about nuance and nudges and unintended consequences. One step sidewards, one back then two forward.

## But Then Again … Safety *is* also very simple

Some years ago, I was at the Singapore safety conference and met a man who said he'd been everywhere, done every job and had seen it all. I asked him which country was the least safe in his opinion, expecting a 'third world' answer. Instead, he said: "New Zealand"!

It reminded me of a visit I made to that country many years back, where I saw a sign by a small airfield saying "sky diving". I stopped and asked how much it was and how much training was required to go up. The instructor said: "Well, we'll get in the back of the crate, Craig will get us in the air, I'll brief you thoroughly on the way up, will kit you out with a chute personally, get you over the drop zone and off you go. You'll be back in your car in an hour, with luck."

I found myself saying: "Hell, that's a bit worrying, to be honest … when I looked into it in the UK they insisted on a fair bit of training and a small test before they'd let you have a go. What if I get it wrong, come over all panicky when it comes to the crunch and forget what to do?"

The tough-looking Kiwi just looked at me with pity and said: "Well I *f!\*!ing* well wouldn't if I were you, mate!"

People and organisations are incredibly unpredictable and complex - but often in a very *very* and simplistic way. I hope you find this attempt to articulate some important elements of that useful.

**Tim Marsh, Feb 2014**

# Chapter 1.
# **Introduction to Safety Culture**

This chapter will provide an overview of the key theories of safety culture, seeking to illustrate what the various definitions of culture mean on a day-to-day basis. It will also reference widely used models (with little academic research behind them), such as the Bradley Curve, as well as academically robust models, such as that developed by Diane Parker and Patrick Hudson. It will use case studies to show how values, beliefs, shared visions and artefacts combine to set the culture – with culture defined in a behavioural way as 'the way we do things around here'.

The list is self-evident except, perhaps, for artefacts, which are physical things and are especially important if they have *symbolic* value. The nation-uniting effect of Nelson Mandela's wearing of the green and gold 'springbok' shirt at the 1995 World Cup rugby final is as powerful an example of artefact as ever there might be. Interestingly, commentators like R.W. Johnson have suggested that the ANC has gone on to overuse such gestures, with too many 'symbolic appointments' to the detriment of organisational efficacy and economic growth. Mandela's act clearly symbolised his values and leadership but gestures alone are unlikely to achieve much.

In particular the book explores the practical use of these models by showing, for example, the direct link between Scott Geller's assertion that "Safety must be in the very DNA of a company" with the story of the mindset of an ex-special forces soldier riding his motorbike on public roads.

Specifically, it seeks to make clear the links between Prof Andrew Hopkins' 'Mindful Safety' model, Sidney Dekker's 'New View' of human error, Professor James Reason's 'Cheese' and 'Elastic Band' models, HSG48 (human error) and the basic behavioural safety principle of Heinrich's Triangle. Finally, it attempts to demystify the increasing controversies surrounding Heinrich's Triangle.

# 1.1 Popular Models and Definitions of Safety Culture

## A case study of culture

In the introduction, I mentioned the tragic suicide of an animal charity worker after her whistleblowing attempts met with a hostile reception from the organisation. Those notes were written in June 2013 as an example of the interplay between the person and the organisation and unspoken assumptions and perceptions. On 7 August a report in the *Times* newspaper on the same organisation by Dominic Kennedy suggested to me that this wasn't a one-off event but perhaps an example of something more systematic – something *cultural*.

Kennedy wrote that the organisation's response to a respected expert on horse care (a Colin Vogel) who had spoken against the charity's policies suggested that it had recently begun systemically to harass experts who speak against it. Branded an 'arch enemy' for supporting from the witness box some horse owners it was seeking to prosecute, one internal memo commented:

"I know it was hoped that we would be able to criticise the content (of his well-respected book) to the extent that we could refuse to be associated with it. To my enormous regret … I do not think that we can easily proceed on those lines. There are a number of minor points that could be raised but nothing to give us a good case. Sorry."

A barrister (a Jonathan Rich) commented that he'd given up defending clients against this organisation because it filed so many complaints against him. He added that "He'd never been subject to a complaint in any case, other than where [this organisation] was involved".

It seems that the worker bizarrely accused of 'tortoise theft' was not a one-off and that the organisation has become defensive and subjective. This mindset always leads to tears, whether we're talking about charities, commercial entities, or even personal relationships! In this case, part of the answer would appear to be an almost doubling in prosecutions by the organisation between 2010 and 2013 – in itself a very good thing – but with the organisation clear that the publicity that accompanied successful prosecutions correlated well with donations. The unintended consequences of well-intentioned actions will feature often in this book.

## Organisational Culture

The concept of an **organisational** culture comes from two books published in 1982: *Corporate Culture* by Deal and Kennedy and *In Search of Excellence* by Peters and

Waterman. To quote the latter pair: "In a strong culture … people way down the line know what they are supposed to do in most situations because a handful of guiding principles are crystal clear." (Obtaining successful prosecutions at all costs, perhaps?)

A weak culture might include a level of 'learned helplessness', where employees have effectively 'learned' from past experience that efforts to improve things will most probably prove fruitless. The term describes an overly fatalistic and passive mindset and was first coined by Martin Seligman in the 1960s.

The importance of culture cannot be overstated. For example, James Reason, in the classic *Managing the Risks of Organisational Accidents*, says that commercial aviation is unusually uniform as an industry. Airlines have the same planes, the same weather conditions, the same air-traffic control and maintenance crews licensed to very similar standards, yet the risk of death varies from 1 in 260,00 to 1 in 11 million! Reason suggests that although resources play a part, "the lion's share is down to safety cultural variations".

**An Important Semantic.** Writers such as Hopkins and Reason have discussed whether the term 'safety culture' is used as a *description* or an *explanation*. This is important as, if it's a description – 'company X has a culture of low risk awareness' – it more readily lends itself to a blaming state of mind (as in, 'it shouldn't have'). If it's used as an *explanation* then, though it's a subtle difference, the emphasis is on 'risk awareness was low *because of* the weak safety culture'. Taking the view that culture is what it *does* makes changing it a much more practical proposition. It's a subtle but important difference and the key question – as so often in this book – is to question why it is as it is.

For example, my company has worked with a lot of oil firms over the years and we often note that two back-to-back OIMs (Offshore Instillation Managers) can have very different safety cultures during their rotation. This is because, offshore, they reign supreme and have a huge and often very direct impact on the culture. In this case, it would be fair to *describe* a poor culture under the OIM who is less interested in safety.

At other times, there may be differences in site cultures within a company that aren't really influenced much by the mindset of the senior management. For example, an audit of BP sites in the US found a variation in culture, with Texas City coming out poorly. Another site (Cherry Point) was scored positively. It had some distinguishing features, though. Firstly, it was smaller and less complex with more interaction and a more family-like atmosphere (it was located in a remote community, which helped in this respect). Secondly, the workforce largely comprised highly educated, former military personnel. Thirdly, the leadership had consciously worked to create an egalitarian environment. You'll note that the first two of these were outside of the control of senior management, except in the long-term.

An interesting question about the third point is how likely it is that the management of Texas City would have looked to set up an egalitarian environment, faced with the same circumstances. This is, in its way, the first reference to the 'substitution' test that underpins much of the Just Culture approach and is defined by Reason as where we can 'substitute' the individual concerned, for someone else coming from the same domain of activity and possessing comparable qualifications and experience. Then ask the question "In the light of how events unfolded and were perceived by those involved in real time, is it likely that this new individual would have behaved any differently?"

If you're thinking 'great, we're only a few pages in and already were wrapping ourselves into a knot about semantics' – please don't. The key thing isn't necessarily to argue which is which – unless you're a lawyer who may well feel it's worth dragging out for some time while the fees clock up – the key thing is simply to objectively and analytically ask "why" a culture is as it is (ideally, closely followed by "what can we do to improve it?")

The more often we lazily use it as a *description* the more often we are likely to slip into a blaming mindset, and blame is a cancer on any culture.

This book isn't really interested in compliance as an end in itself. I'm aiming much higher than simply keeping companies out of court – valid as that goal is. A simple, everyday example: sometimes (when I can see that it's 100-per-cent safe to do so, I should stress) I'll turn left on a red light. Technically that's against the rules in the UK but it *is* allowed in New York and other places I've visited as it's entirely risk free (well, that's a *right* turn in New York, to be precise, but you know what I mean). I must stress that I am extremely interested in road safety and road risk. Without tempting fate, since I was around 21, I've had just one (very small) bump in 30 years and fully intend not to increase that figure in the 30 years driving I hope to have left.

Driving on the roads is easily the most dangerous thing I do, so it's really not something I want to leave to basic compliance! There are symbolic implications to what I've just described, I know, but it falls under the general banner of never doing anything on the roads (like overtaking) when I *think* it's safe (even if it's legal) - only when I *know* it's safe. Risk doesn't care about rules and some rules don't address risks very well.

I'm a great believer in fewer, better rules properly enforced and which are based on high levels of risk literacy. For example, on an oil rig once the behavioural safety team refused to include "trousers outside boots, not tucked in" as part of their PPE checklist. "But it's the rule", protested one team member. "It's to help stop people getting foot rot from oil-dirty trousers". The medic on the team said: "Bugger that, I've never seen one case of foot rot in 30 years working out here!" so the definition stood and the team set off and concentrated (very successfully) on the statistically important aspects of PPE, such as goggles and gloves, as the medic had seen a lot of eye injuries and cuts in his 30 years.

## Vernon Bradley and DuPont

There is nothing mystical about a safety culture. It's not a magic potion, it's just the systematic application of measures and behaviours. It is made up of a number of interactive elements, or ways of doing things and managing people that have enhanced health and safety as their natural by-product. Similarly, a Buddhist guru will stress that the way to a life of 'happiness' is to work at and *practise* being happy as often as possible. They have developed this as a skill in exactly the same way as a beautifully crafted golf swing.

The well-known 'Bradley Curve' was first thought up by Vernon Bradley, an employee of DuPont, who, along with colleagues including Professor Peter McKie, was involved in a series of meetings about a falling away of safety standards within the company in the 1960s. The conclusion of the meetings was that the company rather felt it had 'done' safety because of the excellent results it achieved and had taken its eye off the ball. This hugely influences the tenth and final core value in the DuPont list: "Never think you can't keep improving – because if you're not actively pushing forward then you're almost certainly drifting backwards".

It can be argued that the main learning point of Professor Sidney Dekker's influential book *Drift into Failure* is a version of this principle. The basic premise is that the combination of systems and people is almost infinitely complex and because it is in a constant state of dynamic flux, the laws of unintended/unforeseen consequences complicate matters further, so there will always be a drift away from excellence to the average (a version of the 'regression to the mean', if you would). Literally, if you are not *actively* pushing forwards you will be almost inevitably be drifting backwards towards the ordinary.

I once shared a stage with Professor Dekker, who mentioned teaching his children to use cycle helmets as part of his talk. Recent research (Dinh, Royal Prince Albert Hospital, Sydney, for example) suggests that a cyclist in a helmet is around five times less likely die in the event of an accident. Linking this personal anecdote to his complexity theory I threw in the well-known research finding of Dr Ian Walker from Bath University that lorry drivers have been shown to drive 8 per cent closer to cyclists who are wearing helmets – a very unwelcome unintended consequence based on subconscious risk compensation that the rider is more competent and protected.

Moreover, studies also show that in countries where cycle helmets are compulsory, such as Australia, cycling can decrease by up to 40 per cent, which is hugely detrimental to the nation's overall health. Harry Wallop, writing in the *Telegraph* newspaper in August 2013 stated that after helmets were made mandatory in Australia with failure to comply resulting in a fine cycling numbers fell, especially among teenagers – the group most concerned about their 'cool' hairstyles. Wallop says that "among female secondary pupils in Sydney, cycling rates fell by 90 per cent and the popularity of cycling in New Zealand appears never to have recovered since it introduced its own law in 1994, with rates still 51 per cent lower a decade after the legislation."

In short, despite a slightly increased risk from other drivers, it's perhaps clear what *parents* need to do but for legislators it's very much more complicated.

The other nine DuPont values are:

All Injuries can be prevented.

Everyone is responsible for safety (not just the safety department and/or management);

Safety is a condition of employment (there will be consequences if you don't keep the rules);

Safety needs training;

Never stop checking how you're doing;

Everyone has the right to challenge anyone – and expect action;

There is no such thing as a minor injury (see it as a near major injury);

Workplace safety is only half the story;

Everyone is valuable – we can all learn from each other.

Many are self-evident and none is objectionable, except, perhaps, 'home safety', as many individuals struggle with the philosophical concept that falling off a ladder at home, or not wearing safety glasses when using a lawn mower is anything to do with the their employer! (Except it's very difficult, in the event you lose an eye or fall 15ft from a ladder on a Saturday, that you can turn up for work ready for an 'honest day's pay for an honest day's work' on the following Monday.)

**Milliken.** More recently, the Milliken company has followed the DuPont business model and offers consultancy based on its in-house safety success. There are considerable overlaps, as you can imagine, regarding the likes of visible walk-and-talks, with Milliken stealing from time management best practice and these walk-and-talks being undertaken in 'sacred time'. (The use of the word *stealing* is deliberate, as I'll explain very shortly.)

However, there is a slightly different tone to the core factors of Milliken's model, which include:

Using leading measures, as well as lagging measures;

Using advanced training principles (as detailed later in this book);

Seeking to actively embed the key behaviours with such creative tactics as sending out 'mystery shoppers', who deliberately act unsafely (not too unsafely), with a prize for the first person who challenges them;

Stressing the importance of clear expectation communicated to all (indeed, it's the emphasis on creative communication that catches the eye. For example, Milliken gives extra credit for new *ideas stolen* – so the wheel doesn't have to be reinvented – and shared. It also stresses the importance of getting back to people quickly and maximising genuine workforce involvement and ownership;

Actively empowering the workforce to get involved in safety on a day-to-day basis.

These brief notes are based on just one presentation and a chat over coffee but, frankly, cynical as I often am, I couldn't help but be impressed. By the time you read this Milliken may well be well on its way to catching up with DuPont in terms of market share – good luck to them!

# The 'Bradley Curve'

The classic model suggests an organisation moves from *dependent*, through *independent* and finally to *interdependent*. In making this journey the leaders of the organisation move from an authoritarian 'tell them' culture through to a team-oriented culture characterised by management support and guidance. (To illustrate the point about simple-to-understand messages it's another example of a simple triptych that is resonant and memorable – very many safety people can rattle off 'dependent: independent: interdependent' but few can name all 10 core values.)

Specifically:

At the **dependent** stage the organisation is characterised by rules and regulations, is more reactive than proactive, communicates objectives selectively and the use of control and discipline is prevalent. This might be summarised as "I do it so I

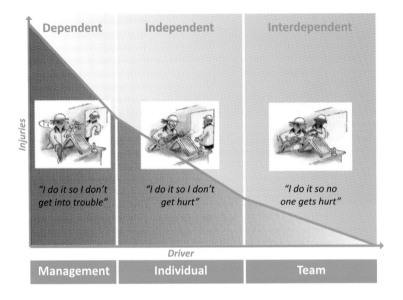

**Figure 2. The 'Bradley Curve'**

don't get into trouble" or "the way we do things around here when we are watched versus when no one is looking". At this point, any 'zero incident' ambitions can be described as merely a *vision*. To a great extent the list of core values described above is largely conceptual.

At the **independent** stage there is a greater understanding of the process complexities of the operation, personal commitment to safety, individuals able to self-manage and able to share logic and ideas. Most improvement will be procedure based. This might be best summarised as "I do it so I don't get hurt". At this level any zero harm ambitions might be considered 'hard but realistic' *goals*. Behaviours flowing from the list of core values above are frequently to be observed in action.

At the **interdependent** stage there is cooperation within and across teams, people acting as a 'brother's keeper', pride in the organisation, and genuine empowerment in day-to-day management and goal-setting. This might be summarised as "I do this so *no one* gets hurt". At this point the very clearly communicated 'zero incident' ambitions can be described as an *expectation*. To a great extent the list of behaviour associated core values above is embedded as "the way we do things around here".

Clearly, a systematic consideration and measurement of either the 'curve' or the 10 core values would be hugely useful to any organisation and constitute the backbone of improvement programmes in many, and this is not a bad way to chart a cultural improvement process. This consideration and measurement would be based on the classic model of:

assess;
plan;
do;
review and learn;
repeat with learning incorporated…

For example, a simple exercise we like to use is the excellent Outtakes DVD *Secret Weapon*, which briefly introduces the 10 core values and asks clients to rate themselves 0 to 10 for each. It's surprising how often really quite bullish organisations will come up with an average score in the 60s, 50s or even lower, and follow-on discussions about opportunities to improve can often prove very animated and productive.

However, my experience is that the model isn't often used in a very systematic way at all and that what Vernon Bradley first came up with is most often used as an inspired and oft-misunderstood touchstone: "That's exactly what we need. We need to be interdependent!"

For example, I attended a contractor day for a major client some years ago and the senior director presenting announced from the stage that any of the contractors hoping to prove successful in the next round of contract awards had "bloody well better demonstrate a commitment to achieving *interdependence* … in fact this is, to me, as important, if not more important, than cost!" (I quote). No one in the room demurred at all and there was much nodding. (Most of the contractors he was presenting to are household names in the UK and the contracts he alluded to were worth, in total, tens if not hundreds of millions of pounds.)

This was clear evidence indeed that this client was taking safety very seriously. Except that when I circulated later and asked them what 'interdependence' meant to them in practical terms, no one could give me any details at all. To my great amusement, nor could the speaker when I asked him!

In a similar vein, management teams will often ask us to cover 'Bradley' because they are working towards, or are committed to working towards 'interdependence', as requested by head office. I often use a simple set of five slides that Peter McKie himself kindly gave me, after we shared a stage at a conference. I am almost certain that hardly anyone to whom I have ever shown these simple slides already knew a tenth of what is on them.

It's the simple concept that resonates but the trouble with user-friendly conceptual models is that they don't often stand up to close scrutiny. Tony Roscoe, a colleague of mine, argues really quite convincingly that the typical organisation starts out from a position of independent and only becomes *dependent* if taught to be that way by the organisation. Certainly, clinical psychologists have much work to do to pull people back from 'learned helplessness' when working with those who have become fatalistic and despondent.

## Building a Case for Proactivity – The Limitations of Compliance

I'd like to start this section with some, perhaps surprising, information, which is that no senior person in the safety culture field pays much attention to the certificates and awards in the foyer that the various auditing organisations deliver. (At least, not unless they aren't there at all, of course)! Clearly, that's a claim that needs justifying.

Certainly, many organisations reach a level of systems compliance that will please the various auditing bodies and will indeed lead to lots of nice certificates in the lobby. These are very reassuring at a glance, so the question is: why isn't this enough? Why bother pushing on to better than compliance? We worked really hard for those certificates and now you're saying "so what?" Charming!

The first thing to note is that for the workforce in the field, the observation "compliance is discretionary" is absolutely true and underpins much of the rationale behind this book. To illustrate the point I offer the following direct quote from a cusomer survey: "The CEO said on the safety day 'if you can't do it safely then don't do it' but in the canteen this translates as if you can't do it safely then do it at night".

More important than that, though, is that basic compliance simply isn't sufficient if you want to achieve any sort of excellence. This is because research suggests that there is a better correlation between workforce *involvement* in safety and incident rate and compliance. (Clarke *et al*, 2012) That's worth re-stating: even if our employees actually do follow all the rules we are still likely to fall some way short of excellence. (This is hypothetical, obviously, because they *don't* always follow the rules.)

If that sounds intuitively dubious please consider this question: would you prefer your 10-year-old to step into the road blindly at a pedestrian crossing because the green 'walk' sign has come on, or would you prefer them to cross 50 yards down the road while 'dynamic risk assessing' effectively as they go?

Companies like Premier Foods in the UK have recently been running much lauded and award-winning safety campaigns, where the emphasis is on fewer but better rules that are easier to enforce consistently and fairly. They are actively seeking to get away from compliance as an 'end in itself' and promote more thinking and empowerment in a search for genuine excellence.

Recently, the expressions 'operational discipline' and 'operating dexterity' have become fashionable, and articles have been published (and well-received) on the topics (see Mei-Li Lin, Safety and Health Practitioner, May 2012). What they mean by these phrases in simple terms is thinking intelligently, imaginatively and flexibly around a solid foundation of controls.

## Case study – a reminder that the challenge that 'compliance isn't enough' is actually quite radical

This drive for 'compliance' can be found everywhere, even in initiatives that quite explicitly seek 'world class' standards and might well be considered really rather leading-edge by the body and organisations involved. For example, in 2013 the EuOHS 'working together' initiative produced a document called *Management Leadership in OS&H*. It contains a useful checklist of 12 behaviourally-anchored items covering issues like responsibility, risk assessment and procurement. However, when moving away from compliance-facing items to what we might consider 'continuous improvement' items it clearly falls short of best practice in the anchors. For example, the maximum score for the item 'workplace inspections' is benchmarked as: "Performed regularly, by the management who take appropriate measures to tackle every non conformity".

This definition scores a 7 (the other three of four benchmarks scoring 5, 3 and 1 descending). An overall score of 61 or more (or an average of 5.1 per item) elicits the comment:

"The OSH prevention policy in your company is situated at a fairly high level. Continue in this way."

I'd argue not unless we can add:

"When we see a non-conformity, first ask *why* to understand the root cause"

to add a Just Culture-influenced learning element; and

"Institute a series of peer-to-peer inspections, or, at the very least, ensure that peers are included in the inspections teams".

Likewise, the item covering 'Consultation' scores the maximum 7 for: "Management is engaged in ongoing dialogue with the workers (representatives) on all OSH matters". This means, you imagine, as major issues arise or in regular (weekly? monthly? quarterly?) meetings. Again it can be suggested that **world class** would include *proactive* questions such as "what's the worst that could happen?" or "anything slow or uncomfortable about doing the job safely?" Further, that there is a methodology in place to ensure that these questions might be proactively asked of anyone on *any given day* so that the search for risk is a far more *dynamic* and *active* affair than items raised at a regular meeting could possibly be.

Certainly I'd argue that any workplace 'walk and talk' should have 'ensuring compliance' as only a *minor* element as first, we must seek to *learn* and then we must seek to *coach*. Only then should we move into a 'policing' role. The Just Culture model (described in detail later) explains how both learning and coaching are more likely to yield success than a basic reinforcement of the status quo.

Overall, looked at from a genuinely proactive and risk literate view, I'd suggest that the whole checklist could do with a fifth anchor (scoring 9) that would take the potential total score to 108. Using the same scale the "great work, keep doing it" feedback response would now only kick in at around 78.5 or more. This is some way north of the suggested 61.

Indeed, the existing scale suggests: "You certainly take care of prevention, but improvement is possible on several aspects." for a score of 37-60.

If a really world-class score does start at around 78.5 as I'm suggesting then such tentative critical feedback for a score of *38* shows how pervasive "compliance is enough" can be as this comes from a really very well meaning and forward facing continent wide initiative rather than the legal department.

**Conclusion**. It can take a lot of work to reach 'broadly compliant' but once there, the law of diminishing returns will set in. What's needed next is not more compliance but a change in mindset. Indeed, my observation as a consultant over the years is that the single biggest issue an organisation in search of excellence faces is the need to understand that once compliance has been reached there is a fork in the road. Turn one way in a search of 'über' compliance, and diminishing returns and frustration lie in store. Instead, what is required is a quantum leap in thinking towards a total culture approach. The Parker and Hudson concept of the 'proactive' culture is a good place to start.

# 1.2 Academic Models of Safety Culture
## The Parker and Hudson Model

The UK HSE developed a model of safety culture that describes progress through:

'Emerging';
'Managing';
'Involving';
'Co-Operating'; and
'Continually Improving'.

Despite having a small walk-on part in its development (I was one of the people interviewed by the researchers) I find I prefer the very similar model Diane Parker and Patrick Hudson developed. It's also a five-factor model of safety culture but one that I find really useful, at it seems the terminology used most accurately describes what I find within organisations. It is:

**Generative** – a 'healthy paranoia' about safety;

**Proactive** – see below…;

**Calculative** (Compliant) – safety is managed on the basis of procedure, documentation and uses mostly lagging indicators;

**Reactive** – safety is an issue once something has occurred;

**Pathological** – safety is an inconvenience and the overriding is aim is 'don't get caught'.

My experience is that the vast majority of organisations seeking to improve their safety cultures are squarely in the 'calculative' stage. That is, they have moved beyond 'reactive' and have good systems, procedures, training and inductions in place and have a set of files guaranteed to deliver a certificate or two for the reception walls. However, despite this baseline of achievement they know that the descriptions in the neat files don't always match with what happens in the middle of a busy shift.

Further, this reflects a broader truth, which is that their safety performance has hit a plateau and has been like that for some time. Headline lagging scores of lost-time incidents are typically waving around slightly as if in a narrow horizontal corridor of best and worst performance – known as the infamous 'safety wave' (see Figure 3 below, which shows a 'typical' recreation and a live example from a real client. At conferences half the audience will nod in agreement when asked "does this look familiar?"). Experience is that the companies in question can easily identify that they 'need to do something about this'. Moreover, since 90 per cent, or more of accidents have a clear human factor element it's clear that this *something* needs to have a person, or behavioural focus.

## Case Study

A working definition of proactivity interacting with systems comes from the director of a large chilled foods company. They enjoy an excellent computerised system

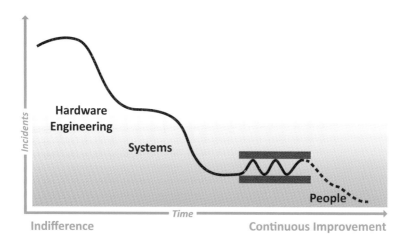

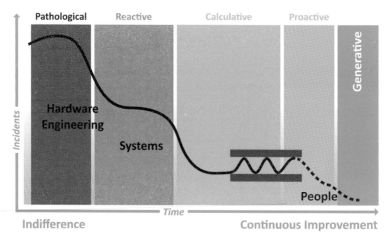

**Figure 3. The 'Safety Wave'**

that allows actions from their thorough in-house audit system to be tracked. She commented that what she wanted from the cultural improvement process we embarked on was, simply:

"That when I get a few red flags from the system instead of rating the local management on just how defensive they are when I we chase them up I just want a simple e-mail the day before the report comes out, to say: 'I must apologise as, tomorrow, there will be a red flag relating to my factory in the reports. Do not be concerned. This is why it's red, this is what we are doing about it and this is when it will be achieved'. That's not too much to ask, is it?"

This is simply the classic 'regret, reason, remedy' communication maxim (see McFarlan) crossed with the basic underpinning premise of the ISO approach. Perfection may be impossible but striving for continuous improvement *is* possible. Andrew Hopkin's 'mindfulness' concept, which was discussed above, is another version of this basic mindset.

A really good everyday analogy with the safety wave is dieting. There have been many books over the years that have said something like "80 per cent of what you weigh is caused by what you eat and 20 per cent by your exercise regime, so it doesn't matter how hard you work out; if you really want to lose weight you have to eat and drink less. Not for the duration of the diet but **for ever**. 'Rude Nike' (aka JFDI!) rules apply!" This was illustrated perfectly by the supermodel Heidi Klum, who once commentated: "Honestly, I've never been on a diet in my life – it's just that I've never allowed myself to eat as much as I wanted to."

Whenever I heard of a safety *initiative* I used to think of the safety wave; now I think of Heidi Klum. Since I hear of a *lot* of safety initiatives this has improved my quality of life greatly. (Incidentally, in edit we researched in vain to find the person who first coined the term 'safety wave'. We also asked around and it seems that quite possibly it was something we came up with in house around 2000 and forgot that we had. If it was *you* before then, then please do let us know and we'll put that right for the next edition!)

# 1.3 Assessing Culture & Climate
## Safety Climate

Traditionally, a safety **climate** assessment was intended to take a snapshot of the organisation as it is today. (For example, it's raining *today* or perhaps even the weather this spring has been unusually cold in the UK because of eastern winds predominating, and this was caused by the Gulf Stream in the Atlantic stopping opposite France, not the UK!) Culture is longer term and less changeable on a day-to-day, or even season-to-season basis.

To continue the analogy it may be that the Gulf Stream will cause problems more often in the years to come. I'd say that this seems to be the result of long-term *climate* change – but that would be confusing!

Certainly the 'political climate' can be hugely influenced by events in the papers – think expense claim scandals and their ilk – but unless something changes as a result the 'culture of petty corruption', for example, will reassert itself once the fuss has blown over. I don't want to be any more cynical than necessary but I'm not alone in wanting to throw things at the TV when someone obviously defensive and of the mindset that we are all idiots says "this can't be allowed to happen again! I'm going to set up a full inquiry". (If they want to change something they change the law – if they don't they set up an inquiry. There's a wonderful scene in the UK satirical TV series *The Thick of It* where a senior politician is in trouble over some impropriety but is told by his permanent secretary: "Minister, news just in from the Prime Minister's Office: they are going to set up an inquiry." The minister lets out a huge sigh and says: "Oh, thank God!")

Similarly, an organisation will nearly always feel very different after a fatality, but unless changes are made and *embedded* it will drift back to its historical standards.

Just to add to the confusion, organisations such as the UK Health and Safety Laboratory have recently claimed that the terms culture and climate are now used interchangeably. Personally, however, I think the distinction is worth keeping. Anyone visiting the UK soon after the death of Princess Diana in 1997, for example, would have observed a mindset among the general population that was very different to the one that reasserted itself within weeks of the funeral. Tides come in and go out on a daily basis but rising sea levels submerge low-lying lands.

## Measuring Safety Climate

There are lots of safety climate measures, supported by online technology and software and can be tailored and customised for each company. This generates some useful benefits:

Areas of weakness can be identified and plugged into 'plan: act: review' processes;

The organisation can be revisited to track progress;

The scores can be benchmarked against other organisations (and, if a suitably sized database exists, against other organisations in the same sector). As more user-friendly versions are used and increasing amounts of data collected this becomes increasingly so;

It's quite cheap and easy to do.

There is a big downside, though, which is that the data comes with an error variance that some find unacceptable. This is because the respondents are often:

self-selecting (for example, only the keenest 50 per cent respond – or perhaps the keenest 40 per cent and the most militant 10 per cent);

wary their responses will be tracked in some way, regardless of assurances – so they are 'careful' rather than honest in the way they respond; offhand in their responses, ticking many boxes with little thought just to get it done – especially in the middle sections. (Psychometric tests of intelligence, too, should take account of error rates as well as raw score to try to adjust for the candidates who randomly tick all the remaining questions when told "one minute left", knowing they're likely to get 20 per cent right by chance. Experience shows that the raw scores are simply fed into the data base.)

The error variance can therefore be quite high and what might look on a colourful chart like meaningful improvement (or a meaningful reduction) can be nothing but statistical 'noise'. My issue is that once these scores *are* on a colourful and official-looking chart people will take them seriously.

Error in the data puts an upper limit on the efficacy of any investment that follows. In short, I don't like to use climate surveys, even though in response to client demand we have developed some very snazzy climate tools of our own. Instead, I try really hard to persuade clients to undertake a more in-depth culture survey.

## Measuring Safety *Culture*

My colleague Paul Bizzell asks delegates to visualise the safety department approaching them with a flashing light on the top of their hard hats. What colour is the light, he asks, and suggests that if you say blue or red, then you probably have a policing problem – a *dependent* culture. Add a sprinkling of amber and that suggests rescue services and a rather *dependent* culture. Predominantly amber is an *independent* culture. Lots of green or white flashing lights would suggest a **caring** culture, where the approach person is there to care for them in a supportive way. This an *interdependent* culture, perhaps.

It's a fun and bizarrely accurate exercise. Another in a similar vein involves asking:

"If your company safety culture were an **animal**, which one would it be and why?"

It was shared with me by the same chap (Lyndon Shearman of the International

Institute of Risk and Safety Management) who came up with the phrase 'Affective Safety Management', which was the title of my first book. I promised him I'd try it a few times and was shocked at the results.

Obviously we get a lot of chickens (headless), ostriches with their heads in the sand, chameleons who change colour with the weather, and so on, but some answers have been even more illuminating.

A personal favourite was the team that told their fearsome boss that he was a bear. "A bear?" he replied, not too put out, macho chap that he was. "What sort of bear, then? A brown bear? A grizzly bear?" They confessed that, actually, the bear they had in mind was a *dancing* bear, as in: "Prod us with a stick and off we go, but our hearts are really not in it…"

This provoked a less benign reaction from the grizzly, and a furious and (ultimately) extremely enlightening debate broke out. I just supped coffee, waiting for my chance to go through my academic results!

Another illuminating answer was at a session with a large utility company that had spent a small fortune on awareness raising sessions. They were always about to do something meaningful but never quite pressed on with it. The answer I got from one group was "A dog, specifically a dog from TV". "Lassie?", I guessed but was told: "No, Scooby Doo. It's large and annoying and makes a lot of noise but it's generally harmless." (At which point a young manager jumped up and shouted: "Absolutely! Got it in one!" and everyone in the room agreed they had indeed nailed it.)

Obviously, many clients insist on something rather more scientific!

What we need to do is to get a collection of operatives together, stratified for department, time with the company, seniority and general attitude. Ideally, the sample will represent 20 per cent of the population unless the organisation is quite large, in which case a 10 or even 5 per cent sample will provide statistical rigour. We need to put them at their ease by stressing that no names will be taken, so that we couldn't say "X claimed this" even if we wanted to. Then we need to ask them a series of questions.

My colleague Matthew Strong coined a phrase that is as true of safety culture generally as it is of this specific methodology. It is:

> "The essence of a total safety culture is that it needs to be truly safe to talk about safety before it can be a truly safe organisation."

Which sums it up nicely.

Reurning to the analyis, we use some standard factors to structure the disccusions.

The five standard factors are:

Procedures;
Concern for safety standards;
Investigation and incident reporting;
Training and competence;
Communication.

And one that we've added in response to client feedback:

A 'Bradley' score (incorporating items on team work, trust, empowerment and 'brother's keeper' behaviour).

These are assessed with anchored responses, where we ask the group:

"Which of these statements most accurately reflect the organisation as you know it and why?'

Then we'll ask for some anecdotes to illustrate.

For example, when looking at accident investigation the scale items essentially ask:

Does a system exist?
Is it a good system?
Is it used well?

Note that to score well here workforce involvement must be high so, to an extent, teamwork and ownership are addressed. However, to really address the 'essence of Bradley' we also need to ask:

Does the majority of the workforce perceive it as a fair system and one in which it is worthwhile being involved?

As we began to use the tool we found an interesting thing: even organisations deep into cultural improvement and employing the sort of high-level skills of analysis, communication and challenging of a strong culture are still some way from achieving their desired levels of *trust*.

Any embedded culture change takes time, of course, and is very easy to undo. However, being able to define the goal and measure the distance to be travelled to achieve it helps management focus on what's required. This is especially true in organisations where data are highly valued. So it's as true of "bring me interdependence!" as it is of quality and productivity.

Figure 4 shows a typical set of findings, with a typical gap between how management rates the organisation and how the employees rate it. The art is in knowing when it's a standard perceptual gap and when it's delusion! As well as the mean score we're also looking for standard deviation as the less the standard deviation, then the greater the

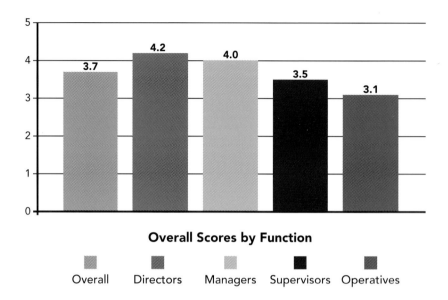

**Overall Scores by Function**

Overall    Directors    Managers    Supervisors    Operatives

**Figure 4. Management and Workforce Perceptions**

consistency within the organisation.

In one piece of work with a mining company we were able to point out "don't look at the mean – look at the standard deviation" (which was considerable). Our research contributed to a more general strategic view about centralising power within the organisation. They'd acquired smaller competitors over the years and let them remain relatively autonomous, for the great benefits of local empowerment. Unfortunately, this meant a huge variation in standards and, in some cases, that standard was far below acceptable.

More recently, we've started to use our own model of safety culture, which lies at the heart of this book. It's more of a road map than just a model. See Figure 5.

This model fleshes out the area in which nearly all organisations find themselves and illustrates the shift in mindset required. As above, it separates compliance into 'minimal compliance' (with an eye on the law courts and clients) and 'broad compliance' (with an eye on the certificates that can be garnered for the reception wall from organisations such as RoSPA and the British Safety Council).

At this point, does the organisation become system obsessed and disappear into a nightmare of ever-decreasing circles and diminishing returns, or does it achieve

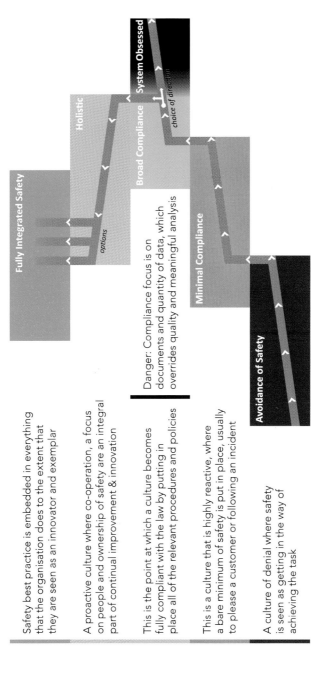

**Figure 5. The Ryder Marsh Roscoe-Bizzell Safety Culture Map**

the mind shift to address its human factors issues in the way I am endeavouring to describe in this book?

## An Intentionally *Slightly Controversial* Case Study: A Reminder that Culture is All Pervasive and Leaks

An example of how culture can 'leak' can, in my opinion, be found in the aforementioned DVD on DuPont's 10 core values (Outtakes' *Secret Weapon*). Criticism of the DuPont approach isn't unheard of, with one of the most frequent observations being that it can feel a bit top-down and paternal. Let's be friendly and suggest that the approach, if not handled carefully, can often be seen that way. (Certainly, some of the early training DVDs beg the question: "You're not actually going to show these to anyone with an IQ of greater than 70, are you?!")

The film, though carefully scripted, edited and sent around for comment to a number of reviewers, has several instances in which a very paternal mindset is depicted. At one point it's suggested with a straight face that *"perhaps the workforce know slightly better than you what really happens with your systems"*.

A contender for understatement of the century, if ever I heard one! Later on, a manager, emphasising the importance of workforce involvement and empowerment, refers several times to the workforce being "down there". Now, either this man lives in a tower, or he's leaking. He meant to say "out there", surely? (Go on, how many of you thought: "Yes, he should – but don't call me Shirley"?!)

# Chapter 2.
# **Defining a Strong Culture**

I've suggested that the key difference between excellent companies and the merely good is that the best companies take that mental jump away from systems and towards learning and leadership. I'd like to look at excellence *in practice*.

I'm not the first person to try to define a strong culture in straightforward terms, so I'll start with an overview of one concept with which readers will be familiar – the High-Reliability Organisation – and then consider Professor Andrew Hopkin's 'mindful' safety culture, which draws heavily on his work with high reliability organisations.

## **2.1 The High Reliability Organisation**

Some complex, technology intensive and high risk organisations must operate as far as humanly possible to a failure free standard. In organisations like these *any* error is a concern in case it becomes a habit, so they habitually worry about errors that they can't foresee. People in these organisations will know the technicalities of a task inside out and will constantly seek to learn from and report error. Mutual monitoring is high and will often increase (rather than decrease) as production pressures increase. This needs planning and resourcing.

Indeed, when the pressure is *really on* in these organisations bureaucratic hierarchies often break down and are replaced with a hierarchy based entirely on technical knowledge. Feedback increases in frequency and clarity. Done well, this is the application of well thought through SOPs alongside brainstorming, active listening and other soft skills done pretty much as the textbooks recommend.

Ironically, to be able to do this requires a strong culture. It is the shared values and assumptions of the organisation that allow this efficacy of decentralised work groups. The quality of front line supervisors is therefore paramount. Many of these high reliability organisations are either military, or staffed largely by ex military, and James Reason and others point out that this sets them up well to have this grounded but also dynamic and flexible safety culture.

In the UK, the most prestigious lecture in safety (the Allan St John Holt lecture) was delivered in 2011 by Paul Thomas, the current head of the rail safety board, previously head of atomic energy safety and, before that, head of safety for the UK's fleet of nuclear submarines. In his lecture Paul's description of safety on a nuclear sub is as good an illustration I've seen of what DuPont has been recently calling 'operational dexterity'.

Most of us do not work on nuclear subs, of course, but I do feel that there are general lessons to be learned. What is key is that the culture is strong and that the desired outcome is known to all, with this clear goal taking precedence over the likes of hierarchies. No time for social niceties and petty politics – we do what needs to be done.

I see this as entirely analogous to an excellent safety culture in a bakery. What's key is a clear and strong vision, detailed knowledge of the 'what' and 'why', as well as the 'how', so that appropriate flexibility can be shown, when appropriate. Most important of all, though, is a commitment to learn where the weaknesses in the system are and to give greatest weight to the person with the best *expertise*. Supervisors need to be empowered and skilled enough to make this happen

This might start with a 'storytelling' consultant who can help an organisation articulate a vision in simple and memorable terms, end with good old-fashioned empowerment, with some good quality safety leadership training in between.

In such a situation there is little opportunity to learn by trial and error and the use of war stories – or, more formally, 'what if?' analysis – becomes key.

I have a pool table in my house and I practise occasionally as an aid to thinking. What I try to do is what is called a '15 to 1'. This is where you break off then try and pot all 15 balls without a miss. Sometimes I'm better at this than others, and I've noticed what causes the difference: it's simply a bit of thought and, specifically, the 'what if?' question. Potting pool balls isn't difficult once you've had some practice but even on a small pool table cue ball position is key, and I simply do not have the cue ball control to nail 14 consecutive pool pots *and* position. What makes the difference for me is when I take a little while to think – for example: "Potting this ball and leaving myself here would be perfect but if I miss the exact position then I'm in trouble. On the other hand, this pot is only slightly harder and I've much more leeway on the position …" In fact, a good title for this book might be 'always try and leave yourself some leeway'!

You might think the pool analogy is a little simplistic. However, consider one of the most infamous instances of a failure to ask 'what if?'. On Piper Alpha a very expensive fire wall was installed when North Sea platform was modified for gas production as well as oil. That seems sensible at first glance – except it's very rare to have a gas fire that is not caused by a gas explosion, and the fire wall wasn't blastproof.

# 2.2 The 'Mindful' Safety Culture

In *Managing the Risks of Organisational Accidents* James Reason suggests that two case studies he presents in the book reveal "a common reason why defensive weaknesses are not detected and repaired: that the people involved had '*forgotten to be afraid*'". He argues that organisations conducting potentially hazardous operations need a requisite imagination – a diversity of thinking and imagining that matches the variety of possible failure scenarios.

It is always possible, with the benefit of hindsight, to notice the presence of all sorts of warning signs, which, if heeded, could have prevented the accident. At the time, however, participants do not have this 'outcome knowledge' and, in their shoes, the accident that is just about to happen looks 'impossible'. At Buncefield, many operators were described as shocked, bemused and struggling to understand what had happened, saying "that simply can't be the case" and "I just don't understand how that happened". With workers undertaking a punishing switch shift programme, and averaging 50 to 60 hours overtime a month, such confusion was entirely predictable, as were the mistakes that helped cause what turned out to be the biggest explosion in Europe since WW2.

In a similar vein is the concept of the 'mindful' safety culture, as articulated by Prof Andrew Hopkins, who has studied the causes of major accidents around the world. He insists that organisations must be 'mindful' if they are to have a strong safety culture. Again, they must *not forget to be afraid*. Hopkins stresses that good safety leadership will occasionally involve the loss of sleep to the thought "but how do I *know* XYZ won't happen?" There will always be lots of weaknesses in the system and the essence of the best companies is that they proactively go out and find out what these are rather than passively waiting for these weaknesses to *find them*. (The key word in the sentence is "find" not just 'go out'. A white paper by Predictive Solutions in 2012 contained the fascinating finding, consistent with Hopkins' mindful theory, that too many '100-per-cent safe' audits correlated well with incidents.)

For example, Reason discusses the Barings Bank collapse. Barings knew they had weaknesses in the system and were actively trying to correct them but "not quickly enough to avert the disaster". The Group treasurer is reported by Reason as commenting: "There was always something else that seemed more pressing." Quite.

This mindfulness must come from the top, and Hopkins says bluntly that "Leaders set the tone and managers have to live with that". He's being simplistic and provocative, of course, to start a debate (and admits as much), as it's the supervisors who set the tone day to day – though always taking their cue from senior management.

The intention of this book is to use the 80:20, or Pareto principle (which suggests that you get 80 per cent of the output from the first 20 per cent of input) to give managers practical tools that will allow any organisation to positively address the key elements of culture change.

## 2.3 The Knot in the Rubber Band Model – Summarising All This Theory into a Simple Exercise/Concept

When I present to a board, CFO, executive directors and the like I try to use a very simple practical exercise to summarise the above theories into one, sticky, hands-on exercise. It's based on James Reason's concept of an overstretched elastic band from the book *The Human Contribution*.

Imagine a knot in the middle of a large rope and a tug-of-war team on either end. When the left-hand side is winning, the company is safe – when the right-hand side is winning, the company is in danger. When the teams are drawing and the knot is in the middle, then there is a genuine balance of safety and productivity. (This could be

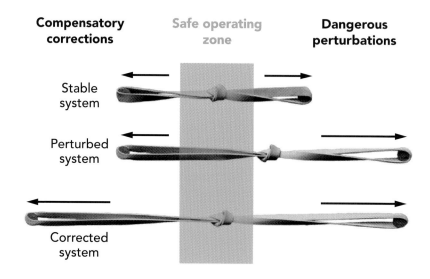

**Figure 6. The knot in the rubber band** Source: Adapted from James Reason, 2008

considered a version of the famous 'Balanced Scorecard' concept.)

Reason says that once we start work in the modern world then all sorts of pressures will automatically try and pull the rope away from balance – such as changes in material prices, contractors who don't perform as they promised they would, competitors, new legislation, and unexpected delays. It doesn't have to be an infamous 'black swan' that causes problems; a few white swans swimming in harmony will do just fine! (The concept of a 'black swan' is being used more and more in the media to describe where something unlikely but devastating actually happens. BP's Deepwater Horizon, the New York storm and the Japanese tsunami are famous examples. The concept is used to encourage in-depth "what if?" worst-case scenario thinking. This is manifest most obviously in such as the Bow Tie concept when teams of experts will map out the various possible causes of an incident and the various ways an incident might be contained one it has occurred. This will be discussed in a little more detail below).

Hopkins points out that a problem with BP at its Texas City site was that the company was overly focused on lost-time injury rates and seemed 'blind' to the possibility of a rare but catastrophic process safety event – despite incidents at its Grangemouth refinery in Scotland. It has been suggested by Hopkins and others that process safety needs a separate and specific focus. I'm not sure I agree, because the (deep) root cause of both personal and process safety issues is nearly always the same (poor planning, poor communication, lack of commitment and/or lack of investment etc) but I do agree that "what if?" questions can help give safety conversations and risk assessments a more holistic feel.

The key is to not ever become overstretched so that the knot moves from a position of genuine balance and the company is *vulnerable*. When vulnerable, an incident is more likely and investigators will take a dim view when it's seen in hindsight that the organisation had overstretched and was indeed 'an accident waiting to happen'.

This is entirely analogous to the key principles of the UK guidance HSG48, which covers human error and says:

Design the job so that error is unlikely;

Make sure you have mechanisms in place to spot it when it (inevitably) happens; and

Make sure you can respond quickly.

# Safety is a Guerrilla War

Related to this, Reason has suggested that safety is best thought of as an ongoing *guerrilla war* and, like any such war, you can't win it in the long run but you can delay defeat almost indefinitely. To do so you'll need keen intelligence and data and use whatever resources you have at our disposal cleverly.

The best organisations have systems aligned with the correct mindset so they can spot an overstretch (or a potential overstretch) quickly and be able to snap back quickly before something goes wrong.

We don't need to get into a semantic argument about whether this is proactive or reactive. It's definitely reactive if we find something that needs action immediately, it's definitely proactive if it's spotted at the design stage, and it's somewhere in between if we find something systemically causing risky behaviour.

# Target Zero?

Some managers I've spoken to report that although they buy into the *concept* of target zero the *reality* can seem daunting – even demotivating. (Summing up the debate my colleague Paul Bizzell often quotes the saying "Zero is the noblest of *aims* but the daftest of *targets*"). If you have 120,000 workers worldwide then the first lost-time injury is likely to arrive early in the New Year, no matter how excellent your safety standards. What's vital is that you don't become despondent and fatalistic about this reality. The rubber band model seems one that managers find best expresses their experience.

At a major conference in Prague in the summer of 2013 a presenter raised the concept of aiming for 'zero *risk*'. That took some moderating, I can assure you, with the more reasoned responses including one from the delegate who pointed out that we'd all flown to Prague, having driven to the airport, in order to learn something useful so that overall risk might best be *minimised…*

This book is intended, to an extent, as a pocket guide to fighting an effective guerrilla safety war. Risk cannot be eliminated in life, nor would eliminating it be very adaptive for our progress as a species, let alone for an organisation. We do not want a culture that is risk-averse; we want a culture that is **risk literate.**

# Summary

Having a strong safety culture should never be your 'number one priority' – it should be a core value. Firstly, the word 'priority' is far too often used in a sentence full of warm vague words with a faint whiff of farmyard about it. Secondly, priorities are political and they change all the time. I do not want my children to work for an organisation where safety may, or may not be, this week's number one priority! It should be an inviolate core value, and organisations where it is understand that there is always bad news to be found and that they need to proactively seek these weaknesses out rather than wait for the weaknesses to find them.

To summarise, I'd like to suggest six clusters of behaviours that best distinguish a proactive company from a merely compliant one:

Learning Commitment – Proactive companies have Just Culture as a cornerstone of their culture, assume from a mindful mindset that there will be a lot to learn, and take every opportunity to learn what's going wrong and why.

Effective Communication – All companies communicate about safety but it is how well and how often that distinguishes the best. Casanova didn't get his reputation from having sex badly, once a month!

Workforce Involvement, Ownership and Empowerment – The best companies seek to maximise these, whenever feasible.

Lead by Example – The management of the best companies know that the worst standards they set are the best they can expect from their workforce.

Challenge Frequently and Constructively – Proactive companies don't turn regular blind eyes but regularly challenge unsafe acts, not just focusing on imminent danger but on day-to-day behaviours that are infrequent and risky.

Lead Measures – Proactive companies, by definition, use lead measures and lagging measures as their most important indicators. More than that, they use good quality lead measures.

# Chapter 3.
# Five Concepts that Enable 'Risk Literacy'

None of us will ever have the technological knowledge to keep an entire company safe on our own. We'll need to be employing (and listening to) experts in loading and lifting, fire safety, ventilation and health screening, among many other specialities. However, there are five concepts of which a good working knowledge will, through the application of the '80:20 principle', stand any individual in good stead, re: their 'risk literacy' score. I think that supervisors, in particular, would benefit from a working knowledge of these principles (as would all managers, safety representatives, etc. but supervisors are, as always, especially important).

The five concepts are:

Heinrich's Triangle – lately much derided by some but it is actually the principle that underpins much that is rational and proactive in this world!

The Safety Hierarchy and Reason's Cheese model – though most widely used in incident investigation it suggests a systematic way of looking for vulnerability (or 'overstretch', if you like);

Reason's 'Just Culture' model;

Dekker's 'new view' of human error, which emphasises the key mindset when out looking for vulnerability (or reactively at culpability); and

Leading and lagging Measures.

These concepts most directly address the 'learning' aspect of the basic holistic model but also inform and underpin the 'leading' and 'personal' elements. Again, we need to understand *why* we are doing something to maximise the likelihood of it being done skilfully and passionately.

## 3.1 Heinrich's Triangle and the Vital Importance of Day-to-Day Behaviour

There are two reasons why an explicitly behavioural focus is vital to a strong safety culture: firstly, because it correlates with loss and secondly, because 'behaviour breeds behaviour' and sets the tone. It's important to bear in mind that the simplistic explanation for bad behaviour is that it is caused by a bad attitude; consequently, attitudes are targeted with posters and inspirational speakers. These rarely work.

## Behaviour and Dissonance

In this chapter, which considers individuals, we will examine the whole notion of dissonance in more detail. Put simply, dissonance is the uncomfortable feeling we get if we think our thoughts and our behaviours are at odds with each other as we generally have a desire for them to be congruent. It's a fascinating, complex and often counterintuitive field. Often, we'll fudge and rationalise incongruent behaviour rather than ponder on our lack of consistency and change the behaviour. The downside is obvious but there is an upside which is that people who regularly behave more safely (for whatever reason) will tend to begin to see themselves as a 'safe' person. This mindset can then generalise to such as citizenship behaviours.

What has become known as 'broken window' theory (from Wilson and Kelling, 1982) and perhaps most famously and successfully applied in New York shows how apparently unrelated issues can have a big impact on day-to-day behaviours, triggering either positive or negative actions. (This was the initiative where broken windows - and other relatively simple issues - were quickly fixed as a matter of priority before they could set a tone that encouraged other negative behaviour like graffiti, shouting or lawlessness!).

Follow-up experiments by Cialdini and others have indeed shown that the amount of litter dropped on the floor increases in the presence of broken windows, litter, or even anti-social noise. The reverse is also true and, similarly, the colour pink has been found to sap violent drunks of their aggression – hence the *New York Times* best-selling book *Drunk Tank Pink*, by Adam Alter.

This is clearly a hugely important and potentially fruitful theme and it will be returned to in the section on 'Nudge' theory, below.

## The Amount of Unsafe Day-to-Day Behaviour Correlates Strongly with Risk

There is always a direct link between the number of unsafe acts and the number of accidents. Heinrich's original triangle (see Figure 7) suggested that there are, on average, 29 minor injuries and 300 near misses for every serious accident. The most recent HSE figures (see Figure 8) suggest – as best as can be extrapolated – 2 million unsafe behaviours per fatality.

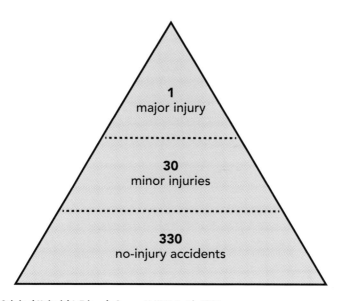

**Figure 7. Original Heinrich's Triangle** Source: H. W. Heinrich, 1931

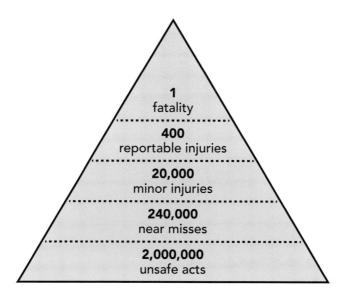

**Figure 8. Extended Heinrich's Triangle** Source: Adapted from H. W. Heinrich, 1950 and HSE figures

Trying to get a definitive study to quote from proved impossible but, that said, arguing over the exact levels in the ratio doesn't matter very much – the simple fact is that there is always is a triangle shaped ratio. (Definitions of 'accident' vary *within* countries, let alone *between* them and they depends hugely on the behaviour in question. If we're discussing driving far too close to the lorry in front of you at 70mph in bad weather, or corner cutting during the maintenance at a high-hazard organisation then 2 million unsafe acts per fatality would be rather optimistic!)

Despite quite a few recent articles questioning the ongoing relevance of Heinrich's work (see Dunlop, for example) on balance, we hurt many more people than we kill and we usually get away with a wide range of unsafe behaviour. Usually…

For example, if the true likelihood of falling down the stairs of a building is 100,000 to 1 and 1 million people use the stairs annually – and none of them hold the handrail – then there'll be 10 accidents a year (give or take). If 90 per cent comply, then there'll be one accident a year, on average, but if 99 per cent comply there'll be just one accident every 10 years, or so – and 'zero accidents' becomes a possibility.

Again, accurate data are very difficult to come by, but my best guesstimate is that the likelihood of falling down the stairs on a typical oil platform is indeed 100,000 to 1 and that the stairs on a typical platform will be used around a million times a year. According to the HSE Hazardous Installation Directorate in the UK around a third of all lost-time injuries in the offshore industry are caused by slips and falls and the cost to the industry is many millions of pounds, as some of those falling hurt themselves badly, and/or are very important to the day-to-day production process. What I can say with certainty is that on platforms with a strong safety culture and a keen behavioural focus few people fall down the stairs, while on platforms with a weak culture, rather more do!

It's a simple numbers game.

I once had a conversation with a wonderful pair of medics called Eddie and Graham on the Cormorant Alpha platform, which illustrates this. The award-winning behavioural safety team they were part of had supplied some sexier tinted sunglasses to replace the standard (unpopular) glasses previously on issue. They gave me a quote that sums up the behavioural approach perfectly:

"We don't say that more people are wearing their glasses when outside but we do say for certain that far fewer are having things blown into their eyes 'around the side of the glasses' they insist they were wearing. It's funny, that!"

# Heinrich, Probability and Immunity?

I was commissioned by the editor of the Safety and Health Practitioner to address why something catastrophic can happen to someone very experienced and safety conscious. The reason is exactly the same as why some children will be pulled alive from the wreckage of a building collapse: it is simply the law of **probability**. Some would suggest that such children's survival is a 'miracle' but the likes of Richard Dawkins would counter that if there was a divine entity with an eye on the building, why not prevent it collapsing in the first place? In Aberfan, in 1966, some 25 children were rescued from the Pantglas school, which was buried when an unstable slag heap slid down the mountain, killing 116 children.

On any given day, in any given situation, some people will be lucky and some will be unlucky. That isn't meant to sound fatalistic – it's just the probability curve. We simply can't guarantee good luck, not even for most vulnerable and deserving; we can only significantly impact how much luck we need. As will be discussed in a later chapter, training in 'situational awareness' skills (Flin *et al*) will help (think defensive driver training, with its proactive focus on driving to the distance, etc). Alternatively, we may give them some inspirational and/or high impact, person-focused input (sometimes claimed to be 'advanced behavioural safety'), where we seek to embed, for recall at important moments, a key motivational image, like our children at our funeral. These can be helpful for average workers (ideally as part of a holistic package and to *supplement* an analysis focus) but are really of little use to those workers addressed by the editor's question, who are already experienced, conscientious and motivated.

A much better strategy is **constantly** to try to move the task up the safety hierarchy by designing out the risk. This might involve foolproof fall-arrest technology that *never* needs unclipping. It might mean replacing all windows at height with the self-cleaning make. Instead of reminding workers to "be careful not to stand there", whenever possible, we must make it *impossible* to stand there or perfectly safe to stand there.

In some cases, a design solution is not possible, of course, but we should always be looking for one and never allow ourselves to get comfortable with a 'standard risk'. A mindset that 'that's just the nature of the beast – what can you do?' is the enemy of creative design necessary for continuous improvement.

Every normal distribution curve has outliers. Bad things happen to the best people because they are merely *less likely* to happen to them, rather than them being immune, and bad things are more likely to happen to good people in organisations with a weak safety culture simply because more bad things happen in general. Weak cultures focus too much on the individual and not enough on the environment so, to be perfectly safe, those people need superhuman levels of focus and concentration that simply can't be maintained, no matter how impactful the safety posters are. Worse, we must never forget that many experienced and conscientious workers get killed at work simply because they are standing next to something that blows up. (The folly of focusing too closely on behavioural safety at the expense of process safety is covered in other chapters.)

In my view, the Heinrich *principle* remains as valid as ever. It underpins every self-help book ever written and even the Buddhist philosophy from which the concept of 'mindfulness' comes. Gary Player didn't win every golf tournament he entered and some he even lost *unluckily*, but you've probably heard of him – he had a great career. Applying his advice to safety certainly helps individuals keep out of harm's way on any given day, but even more important is that the organisation works hard at developing a **holistic** culture of analysis, design, facilitation, empowerment and continuous improvement because the very best way to minimise the number of injuries to experienced, conscientious and safety-conscious people is to minimise the **total** number of injuries.

## Heinrich's Principle and *Gravity*

The Heinrich principle is important since, for most companies, the majority of accidents will be the result of simple slips, trips, falls and 'struck-bys' so although excellent process safety is utterly vital to ensure something catastrophic doesn't happen it's virtually impossible to have world-class safety figures without a behavioural approach.

The staircase example above is illustrative as the majority of accidents have gravity as the root cause and, however sophisticated our systems are, we can't design out gravity if we want to move our product or our people. (Think of any famous people who've been in the media following an accident. It's difficult to find any reports in which the word 'fall' isn't mentioned – from the tragic death of actress Natasha Richardson after a fall on a nursery ski slope, to Ozzie Osbourne falling off a quad bike and Keith Richards falling from a coconut tree.)

The Keith Richards example illustrates the point well. Richards enjoyed decades of quite alarming drug abuse that would have killed most ordinary people (in fact *did* kill many people who tried to keep up with him, such as fellow musician Gram Parsons). The Stones guitarist explained to a US 'men's journal' in July 2013 that he only cleaned up his lifestyle after he climbed up and fell out of the tree while intoxicated. He was badly injured and needed brain surgery and it was these injuries he suffered in a **fall** that finally convinced him to cut out the substance abuse.

Even call centre employees will usually have to climb stairs daily and for many giant utility companies the single most common type of accident is their salespeople tripping over in the street walking from house to house while trying to update their handheld devices as they go.

I'd like to give two other 'interesting facts' to illustrate the principle under discussion. The first is that 10 to 20 times as many people are killed each year by falling coconuts as by sharks, with the numbers usually around 150:10, according to George Burgess, director of the University of Florida's International Shark Attack File. So, we shouldn't be pointing out to sea shouting "Shark! Run for your lives" – we should be pointing at the trees behind us shouting "Coconut falling season and a stiff breeze – swim for your lives!" Similarly, though not wishing to down play the long-term dangers of nuclear energy, more people have already been killed in falls erecting wind farms than have ever been in nuclear accidents over the decades.

Please note that these figures are reported from the likes of 'awesome facts' websites, so not sources that necessarily merit inclusion in the reference section! It's the principle that's important.

**Home Safety Behaviours.** Because unsafe behaviours very rarely result in a near miss (let alone anything more serious) it's easy to assume they never will, and forget Heinrich's principle. But here's a final example to bear in mind: the first sunny weekend in spring in the UK will see lots of children bouncing around on trampolines all day, and many of them will be unguarded. By the end of the day, inevitably, a handful will have suffered what are called 'life-changing' injuries. I just can't tell you their names yet.

Again, it's a simple numbers game: the bigger the number at the bottom of the triangle the bigger the number at the top will be. More positively, the opposite is also true: the smaller the number at the bottom of the triangle, the smaller the top number will be. The more trampolines with good guarding, or that are sunk into the ground, the fewer accidents there will be. This time, of course, we'll *never* know the names of those saved.

# Behaviour Sets the Tone and is Self Reinforcing…

As well as the simple relationship between the bottom of the triangle and the top the second reason why behaviour is so important is that in many respects it *is* the organisational culture. The very best simple definition of safety culture is 'the way we typically do things around here' and in all walks of life a handful of key behaviours will set the tone, and the first thing we do in a new situation is look about and 'check out what's what'. If we see half the 'regulars' acting safely and half unsafely then, as a new start or sub-contractor, we can do pretty much what we want and not stand out. However, if we can improve these key behaviours so that 90 per cent (the fabled 'tipping point') then these behaviours become self-sustaining.

These key behaviours will range from simple 'hold the handrail', 'look where you're walking' and 'use PPE', as above, through to the quality of a toolbox talk. Are these delivered with passion and clarity and confirmed understanding, or are they rattled off with a mumble and a "sign here, I don't even care if you don't speak my language and didn't understand that, just so long as you sign" approach. At board level this could be manifested in the form of an MD who closes out a strategy meeting that discussed cost cutting with an aggressive "any problems with that!? No? Good! Get on with it, then."

## Behaviour and Peer Influence

Studies suggest that the majority of what we learn is from our peers and only a small minority from formal training. Lombardo and Eichinger, in *The Career Architect Development Planner,* for example, posit a 70:20:10 model. They suggest that learning comes from "feedback, a mistake, watching other people's reactions, failing or not being up to a task – in other words, from experience". Around 70 per cent of development will be the result of on-the-job experiences and working on tasks and problems; about 20 per cent will result from feedback and working around good and bad examples of the need; and 10 per cent will result from courses and reading.

It's important here to distinguish between peer pressure and peer influence. The latter is a much more subtle and subconscious phenomenon. Peer pressure is where individuals make active efforts to influence your behaviour. As well as obvious examples from gang culture a famous example in the UK would be the politicians' expenses scandal. The culture had developed of claiming lavishly to top up what were seen as rather low salaries (because MP pay rises tend to play very badly in the press). This left many MPs seeing their expenses as part of an overall and perfectly legitimate income. Several of the newer MPs who didn't 'over' claim testified at the subsequent inquiry that they had been taken to one side and told: "You don't understand. . .people like you are making things difficult. Claim more!" This is peer *pressure.* Peer *influence* is a subtler and less conscious process.

A practical example of that principle: imagine arriving in a new country and being told by the hire car people "We're very strict with speeding on this island. . .don't even think about exceeding 80kph" and seeing this reinforced by huge threatening signs on the road as you drive out of the airport. (See Road sign Reconstruction) You'd very probably join the motorway at 75kph but you quickly determine that the inside lane is averaging 90, the middle 120, and the outside lane is a complete free

**Photo 1. Road sign** Reconstruction

for all. What speed do you think you'd be doing five minutes later? (At conferences I used to ask the question "what speed would you be doing 10 minutes later?" However, on the back of a number of "well, you have to keep up with the flow for safety" comments, I started asking "how many of us would have used the outside lane within half an hour?" Interestingly, it's always about 50 per cent – or more – who say they would!)

Even a reference to a social norm can have a meaningful influence on behaviour. For example, it's important never ever to suggest that the individual is part of a bigger problem and that lots of others are guilty, too. When a problem is raised in an organisation, pointing out for emphasis that "everyone does it" hardly ever makes peole think "oh, that's terrible!" Instead, most people would take that to mean "that's OK, then", and the closer to home the reference group, the more powerful this effect is. So, if you could get away with it, an ideal thing to say would be something like: "No one else who works here, now or ever before, has ever done this unsafely." On motorway signs in the UK we've started displaying signs saying "Take litter home, other people do". Similarly, tax reminders will say "You haven't returned your forms yet and nearly everyone else in your district has" using this showed an increase in compliance, compared with simple reminders, from 68 to 83 per cent

(Lawton, 2013). These are attempts to influence behaviour by the government 'nudge' team – a concept we'll return to in depth later.

### Taking this One Step Further – A True Imperative to Active Peer Intervention: Taboo

Though this 90 per cent compliance rate leads to the majority of new starts and subcontractors following suit, and is self reinforcing, there is another level of norm at which a more active response will almost certainly be elicited from colleagues. This is where the norm is both strong and valued, so that in the event of someone undertaking this behaviour they will almost certainly be actively challenged. For example, imagine a visiting rugby fan at the Millennium Stadium in Cardiff. The norm is very much to be welcoming and friendly, win or lose.

(In truth, if the visiting fans are from England and the England team is winning, then the friendliness might be absent but the worst you'll see is Welsh fans suffering in silence! Even then, what you'll hardly ever see is hostility, or even verbal aggression. If someone has just got too upset and/or drunk and forgets themselves, as does happen from time to time, then, without fail, someone will lean forward and tap the miscreant on the shoulder and warn them to "cut that out!" On the rare occasions where they *don't* cut it out, then their own fans will alert the stewards to the problem. Well, I'm assured that's what happens – I've seen only a handful of 'taps' in all my years and never seen one ignored).

The same is true of junior rugby. Occasionally, a player's father (almost inevitably more used to watching junior football) will loudly offer a few choice remarks about the referee's objectivity, competence, or parentage. This is still totally taboo at junior rugby level and simply won't be tolerated. Automatically, other parents will say something and insist the person cease or leave. Resistance is futile, as having two teams, a referee and all other spectators stop and unite against you is almost impossible to battle on against – although the language as they walked off on the two occasions I've seen this first hand *was* pretty colourful.

(Mind you, at international matches the referees' objectivity, competence and parentage may well be savagely abused by these self same touchline-policing parents! Alternatively, if some thuggish prop forward has illegally felled a local player and is abused as an "effing French &%$£" then the person will most often turn to the nearest French fan with a cheery "no offence boys!" as the spirit of welcome must be maintained.)

Where what is allowed and *not* allowed is clear and widely understood we might like to think of such behaviours as 'taboo' – something that 'just isn't done', to give it a behavioural definition. Overriding a lockout system, photocopying a risk assessment, or signing a permit blindly in organisations where that simply isn't done would be obvious safety examples. Just about anything safety related on a nuclear submarine and other genuinely high-reliability organisations would fall into this category. Finding out if a risky behaviour is indeed actually 'taboo' isn't difficult with the right conversational approach. If it isn't, the culture can be strengthened.

## Linking Behaviour to Habits and Culture: Everyone is Involved

To summarise the issues covered so far: although vision statements and company values are vital in setting the tone they are the very definition of 'necessary but not sufficient'. They (should!) certainly influence the culture but they are not *it*, the day-to-day behaviour is – and it is almost impossible to overstate its importance.

For this reason, absolutely *everyone* is involved in the safety culture. Everything we do, or don't do ripples. Every time we say something, or don't say something we contribute. We contribute to the culture of an organisation all day and every day, whether we want to or not.

On training courses I often use some real life closed-circuit television footage of a young man being knocked off a motorbike by a driver undertaking an illegal U-turn to escape a traffic jam. The motorcyclist is compliant, as he wasn't speeding and had every right to be using the outside lane. However, he wasn't driving proactively (proactive driving principles being such as 'always give yourself the time and space to deal with the mistakes of others as well as your own' and 'assume everyone else is a drunken idiot').

I once showed this footage to some managers when team training with an ex special services soldier, who was waiting to teach them defensive driving techniques. He said something very interesting:

"You all know me as someone very risk tolerant (we knew him to be an ex SAS soldier) and if you saw me riding my motorbike in the woods on a weekend you'd be mortified at the risks I'm comfortable taking. But this simply wouldn't have happened to me because though I'm very risk tolerant, I'm also very risk aware and I'd have noticed the curve in the road reducing visibility; I'd have noticed all those frustrated drivers and that there was no barrier separating them from me – and without thinking about it, I'd have moved to the inside lane to give myself some space…"

As well as a simple demonstration of the American behavioural safety expert Scott Geller's assertion that "Safety must be part of the very DNA, something we do without thinking about it – just part of who we are" this also illustrates a key point about behavioural safety.

Often, when we're tired and distracted, the **only** thing that can save us is our good habits.

## Behaviour, Heinrich and Process Safety

It's worth acknowledging that the Heinrich ratios do vary, depending on the behaviours in question and the potential outcomes. Some of these behaviours are frequent and reasonably trivial in terms of likelihood (though note that, as above, even trips on flat surfaces cause multiple fatalities every year).

Others are less frequent but more likely to cause fatalities – a steeper triangle, if you like. This is especially true in terms of *process* safety issues. For this reason, much of the criticism of Heinrich has been along the lines of 'they were too busy counting hard hats, people holding the handrail and the like to notice the place was falling apart and about to blow up!' Lynn Dunlop, in *Beyond the safety triangle* quotes an Andrew Hale as saying: "We are not going to get very far in preventing chemical industry disasters by encouraging people to hold the handrail when walking down the stairs." It's a great quip but whoever suggested we would? (In response, we are never going to get close to LTI-free, either, without a focus on handrail holding, as, typically, a third of accidents – or more – at any site are falls.) BP at Texas City didn't have an *active* strategy to keep process safety under control through a low LTI rate – they simply sleepwalked into a vulnerable position because they were unduly reassured by strong personal safety scores. That's just a lack of holistic risk literacy.

I'd like to mount a defence of behavioural safety here and argue that the two things aren't separate but instead interlink and overlap. A good example of an overlap would be the housekeeping on the Piper Alpha oil platform, which was notoriously poor. The North Sea platform exploded in July 1988, with the loss of 167 lives.

Again quoting Hale, Lynn Dunlop says: "A large release of flammable chemicals. . .will produce more fatalities than objects dropped from scaffolding. . .at this level of cause there is only a very limited overlap between major and minor injuries" but the implication of this line of reasoning is far too black and white and focused on the wrong level of cause. Any meaningful analysis of the poor housekeeping before the accident would have taken the auditor straight to the permit-to-work system (weaknesses in which were, arguably, considered *the* key cause of the explosion). The permits contained a 'has the housekeeping been put right?' element, which, in light of the poor housekeeping would have clearly demonstrated a tick-box mentality lacking control. Obviously, this would have been a very useful issue to have addressed in early 1988.

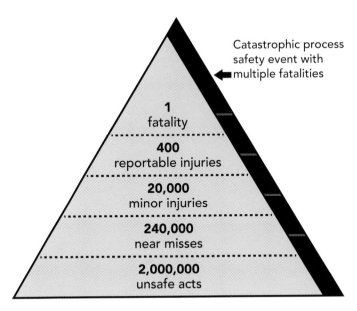

Catastrophic process
safety event with
◀ multiple fatalities

**1**
fatality

**400**
reportable injuries

**20,000**
minor injuries

**240,000**
near misses

**2,000,000**
unsafe acts

**Figure 9. Extended Heinrich's Triangle and Process Safety** Source: Adapted from H. W. Heinrich & HSE figures

We know that much unsafe behaviour will be caused, in large part, by complex organisational weaknesses around communication, ergonomics, staffing and resource that can have devastating organisational consequences.

The basic Heinrich (or Gary Player) principle still holds: halving the number of poor handovers, weak communications, simplistic decisions, or mindless 'tick-box and file' audits **will** reduce the number of process-safety incidents, big and small. In-depth, analytic conversations are much harder than hard-hat head counts and that's why they happen less often. It takes more effort.

Anyone suggesting *their* data don't support the above position is somehow collecting the wrong data and/or collecting inaccurate data! Drilling 'kicks' are a good example: on Deepwater Horizon, though personal safety was being very well monitored, nobody was really monitoring the likelihood of a blow-out. No one even reacted effectively when it started to actually happen. (The mindset that they were *confirming* capping success rather than testing for it combined with some groupthink when one person raised concerns was mentioned earlier). Before a well blows out it 'kicks' – a kick being the entry of enough oil and gas into the well bore to create upward pressure. If employees do not realise that a well has 'kicked' and take corrective action, then it can blow.

Again, the very definition of a strong safety culture is the speed with which it is noticed that something has gone wrong and the speed with which action is taken to contain the risk (if it's something dynamic) or rectify the problem (if it's something incremental). In hindsight, it's alarming that few oil companies collect data either about the number of 'kicks' they experience, or the speed with which they are spotted.

So, although the dedicated safety conversation that this book covers can never take the place of effective and interlinked systems, monitoring and auditing it certainly should complement them, and a good safety conversation really should seek to directly address these in depth issues when possible. Even when it doesn't directly address them an intelligent, open conversation even about something as 'relatively trivial' as housekeeping, or PPE compliance could reveal an underlying cause that could be instrumental in causing a catastrophic process issue.

Andrew Hopkins, in *Disastrous Decisions*, points out that it makes no sense to tour a site looking for trip hazards and lack of PPE when there are process issues to be spotted too. Not only should we take the opportunity while out there ticking boxes to talk to people about their problems with skips, lay-down areas, and access to user-friendly PPE we must also talk about process safety issues and not worry about 'looking foolish' and thus only stick to the obvious and visible items.

To refer back to the Bradley curve, admitting that you don't understand something doesn't make people think you're stupid. It actually does two very positive things, according to researchers like Robert Cialdini and Noah Goldstein. First, it makes people think you're *interested* and second, it has the very welcome side effect of increasing their levels of trust in you because of your humility.

# Situational Awareness

A link between behavioural and process safety is the concept of situational awareness, as discussed by Rona Flin *et al* in *Safety at the Sharp End*. This, quite explicitly, describes a day-to-day combination of the experience and awareness of our special-forces motorcyclist and the 'mindful' mindset, as recommended by Andrew Hopkins. It is most often attributed to high risk activities, like aviation and surgery, but is a simple model that is useful for all aspects of safety, or even for managing life itself.

It suggests that individuals are best advised to effectively gather data, interpret that data skilfully and then accurately anticipate what's likely to happen next. A simple example might be driving along a normally quiet country lane and noticing two children with painted faces and carrying a goldfish in a plastic bag. This means a country fair of some description is almost certainly nearby and that slowing down is advisable, as there are likely to be a lot of excited (and unpredictable) children about. The person low in situational awareness would barely notice the children, or would simply think: "They should be careful walking along here!"

The most obvious example of this in action would be in a 'commentary drive', where the student would get good marks for articulating: "We are coming to the end of the M6 toll, where the signage is notoriously confusing. I'm assuming half the drivers around me are looking up rather than at the road, and that half of them will soon change direction suddenly, so I've taken my two-second gap and doubled it to a four-second gap, though remembering that that two-second gap is a minimum, not an ideal – even in good weather." It would also be seen in the sort of in depth task analysis often undertaken in safety-critical organisations

Factors important for encouraging situational awareness would include: clear two-way communications; minimising fatigue and distractions through good planning and design (especially at critical times); and regular monitoring. The only elements that can't be taught or designed for are experience and natural 'monitor evaluator' intelligence. Think Sherlock Holmes versus Homer Simpson, perhaps.

## Why You Can't Address Behaviour by Exhorting "Have A Good Attitude"?

The most obvious approach to safety that focuses on the individual is the behavioural one – hence, the 1001 versions of 'behavioural safety'. Unfortunately, many simply exhort people to behave more safely, trying to encourage a 'better attitude'. This is an approach doomed to failure, as no one thinks that they have a bad attitude. As mentioned above, most of us think we're entirely rational and reasonable!

Just about every study of anything shows that 50 per cent of us think we have an average attitude and 50 per cent a good attitude. A Scottish study of drivers reported in the UK media quoted figures of around 48 per cent above average and 49 per cent average. I couldn't find the original source to quote accurately but, in searching, I found an older American study, in which more than *80 per cent* of drivers rated themselves as 'above average' on a whole range of scales (see McCormick *et al*). So, when we talk about people who cut corners and take risks and say "you know who you are!" everyone will point to the person next to them and say "I hope you're listening to this – they're talking about you" (because any risks *I* take are thought through and appropriate, and because there's nothing wrong with my attitude, thank you very much).

Here's a question for you: have you ever won an argument about sport, politics or religion? Ever? and another: Have you changed an attitude about any of those subjects in the last 20 years?

Inspirational speakers can help get through this denial in the short-term, just as new football managers can induce a sudden boost in performance – the 'honeymoon period'. After listening to an inspirational speaker, who may be talking from a wheelchair after being paralysed in a fall, we may find ourselves thinking: "Yes, I suppose that could be me" and vowing to make a greater effort to cut fewer corners. However, this honeymoon period hardly ever lasts and, soon enough, we are back to the old levels of performance.

Unless, that is, we change something. In football terms, it might be cleverly re-organising the team, better organisation at set pieces, or improving fitness levels. In safety terms, we need to change the working environment – otherwise, the maxim 'If you do what you always did, you get what you always got' applies. That's the bad news, but the good news is that the relationship between behaviour and attitude is two-way and dynamic and something we can use in our favour. This is discussed in depth under the section on individuals' cognitive dissonance below.

## 3.2 The Safety Hierarchy of Control and Reason's Cheese Model
### Safety Hierarchy

A key element of risk literacy for all is an understanding of the safety hierarchy. This suggests that the higher up the hierarchy our solutions, the more effective they will be. There are several versions of the basic hierarchy, and most safety professionals will find the following few pages superfluous. They are included for the line manager, as is the Cheese model, which may also be familiar to readers with a safety background.

One simple model goes by the acronym 'ERICPD', where the last letter stands for discipline, though this is not about monitoring and disciplining but rather situational awareness, as introduced above.

To consider the other elements in turn, from least to most desirable:

**PPE.** PPE is the least effective way to control hazards because of the high potential for equipment to become ineffective owing to damage, or for it not be work appropriately. In addition, some PPE, such as respirators, increase the physical effort required to complete a task so there may be 'unintended consequences' to deal with. For example, wearing ear plugs helps protect against long-term damage to hearing but may lead to an infection if plugs are dirty, and certainly means that you'll

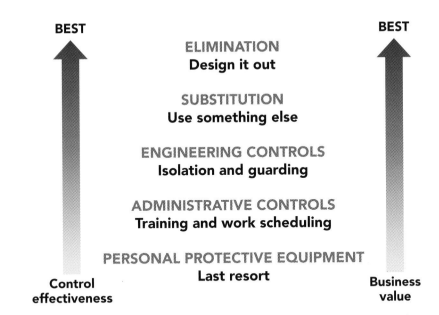

**BEST**

**BEST**

**ELIMINATION**
**Design it out**

**SUBSTITUTION**
**Use something else**

**ENGINEERING CONTROLS**
**Isolation and guarding**

**ADMINISTRATIVE CONTROLS**
**Training and work scheduling**

**PERSONAL PROTECTIVE EQUIPMENT**
**Last resort**

**Control
effectiveness**

**Business
value**

**Figure 10. Hierachy of Controls**

have one of your key senses impaired. Similarly, heavy overalls increase fatigue and reduce speed. Protective gloves reduce feel and manual dexterity. And so on.

Risk literacy is moving from Kahneman's fast thinking to slow thinking, with a consideration of the unintended consequences.

**Engineering.** Engineering controls do not eliminate hazards, but rather keep people isolated from the hazard – using extractor fans to remove harmful particles would be a good example, as would using platforms instead of ladders for work at height.

**Administrative Controls.** These controls do not eliminate hazards either, but seek to limit peoples' exposure to the hazard by changing the way people work – for example, completing road construction at night, when fewer people will be driving.

**Substitution**. The second most effective way to control hazards is substitution, which involves removing something that produces a hazard (similar to elimination) and replacing with something that does not produce a hazard. An example of substitution is replacing lead-based paint with acrylic paint.

**Elimination**. Finally, elimination of the hazard is the most effective means of hazard control. It involves the physical removal of the hazard. For example, if employees are required to work high above the ground, the hazard can be eliminated by moving the piece they are working on to ground level to eliminate the need to work at height.

**Cost Effectiveness and Unintended Consequences**. As you can imagine, the costs of engineering controls tend to be higher than those of the less effective controls within the hierarchy. However, they may reduce future costs and prove cost effective in the long-term. For example, a one-off cost of building a work platform may be cheaper in the long-term than maintaining and replacing fall arrest equipment.

On the other hand, we must be wary of applying this simple model without risk literacy. For example, I've seen very expensive extractor systems installed to remove the need for PPE. The new senior manager ordered the one he had used at his previous place of employment. It was the most expensive but it wasn't the best choice and, worse, it was badly installed and badly maintained and didn't provide anywhere near as much protection in practice as the PPE did!

# Case Study

Nestlé reported (HSW, January 2013) a reduction in their accident frequency rate from 6.5 per million man-hours to 1.6 million – due, in large part, to a design-stage risk assessment scheme. It simply made every effort to design out hazards before machinery and processes were engineered and installed. The company aimed for 'right first time, rather than the expense of a retrofit' reasoning that not only is machinery downtime expensive but the retrofit adjustments might be limited in scope. It recognised that while it was good at designing machinery it was less good at the machine/worker interaction and building in slip hazards and manual-handling issues.

The assessment of risk at the design stage was conducted by a group led by process engineers and including craftspeople, engineers and union reps. They systematically assessed goods receipt, manufacturing, packaging and despatch. They considered the issues around normal operations but also abnormal operations, cleaning and maintenance. Each section was thought through for slips, handling issues and health risks, the aim being to eliminate the risk, or at least mitigate it.

Nestlé reported that the involvement of the shop floor helped because of their hands-on knowledge and that the element of ownership proved motivating. I'm very tempted to make the famous sarcastic comment that references Sherlock Holmes but will simply note that it was deemed worthy of a dedicated article in a magazine because it isn't a standard approach.

Rather than say something as obvious as "I think it *should* be standard" can I suggest that anyone tempted to plonk a machine or process into the middle of a workplace without going through this process should then have to work on it for a week. I'd like to argue that, very predictably, the Nestlé management noted that the process was 'quite straightforward', with a review of a simple piece of plant taking just a day and workers being 'keen to get involved'. The changes suggested in the pilot project included making access easier where tools were required to be taken in, and ground-level testing facilities to remove the need for workers to carry out work at height and in confined spaces. The manager of the scheme reported that: "All of these (changes) involved just a little thought up front. Though we didn't get everything, we got 90 per cent, and most equipment is designed to last 30 years."

## Reason's Cheese Model

Reason's famous Swiss Cheese model (figure 11) shows that the more weaknesses there are in an organisation (or holes in the Swiss cheese) – from strategy management decisions, through supervision and process safety, on to individual actions – the more likely the holes in the slices of Swiss cheese are to line up and an accident occur. It is arguably the most influential model in all of safety literature.

The model shows that *with the benefit of hindsight* all accidents could have been prevented, and it has directly influenced the various 'target zero' campaigns.

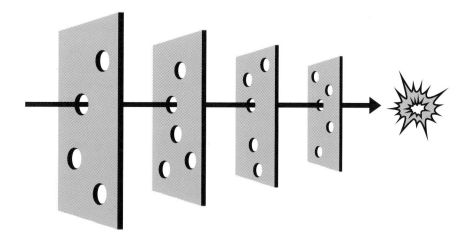

**Figure 11. Reason's Swiss Cheese model** Source: Adapted from James Reason, 2008

(Hindsight will be discussed in the next sub section).

Reason gives the financial example of Barings Bank, where the structure of the overseas operation was such that 'rogue trader' Nick Leeson's activities "were not closely monitored by anyone. . .with his local supervisors reluctant to supervise him. He was always regarded as someone else's responsibility."

This case study is the very definition of the phrase 'if two people think they're responsible, then no one is' and a classic example of a latent failure just waiting for an opportunity to break out. Leeson had access to an awful lot of money.

Another memorable example from Reason is the Nakina train derailment. In this incident, a train track was built on a beaver dam, which was long a *latent* problem since the track was built in 1916. It wasn't a *practical* problem, however, until the rail company enacted a policy of killing beavers in the vicinity of the track, some 70 years later. On the surface, this operation – to 'minimise the problems of flooding and washouts of railway infrastructure associated with beaver activity' – made sense but the subsequent lack of beavers meant the beaver dam soon fell into disrepair through lack of regular maintenance. . .

This is an unusual accident, in that there were no active failures on the part of maintenance or users – the only 'cause' was a latent weakness that lay undetected for 76 years.

More recently, there was the sinking of the cruise ship Costa Concordia off the coast of Italy. The ship's captain's alleged refusal to get back on board once he was safely on a life boat didn't play at all well with the media and ensured he received very little sympathy. As discussed in the introduction, often the most important factor is not the facts of the matter but norms, expectations and psycho-social elements.

However, there is, as always, more to the incident than meets the eye. For example, every newspaper reported that having completed a successful pass of the coast previously the captain had been sent a congratulatory note by the mayor of the town, thanking him for the 'wonderful spectacle'.

Reason summarises the latent weaknesses as relating to the organisational weaknesses: designing, constructing, operating, maintaining, communicating, selecting, training supervising and managing. This is an 'incomplete list' but it contains the 'generic essentials' of any productive process that shows why safety should not be treated as a separate issue.

**Practical Application of the Cheese Model**. I once gave a talk to a shipbuilder about this model, who, after thinking about the strategic implications of the dangers inherent in the business, approached me and said: "We should never have agreed to build this ship this way."

Recently, however, Reason himself has suggested that the model isn't *always* entirely helpful and his later 'knot in the rubber band' model illustrates why target zero campaigns can prove so controversial. (I wish I had a pound for every heated debate about whether target zero is best seen as a concept!)

To return to the shipbuilding example, we can say that in an ideal world we wouldn't build ships this way but it is, of course, *not* an ideal world. A more pragmatic view would be to say that *somebody* was bound to agree to build the ship this way, so it might as well be us, as we need the work. Consequently, pockets of vulnerability were **inevitably** going to pop up from time to time and from place to place, even if, overall, the culture is strong and the planning thorough. The trick, then, is to be geared to spot these emerging vulnerabilities quickly and respond promptly – an approach that is entirely consistent with the 'overstretched elastic band model' described above.

## Haddon Cave Variation on Bow Tie

A simple and much-used variation on Reason's Cheese model has been the 'bow

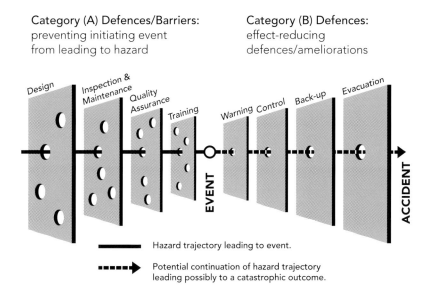

**Figure 12. Haddon-Cave Report's 'Bow-Tie' analogy**

tie'. The aim of the  bow tie is to facilitate a systematic assessment of events after an incident, or potential incident. Similar to the overstretched elastic-band model, it describes not how quickly an organisation can respond to vulnerability but how effectively it can respond when something has gone wrong. Infamously, in the case of the Piper Alpha platform, it was not very well at all starting with the lack of emergency-response training and the fact that the fire wall wasn't blast-proof.

Recently, Charles Haddon Cave QC led the inquiry into a Nimrod plane crash and proposed the variation in figure 12. Used proactively and systemically these clearly hugely useful when planning defences. Patrick Hudson has pointed out that often these analyses can be weak at incorporating the human factor and has suggested a third level of analysis with Bow Tie looking explicitly at Human Factor and cultural issues. (A simple example: The only line of defence is a nurse not mistakenly reading a doctors notes or the label on a phial and both doctor and nurse are fatigued).

Much has been written about and excellent research undertaken into these models before. The intention of this book is not to reinvent the wheel but to try to set them in proper context and to provide some material that will help users of these models understand the cultural and psychological issues associated. Forgetting that you can't have a gas fire without it starting with a blast and that, therefore, if the fire wall isn't blast proof it will be little use as a fire wall is, thankfully, a rare event. Mistaken assumptions about culture and psychology are rather more common. For example a bow tie analysis might identify that a level could overfill (as at Texas City) and that poor maintenance of a gauge could therefore be a threat as could a failure to check the gauge as often as scheduled. Ideally, this analysis will decide this non compliance is possible and will beget a physical failsafe – another barrier.

An explicit aim of this book is to produce a text that will be useful to even experienced individuals about to undertake a bow tie exercise. As standard, we should be asking the following questions of the engineer tasked with checking the gauge: How easy is the gauge to physically check? How easily might a reading be misunderstood? How easily can an engineer realise the gauge is faulty? How well does the engineer understand the task and the importance of the task? How does an organisation react to an engineer who fails to undertake the task? If the answers to these questions make uncomfortable reading, and I reference Piper Alpha, early flight decks, Texas City, Bhopal and any number of other well known incidents, then sooner rather than later that physical failsafe is going to be tested in anger.

# 3.3 'Just Culture'
## Rationale

Like Hopkins, Reason suggests that key to a strong culture is that it is an informed one. The only way to maintain a state of respectful wariness is to gather the right kind of data, as we cannot assume no news is good news. This will require a reporting culture where hazards are actively sought and reported upwards.

This only works well where there is little blame and high levels of trust, as we cannot have excellent reporting without a belief that the effort will be worthwhile. If not, the inertia of 'extra work', the embarrassment of making an error, and a residual concern that someone will get into trouble (maybe you!) will see to it that the best response is to keep your head down.

This *literally* reminds me of an accident in a large pharmaceutical company, which was reported to me on a training course. A forklift truck driver had got into the habit of timing his run under a lifting door to perfection, except for the day when he mistimed it and knocked himself unconscious. He lay on the floor undiscovered for four hours before coming round and dusting himself down. He never reported it and the opportunity to look at some lone-worker issues – if nothing else! – was lost.

Clearly, to get useful information reporting needs to be confidential, blame free, easy to do, and perceived as valuable. Anonymity isn't easy in small companies and follow-up questions may be needed, so systems that close out the learning then erase all names are best. (Third parties like universities are useful, as are dedicated reporting bodies. In the UK, the rail incident reporting body CIRUS has proved very useful). Questionnaires need to be concise and questions worded in a way that encourages thought and depth of response but puts the onus on the person receiving the information to categorise it.

The technicalities of what to do about information that requires a disciplinary response are for other books to discuss. However, I'd like to say here that two things are true for a risk literate culture:

The greater the perception that 'keeping your head down' is best, the less the information flow; and

Accessing this learning proactively avoids the problem entirely - which is where learning-focused 'walk and talk' methodologies and workforce behavioural analysis teams come in. Don't learn from incidents when you can learn from near misses but even better, don't learn from near-misses when you can learn from behavioural risk analysis. (Please see chapter 9 for methodological details).

Of course, an entirely just culture isn't possible but one in which "the majority of members share a belief that justice will usually be dispensed" (Reason) *is* possible. Complete immunity from punishment isn't just in the case of genuinely reckless or vindictive actions, and an agreed set of principles needs to be in place before incidents occur. Dekker makes the point that "who gets to draw the line" is key; those on the receiving end must have contributed to the definitions to be used.

Dekker also makes the point that the more you look at the nature of 'truth' or 'justice' the greater the debate and controversy. It is "basically intractable, unmanageable" and his book, *Just Culture*, is full of examples in which the response to incidents appears arbitrary, unfair, simplistic and/or self-serving to an organisation. Relationships, on the other hand, *are* manageable. He concludes: "If you want to do something about just culture, then that is probably where to start."

For example, in a series of radio shows Reason made the case that patients who have suffered because of medical mistakes do not typically take the hospital to court unless they feel that's the only way they can get an honest account of what went wrong. (See also research by Berlinger.) The motivation to take action isn't primarily financial, or even to extract retribution – it's to force transparency and fairness.

Most staff know who the 'cowboys' are, and watching them get away with it time after time sets a bad precedent and is demoralising for more conscientious colleagues who have to watch this behaviour. The occasional 'head on a stick' not only demonstrates management's commitment it can have a symbolic importance. What's vital, of course, is that it's the *right* head on the stick! A knee-jerk 'right, the very *next* person who is caught doing X…' reaction, regardless of why, will reduce motivation, reduce trust and undermine the foundations of any organisational culture. It will seem arbitrary and unfair.

That last point is important. Everyone wants to be protected from the unsafe behaviour of others but we should never underestimate the power of perceived kinship. In 1001 films and books the line has been delivered "I know he's an idiot, but he's *our* idiot so what can you do?!" The same is true of the workplace.

As ever, it isn't about laws, rules and academic models, it's about the unspoken 'rules' that consciously or sub-consciously determine how we genuinely judge a situation. In almost every culture in the world it has proved adaptive to 'look after your own'. In short, it's no good an organisation bemoaning a lack of information about incidents if the organisation looks as if it were designed to discourage reporting.

James Reason (who coined the term and did much his work in aviation) gives a simple example asking us to consider a worker checking rivets on a plane. (This some years before the events at Heathrow of May 2013 described below)!

He says if the worker has the time, the torch, and the gantry, does the job conscientiously but misses as few rivets, this is out-and-out human error. We should go away and invent a machine that works better than the human eye. If a worker is working conscientiously but is missing a torch, a gantry, or is under time pressure then they are entirely blameless and it's an organisational resource issue. Finally, he asks us to consider the worker who has the time, the torch and the gantry but chooses to work quickly from the ground so they can get back to the canteen and their crossword. This is their fault and they should suffer accordingly.

This user-friendly sketch works very well. Even when presented to an audience entirely made up of union officials it's unlikely to draw negative comment. It should, though, but before explaining that, it's worth walking through the basic model.

## Basic Model of Just Culture

The basic model separates unsafe behaviours into errors (*unintentional*) and violations (*intentional* acts). This could also apply to unhealthy acts, environmentally unsound acts – or unproductive acts. It's a model with very wide applicability.

Basically, in order for there to be a **violation** there must, by definition, be a rule and

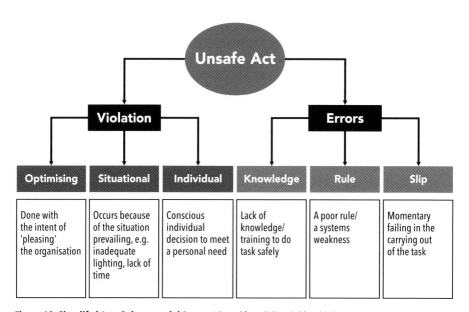

**Figure 13. Simplifed Just Culture model** Source: Adapted from Sidney Dekker, 2012

secondly, a deliberate intention to break it. It's worth reiterating that, technically, if there's no rule then no violation is possible! Any omissions in the system are management responsibility to fix (but also everyone's responsibility to highlight when they become aware of them).

Errors occur when there is no intent. This might be a slip or lapse.

**Slips** and **lapses** can be differentiated as a physical act (a *slip*) and a mental *lapse*. Yesterday, I managed to break a desk lamp by pushing a book that pushed another book that nudged my lovely lamp over the side of the table. This was both clumsy and absent minded simultaneously. In both cases, the solution is the same – using ergonomics to come up with a safe design, or a safety net of some sort – in this case, a lamp that isn't fragile, or a table that is edged. Or I could use a bigger table. Or, in former times, when the consequences of knocking a lamp off a table could be far more severe, we might see a rule about only one book on a table at any one time. (And indeed we did).

## Why Error is Inevitable

It may be asked: "Why didn't I simply pay better attention?" and the answer would be that, like everyone else, I can only pay attention for a maximum of 55 minutes an hour when fit, rested and stress free, as it's said that we are doomed to five minutes of what some call 'mind fart' territory every hour, on average. (A better question might be why I had so many books on a cluttered desk and why hadn't I tidied up a bit before starting work during my 55 minutes of alertness!)

It must be pointed out that trying to pin down a definitive study confirming this '55-minute' claim is next to impossible. Any number of populist sources will state that "scientists have proved we can only concentrate for 45 minutes an hour before we need a break" but it depends on so many factors, such as interest in the subject matter, the flow or ease with which we can work, and the specific task at hand. Is it learning? Actively monitoring? Passively monitoring? Are there distractions such as noise? Most people, for example, will work flat out through a three-hour exam and certainly wont spend five minutes an hour relaxing or meditating (though perhaps they should!)

The key point is simple, however, and goes directly to the issue of the mind-shift from 'über-compliance' to a more proactive, risk literate approach, as discussed above. Whatever the exact limits are on a given day, or in a given situation, it is true that there **is** an upper limit and that exhorting people to take more care and pay full attention at all times is doomed to failure. The more concentration required of the workforce, the more lapses of attention there will be.

A *rule-based* mistake is illustrated by Reason's example that "if you solved a problem with a hammer yesterday, then today everything looks like a nail". (We'll discuss the psychology behind how we can so easily get into bad habits in more detail when we discuss ABC analysis, later). Obviously, always stepping back and applying a logical reasoning approach is essential here, as is ergonomically consistent design.

A rule-based mistake is, for example, where you get annoyed with another driver (in your partner's car or in a hire car) and angrily wash the windscreen wipers at them having first sprayed the windscreen with water! Your anger makes you react instinctively and you do what you would have done in your *own* car. (Apply the 'rule' that it's *always* the left stalk that flashes the lights. Although it's true for your make and model it's a mistake to extrapolate that to *all* cars.)

Similarly, it's far easier to learn to drive a car in the UK after learning to ride a motorbike here, as so many of the skills that become habits are directly transferable. Adapting to driving a car on the continent, where they drive on the 'wrong side' of the road is rather more hazardous.

A *knowledge-based* mistake is, for example, where doctors killed thousands of people every year in previous centuries because they didn't know about germs, which were invisible to the naked eye.

To an extent, it's so far, so simple. When we can see it was an unintentional error we can call for the trainers and/or the ergonomists. Only if that error has legal consequences – or if you work in a blame culture – is there an issue. But again, pure logic simply doesn't always apply.

For example, your car has been badly designed and has a blind spot, so you do not see the motorcyclist you pulled in front of and killed, even though you did consciously look for them. But it's not just about consequences; norms and expectations play a role here. A similar example: imagine you are waiting at a junction to turn right and are shunted into the path of an on-coming motorcyclist by a lorry that brakes too slowly. You're entirely blameless, of course, but anyone who has been on a defensive driving course will know that when you pull up to turn right you automatically point in the direction in which you are about to travel, which means if you're shunted from behind, then *out you go*. So, it's far safer to get into the habit of pointing *ahead* and only start turning when you need to.

Who is more culpable? The driver who consciously tried to look but was undone by a poor ergonomist, or the driver who *had* been on a defensive driving course but who didn't make the effort to point his car in the right direction while he waited a few seconds?

Again, I'd like to make a plug for my own model of safety here. So often it's not about the facts and figures, it's about individual, national and societal norms and perceptions. Even if the driver shunted out by the lorry broke down sobbing, saying to the Police "but I could have saved him if only I'd remembered to point straight ahead. . .I only went on the course last month!" it's not difficult to imagine the constable offering nothing but consoling words: "Hey, come on now. . .you can't be blaming yourself."

In the next section, on Dekker's 'New View', I'll expand further on the contradictions and inconsistencies of objectively assessing the role of the individual.

**Nature of Error.** Error is, by definition, unintentional and this must be borne in mind when we respond to it. A client once described how a driver of one of their trains 'admitted' they'd made an error and had been sent off for training in situational awareness. That sounds credible but will achieve little, as it's not a million miles from defensive (car) driver training or, importantly, from what they already knew from when they were first trained. If it's an *error* you get an ergonomist in, or you deliver some specialist training. Going through the same training a second time is a refresher only – it doesn't address the root cause of the error.

# Violations

In the basic Just Culture model three different violations are identified;

Situational:

The person genuinely believes he had no choice but to break the rule. Three common causes are:

1. A physical constraint, which meant they simply can't do it physically, no matter how much they want to. For example: stand up and stand on your left leg. Try to rotate your right leg *clockwise* while drawing in the air with your finger a figure of 6 from the top down. How did you get on? That's a contradictory movement and almost impossible to do. It's easy if you start in the *middle* of the 6 and work up while rotating your right leg clockwise, because that's a complementary movement. (Experienced drummers seem able to do this but as an exception that proves the rule, have you ever tried to learn to drum? Goodness, it's hard!)

2. There are conflicting rules or requirements – they can do one or two things of the three requested and have to choose which of the three they don't do. (See, for example, the well-known truism: 'quick, cheap, top quality – pick any two of the three'.)

3.    There are emotional pressures (either internally or externally applied). This won't get you very far in a court of law necessarily, but such pressures are often hugely important, as anyone who has ever watched a film about a young person getting caught up in a gang conflict will know. The young lead male in West Side Story is as nice and intelligent a chap as a girl could take home to meet her mum. But that would be the same young man who goes on to kill and then gets killed in a knife fight.

In all these cases the solution is to change the environment.

Optimising Violation:

This is where the action is undertaken with a genuine belief that this is what is really wanted. For example, I do a job and do it safely but cut a few corners and my supervisor knows I cut those corners. However, the feedback I get is "good job, well done" which guarantees I'll cut those corners again next week. Frankly, if you want to be emotive about it you could call this 'grooming'.

Again, I'd argue that this is the very epicentre of safety culture because 85 per cent of communication is in the voice tone and body language and only 15 per cent in the words used. The old expression "It's not what you say, it's the way that you say it – that's what gets results" is the core message of this book.

Imagine you walk into a bar on holiday with your children. The sign promises a "warm Irish welcome in this Traditional Family Pub". How long would it take you to work out the only family that would be comfortable would be the Manson family? It's seconds - even without anyone as much as looking at you. The 'atmosphere' is obvious instantly.

Similarly, in the next pub (which, by chance, is frequented by ex rugby league players who are twice as large and mean as the characters in the first pub) how long would it take you to consider it safe for the family – again, without anyone even looking at you? Again, I'd argue seconds, as the atmosphere is obvious almost instantly.

This ability to sense the atmosphere is highly genetically adaptive and based on millennia of survival in hostile environments. In his bestselling book Blink Malcolm Gladwell suggests that if you find yourself uncomfortable somewhere then you're a bloody idiot if you don't try and work out why from near the door!

It's a little out of place but I'd like to give a simple practical example of a frequently seen cue for an optimising violation that can be readily denied at a later date when something has gone wrong. "I made a point of saying work safely" is the defence but before we even talk about how it was said let's consider when it was said.

**The Killer 'But' Says What's Really Important.** If you've ever been told "You're really nice and I really like you **but** …" you didn't need them to finish the sentence, did you? We know that everything before the 'but' in the sentence is merely intended to soften the blow of what comes after it.

Therefore, being told "Do this safely but *by Friday*, please" means something very different to "Do it by Friday *but safely*, please". The interesting thing is that neither the speaker nor the listener might be aware of how the message was communicated – but communicated it most certainly is. Such simple cues, along with body language and other ways of letting someone know what we really mean, are covered in more detail in sections on leadership and communication but are central to the whole notion of optimising violations, as a workforce will nearly always do what they think management *really* want.

Indeed, to a great extent understanding the subtle cues that lead to optimising violations is really the core of this whole book. What's key is to look for these cultural issues proactively. Looked at *reactively* the cues are too subtle to be proved. In every investigation or court case a verbal communication "safely but quickly" will become "safely and quickly". (If it were the *later* there would have been a *debate* about priorities and feasibility between the two parties and the behaviour that followed wouldn't have been typical but you'll need a really good lawyer to prove that point when CCTV shows you standing next to an injured colleague with a smoking (nail) gun in your hand).

Individual Violations:

This is a violation done intentionally for personal gain or satisfaction. It is, technically, not so much a safety issue as a personnel/line-management function, as it is likely to fall into the area of breach of contract and trigger disciplinary procedures.

We should remember Elvis here – as in his statement that "You should always walk a mile in a man's shoes before you judge him" (and the almost as well known joke that this is because 'if you judge them harshly, you'll be a mile clear and they'll be barefoot!'). As however, even where the worker seems a bang-to-rights reckless halfwit we should (as with *optimising* and *situational* violations) always look at the environment and clarity of leadership. They may provide a degree of mitigation, or at least an explanation that we can learn from.

This is where a supervisor will claim "but I told him to be safe …" and we need to know whether that was "quick but safe" or "safe but quick". And their voice tone as they told him and so on. Norms of behaviour in the past will provide the best clues.

For example, the 2012 Cavendish review of health-care support workers gives a clear example that things might not be as they first appear when a little empathy is applied. The author, writing in the *Sunday Times*, said: "The Francis Inquiry had suggested that some of these people might be a risk to patients, and my job was to consider what needed to be done about it." However, she adds: "But to cut a long story short, when I started looking at things from the perspective of the people at the bottom, it became clear that we needed to fix the top. The situation is. . .deeply distressing. . .and also dangerous." The review recommended learning from industry and highlighted, as an example of good practice, a hospital in Cambridge that had halved incidents with a simple 'stop the line' empowerment process 'borrowed from Toyota'. As mentioned above, they simply made it 'safer to talk about safety concerns'.

Have you ever met anyone who got so stressed that they 'accidentally on purpose' hurt themselves so that they could say "now look what you've made me do!" (Yes, so have I). Or do you remember a child in the playground who bullied others because they were pushed around at home? One of the key drivers in life is to be in control (see Maslow's 'Hierarchy of Needs' or Warr's 'Vitamin Model' of job satisfaction) and we'll strive to take that control when and where we can. In short, we'll undertake a little bit of risk and autonomy here and there, just to make ourselves feel a little less emasculated. This isn't a lot of use once the lawyers get involved but is something we can look for proactively and empathise with. In short, when we look deeply it's very hard to tick the 'individual' violation box without caveat.

Similarly, Dekker suggests that even where something has happened and it's a clear case of complacency then even that shouldn't be seen as the *cause* of the event but the start point of the investigation (starting with asking the question *why* were they complacent?)

I have a practical case study I use at conferences, in which the majority of unsafe behaviours can be seen to have environmental causes (lack of availability of PPE, lack of training, and so on) but where the last unsafe act is a man walking around the (steel production) factory smoking through a hole in his face mask. This usually gets a laugh and we can all agree that this is the '1 in 10' who is guilty of an individual violation. However, following Dekker, there are still questions to be asked. Where did he learn this was acceptable? How many times has he done this before? Who saw him and what did they do or say? And finally, I mean – who owns and runs this factory anyway?

With this in mind, let's return to the 'bang to rights' rivet-checker described by James Reason above. Imagine this person has been undertaking this task without break or rotation for several years and is now bored senseless. Imagine they had never been properly trained, and so were uncertain what they were looking for from the off? Imagine that when they started taking short cuts they had been seen but the supervisor said nothing and, moreover, when the supervisor stands in, they do a perfunctory job, too?

Are they still 'bang to rights?' (That's intended to be a rhetorical question). This is why I think the union delegates could well have challenged Reason's simple example. It also illustrates why there are so many opportunities to develop this concept of 'risk literacy', even in populations where we might assume a high level.

This is important, as this book makes the case that applying these principles really makes for a safe, vibrant, productive and profitable organisation. It isn't free; a lot of time and effort needs to be invested in change **but** it is the very definition of a 'win: win'.

## A Recent Adaptation - Blending Just Culture with HSG48

Figure 14 shows the original Just Culture model adapted to incorporate HSG48, as many companies prefer. Please note that the addition of an 'exceptional' violation

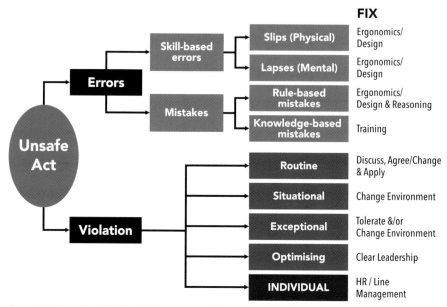

**Figure 14. Adaptation of the Just Culture model to incorporate HSG48**

reflects those times when it is adaptive to break the rule – for example, jumping in the sea from Piper Alpha, which was against training but saved many lives).

All simple models have weaknesses but I think the major weakness of this version is the inclusion of 'routine' as just one of the list of violations. For me, violations that have become routine nearly always commence life as **situational** ("I had to get the job done") and/or **optimising** ("I thought that's what you really wanted"). I'd argue strongly, then, that this model needs a third dimension that reflects the root cause: 'routine was originally situational' or 'routine was originally optimising').

Recently Patrick Hudson (of the Parker and Hudson model) has suggested an alternative taxonomy including the very interesting concept of perceived 'powerfulness' – the feeling that the person has the ability and experience to do the job safely without following the written rules. Above, we considering the limitations of compliance we discussed the preference for our children to cross a road downstream from a crossing (but dynamically risk assessing as they go) rather than stepping out blindly because the light has flashed 'safe'. It's a useful example when we consider how this 'powerfulness' might interact with the basic five violations of optimising; situational and individual. When is using the crossing considered too slow so that this is an optimising violation in the face of productivity pressure? When is a crossing badly situated (or entirely missing) so that it's perhaps situational? When is it an attempt to regain control so that the individual feels more empowered and scores a little victory over a company they feel undervalues or oppresses them?

There are a number of taxonomies of error and violation – all of which are interesting and scientifically persuasive as you move from one to the other. Their strength is that they remind organisations to ask "why" curiously when an unsafe act is seen. I'd like to argue that it's that thoughtful analysis that's key (which will usually throw up an interlinked *blend* of causes) rather than the specific label that's most important.

## Applying the Model through HR

Many organisations have incorporated models such as Figure 15 to add consistency and logic to the discipline process. Obviously, best practice is to consult all possible stakeholders, including workforce representatives, in the development of the model before rolling it out. When we undertake group exercises asking people to identify what makes for good leadership (in safety or generally) they always include 'consistent', 'transparent', 'thoughtful' and 'fair' in the list. Developed and applied at all well, this model cannot fail to help with this.

A word of warning, however: Sidney Dekker himself has found in health care that the leniency with which a Just Culture algorithm is applied increases with power, with

**Figure 15. Just Culture example**

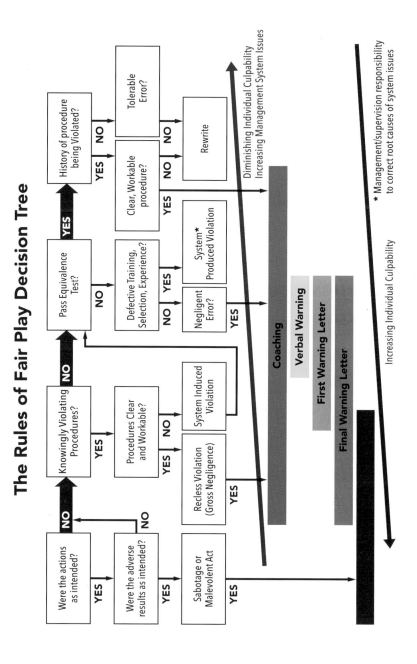

The Rules of Fair Play Decision Tree

those 'yes: no' branch decisions going in the favour of doctors more often than they go in favour of nurses. This will apply in all industries, with the infamous expression from the BBC that "*junior* heads must roll" coming to mind. Patrick Hudson has also stressed the vital importance of context and the overall culture when developing such models. It's difficult to use an objective tool effectively in an organisation shot through with subjectivity.

Therefore, both the development of tailored models and their application in practice must involve representatives of all stakeholders.

## Just Culture – Summary

Once you have blame and any sort of 'scapegoating' you will inevitably have indignation, shame and under-reporting. However, although the legal process often looks arbitrary and counter-productive it simply isn't possible to operate with *no* accountability. Further, though almost every prosecution seems flawed and actively counter-productive *locally* when looked at closely (especially with the Cheese model in mind), the (real) threat of possible consequences probably minimises the total number of flawed prosecutions and disciplinary procedures required.

More positively, the practical implications of proactively adopting a balanced Just Culture approach are many:

Greater buy-in to the key behaviours addressed;

Fewer people (usually *far* fewer) will be undertaking unsafe acts;

A greater percentage of these will be doing so for individual reasons and they will therefore stand out more; and

Following all feasible efforts to facilitate safety any punitive action undertaken will be viewed as more legitimate.

Therefore:

Risk and incidents are reduced, trust and transparency are enhanced and the overall culture strengthened.

Apart from that, it achieves nothing.

The whole tone of this book is to be proactive and I think the best use of the Just Culture model is a very simple one: to educate the whole workforce on why people do what they do, in order to move the culture from one of blame to one of *analysis* and *empathy*. Any good analysis will try to come to the right conclusion and action, regardless of a model. The clear message here is that training is only the appropriate response to an error once and, even more importantly, that training is *not* a punishment to be endured because 'the buggers clearly didn't pay enough attention the first time they sat through it'!

However, for me *the* key learning point of the Just Culture model for organisations is that if 90 per cent (or more) of the cause of unsafe acts and conditions is environmental, then at least 90 per cent of the *resources* of a company devoted to safety need to be spent on *analysis* and *facilitation*. Only 10 per cent can be spent on inspirational speakers, posters and exhortations to take more care. In my experience, many organisations stuck in a compliance-driven mindset get this the wrong way around and although there is *some* analysis and facilitation, the majority of time and resource are spent encouraging people to take more care.

This isn't a political point of view, or even a philosophical one. It's just logic.

## 3.4 Sidney Dekker's 'New View' of Human Error, ABC Analysis and the Fundamental Attribution Error

This section addresses the human factor in more depth and in a way that drills down into the nuance of the individual side of the holistic model described in the book. To reiterate that proposes that to understand risk we simply need measures relating to four factors. First: the quality of the organisations systems and procedures. Second: the objectivity of learning about what's wrong with those systems. Third: the strength and quality of its leadership. Fourth: the people. This section therefore also takes a very close look at the 'individual' box in Reason's Just Culture model.

This individual focus might also be known as the 'Elvis Rule'. Hindsight bias is one of the 'seven deadly sins' listed in Piattelli-Palmarini's classic book *Inevitable Illusions*. Two of the others, overconfidence and our general uselessness at predicting probability accurately, explain why the individuals involved in a negative outcome are comfortable that nothing will go wrong before it does, whereupon someone inevitably comes along (with the benefit of hindsight) to point out that the negative outcome was obvious.

We have seen that ABC (or temptation) analysis helps explain how this works. The everyday cognition "I really need to crack on, so I'll just have to do X/not bother this time with Y … but it'll probably be all right and anyway I know what I'm doing" combines several of these principles. (The other four: availability heuristic, rationalisation, anchoring and simplistic – or 'magical' – thinking are also covered elsewhere in the book).

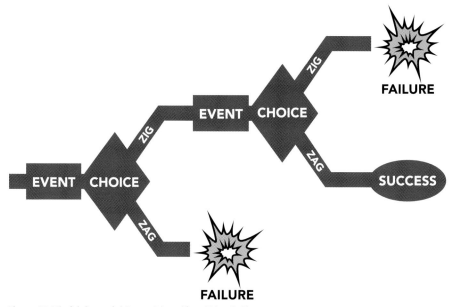

**Figure 16. Hindsight model** Source: Adapted from Sidney Dekker

Before getting into the practicalities of this model it might be worth stressing just how subjective people can be and how simple mistakes can be made. The essence of Kahneman's *'Thinking, fast and slow'* is that we can think we were reasoned and objective (i.e. thinking *slowly*) when, in fact, we were thinking subjectively and instinctively. For example, if I tell you that pie and chips are £2.90 and the pie costs £2 more than the chips, most readers will have worked out instantly that we're talking about a 90p portion of chips. Except we're not; when you work it through you'll realise that the chips cost 45p and the pie £2.45.

Similarly, we often see hindsight reasoning that says that "X was bound to lead to Y" so "doing X was clearly negligent" and therefore "someone must pay for X". But excellence is about using proactive logic and reasoning to minimise fatalism and simplistic thinking.

However, if we put ourselves in the shoes of the individuals concerned we often see that, *at the time*, several other outcomes looked (and indeed *were*) equally likely. Only *after* the event, with the benefit of hindsight, does the sequence seem inevitable. The more obvious outcomes of this are anger and **blame**. For example, the *Times* newspaper reported in September 2013 on the story of a young man of 21 who argued with his girlfriend in a nightclub in 2006. They subsequently made their way home separately and, tragically, the girlfriend was murdered before she made it home. The boyfriend was convicted of her murder and served six years in jail before being released on appeal. However, the girl's parents commented that they had "little sympathy" with him and still blamed him for their daughter's death because "he should never have left her in the nightclub".

Basically, *hindsight changes everything.* What we must try to do is clear our minds of what we know now and look at the world through the eyes of the person *before* the incident occurred. Dekker gives the excellent example of the Mid Staffordshire Hospital debacle in the UK in 2013, in a paper submitted on invitation of the *British Medical Journal* but (at the time of writing) not yet published. He discusses the second set of victims. By this he means that the first victims are the estimated 1200 who are considered to have 'died needlessly' owing to poor care and mismanagement between 2004 and 2009 *and* their loved ones. Turning to the *secondary* victims he also asks us to consider the hundreds of dedicated *employees* caught up in these infamous events. What about their feelings of self-worth and professional pride?

It's natural to want to leave objective truth to one side and tar and feather a few senior managers just to satisfy the urge to 'make the bastards pay', but Dekker argues convincingly that this is nearly always counter-productive in the long run. It's perhaps easier to empathise with the nursing staff – but also easier to be angry with them. Consider, for example, a nurse who was genuinely dedicated initially but was hugely influenced by the prevailing culture and who now realises, with the benefit of hindsight, that they drifted imperceptibly into sloppiness and indifference? On a practical level, their CV will have a toxic element forever but that's an awful burden to carry existentially, too.

## Case Study. The Atherstone fire

In November 2007 four firemen were killed attending a blaze in a large empty warehouse in Atherstone, in the UK county of Warwickshire. The question was asked: "Why send men to their deaths when no one was in the building?" and media momentum built for someone to be punished for this senseless loss of life. After all, if there are four people dead then someone must, by definition, be culpable. In the end, no fewer than 12 individuals were arrested, with three commanding officers eventually standing trial. They were all acquitted, and the case study is an excellent example of hindsight bias and the need to blame.

Assistant Chief Fire Officer Jim Onions, in a subsequent talk, explained exactly how terrible the situation in the warehouse was and the confusion that was caused when firefighters tried to make their way to the source of the blaze along corridors and through internal doors. (Along with several other issues, the building manager, in his original briefing, forgot a double door half-way along a corridor.) They simply weren't able to retreat quickly enough when it was obvious the heat was too much, and the rescue crew who responded to the automatic distress signals also got into difficulty.

At the talk, the horrific situation the firefighters encountered was detailed and a very specific time line given. Film from outside the building taken by a BBC film crew who were shadowing one of the firemen in attendance for a 'day in the life' programme showed smoke coming out of the windows near where the fire-fighters gained access. There are no flames and though the smoke is steady, it certainly isn't dramatic, or at all intimidating. In fact, it looks relatively benign at a glance.

The presenter paused the film and asked – particularly of the other fire services in attendance, who would know well what such levels of smoke might mean for the situation deeper in the building: "OK, what time was this film taken?" and: "Would you have gone in?" It's worth stressing that the point had already been made that putting out fires, even major fires, where no one's life is in danger, is simply standard firefighting work. It comprises the vast majority of what fire services do every day – rescue operations are unusual. The "why even *think* of going in?" question is a post-hoc rationalisation and very much a response to the outcome.

The three services in the room all agreed "Yes, we'd go in based on what we can see". Trying to second-guess the time of the film it was suggested "We can see where you're going with this, this was only 10 minutes before the fatalities, isn't it?" Another participant suggested: "You're going to say this was actually when the fatalities happened." The answer, which stunned the room – as intended – was that this was the scene some *45 minutes after* the fatalities had occurred.

This simple exercise alone provides strong evidence that, clearly, no one was anywhere near 'grossly negligent', as is required by law for a manslaughter conviction.

# 'ABC' Analysis and the Fundamental Attribution Error

I wouldn't be surprised if the single most important concept for the world of safety is an understanding of ABC (or temptation) analysis, the fundamental attribution error and what it means for the way we manage safety. The model comes from the field of Applied Behaviour Analysis and is based on the observable relationship between behaviour and the environment. It was originally based on the work of psychologist B. F. Skinner in the 1930s.

It has already been suggested above that once we've reached the law of diminishing returns in terms of compliance we need to look at our organisation in a different way.

A working knowledge of these theories is utterly central to that.

First, however, a fun quiz: please complete the following questionnaire and answer honestly if you have you ever been guilty of:

Drinking your weekly allowance of alcohol in a single 24-hour session?

Smoking?

Taking a drug given to you by a friend, rather than prescribed by a doctor?

Making a healthy resolution because you want to be the sort of grandparent that can play touch rugby with your grandchildren, so it's improved diet, less alcohol, stretching exercises and yoga, and regular visits to the gym. And really meaning it! But it's all out of the window in weeks – and the last two visits to the gym before you cancel the membership cost around £600 each!

Driving at 50 per cent above the speed limit (so, 75 in a 50mph zone; 45 in a 30 zone, and so on)?

Driving through a traffic light as it turns from amber to red because you responded to an amber light 30 yards ahead by accelerating, not braking?

Driving when you think you're under the drink-drive limit but you're not entirely certain and would worry if breathalysed (because you had a drink more than you intended with your meal out, or perhaps had a late and heavy night and it's only 8am)?

Having unprotected sex with someone in the last 15 years, even though you have little or no idea where they have been, or who with – but they look healthy and wholesome enough, so it'll probably be ok?

Having any sort of sex, protected or otherwise, with someone other than the partner who would be very upset if they found out?

At conferences, we'll often get someone young in the front row shout out "house!" at the end of this list. Some younger ones even add "and all last week too … living on the edge, me!" More usually, most people, up to and including heads of state, will fail some of the items, if not lots of them.

The hugely famous photograph on the facing page is often shown to illustrate the importance of PPE but the story behind the fire is that, as well as removing an important filter to save 1.2 seconds of refuelling time, two maintenance engineers had, crucially, taken a short cut in their maintenance of a valve in the nozzle because one of the two had a 'hot date' lined up for that night back at his hotel. This is a good example of ABC in action and of the basics of psychology (never overlook the

**Photo 2. Verstapen pit fire 1994** Source: ATP Arthur Thill

most *basic* basics!) but also a good reminder that, when told something would be safe 'if only we'd taken a little more time', sometimes 1.2 seconds is perceived as a long time.

Oscar Wilde famously said he could resist anything but temptation, and the UK writer and TV presenter Stephen Fry jokes that what he does with temptation is "yield to it straight away, as it saves time on the faffing about". We laugh at these quips because we understand them, and Aristotle noted that humour is merely 'common sense speeded up'. However, in a calculative (i.e. compliance based) safety culture we forget these truths and assume that people become rational, long-term and logical when they enter the workplace. When something goes wrong, we ask: "What *were* you doing? Didn't you realise the risks you were running?" and: "How could you have been so foolish?" But people don't change personality entirely when they come to work, and if there are temptations to take risks because the safe way is slow, uncomfortable, or inconvenient then it's just a question of how many will cut corners and how often.

Indeed, this is an area of health science that seems ludicrously under-researched. Books with such direct titles as *Change or Die* (Alan Deutschman) show that, left to their own devices, 90 per cent of heart-surgery patients, for example, regress to their bad habits and do not maintain the changes recommended by the doctors who saved their lives. Similar percentages of recidivism are true of many other serious health issues and, as ever, successful change is found to be far more likely to sustain when there is also support in changing the social environment. (The most obvious example of this is the advice that a patient should get themselves a new set of friends on leaving 'rehab' after a successful stay.)

## Why Would We Behave Unsafely?

The philosopher Derek Parfit controversially suggested that we "not judge the smoking boy too harshly" as the personality is not a consistent moving entity through time but rather a chain of successive selves, linked, but distinct from subsequent and previous selves. It was controversial at the time but recent research backs him up though. Hal Hershfeld of New York University's Stern School of Business suggests that at an emotional level we consider our future self as another person. Using MRI scans of the areas of the medial and anterior cortex that are more active when we are thinking of ourselves they found that the patterns are similar when we are thinking of our future selves as to what they are when we think of a famous person like Madonna or David Beckham. In effect I get the soon, certain and positive benefits today. Future risks and costs (not certain anyway) are, at a physiological level, literally for *someone else* to worry about.

Hershfeld has used computer technology to artificially age images of subjects before making pension related decisions and found that these subjects put twice as much money went into the pension pot following such a session.

This helps explain the power of inspirational speakers who have suffered injury as they make potential future outcomes seem more tangible. Even more effective perhaps would be blind or disabled for a certain period sessions similar to the 14 year old girls given defecating and crying dolls to look after for the weekend.

## Distinguishing consequences in 'ABC Analysis' and 'Consequence Management'

It's important to distinguish between the consequences discussed here, which are normally positive and important to the individual, and the more traditional meaning of the word consequences, which is nearly always negative. For example, when the need for better 'consequence management' is mentioned it rarely, if ever, means management seeking to understand temptations, or even the systemic application of Just Culture principles (which will be discussed presently). Instead, it nearly always means ensuring that punishment is more likely to be applied to a transgressor.

And the bottom of Heinrich's Triangle will fill up and people will **_inevitably_** get hurt sooner or later. We all know there are risks associated with these behaviours but they tend to be long-term and uncertain, so we tend to get on with things and let the future take care of itself. But the 'bad' behaviours I listed two pages ago will kill hundreds of millions of people worldwide every year.

Basically, everything we do has a trigger and associated contextual issues. Collectively, this is called an antecedent, which is everything relevant before the behaviour occurs. (This is the A in ABC.) We want to do something and have tools to do it with but we are tired. Or we're told to do something, don't have the tools but are bright and alert. And so on and so on. Then there's the behaviour itself (B) and then the consequence (C) of the behaviour.

In a compliance-based culture we tend to focus on the antecedents. The view will be that the workers have been trained, have the appropriate tools and were thoroughly briefed in a toolbox talk. However, it's the consequences that far more often determine the behaviour, especially once the behaviour becomes routine. (Early behaviours tend to be more driven by antecedents like rules and training, and that gives us an excellent opportunity to start people off correctly. However, it's once we relax into the task that the problems start.)

Consequences can be:

- soon or delayed
- certain or uncertain
- positive or negative.

Anything with a soon, certain and positive consequence will be tempting. Again the 'bad behaviour' list a few pages back illustrates the range of temptations we can give in to as do the outcomes of misbehaviour by the likes of Bill Clinton, John F Kennedy and Richard Nixon!

In the world of safety and health if the safe or healthy way is slow, inconvenient or uncomfortable then people will be tempted to cut a corner for the soon, certain and positive consequences of speed, comfort and convenience. If we are _tempted_ to do so, it is simply a head count of how many give in to that temptation. This is just a law of nature and I'd like to argue that laws of nature supersede the laws of countries and the rules of organisations.

One of the criticisms of the four-man visit to the Macondo well (Deepwater Horizon) just prior to the explosion was that they focused on visible behavioural issues that were easy to see and didn't require preplanning. One of the reasons for this is simply that it was much more convenient on the day.

# The Fundamental Attribution Error

In the chapter on individual we discuss some of the many causes of mistaken thinking. However, the most important error of them all, when viewed from a Just Culture perspective, is the fundamental attribution error and it needs addressing here because of the way it interacts with ABC analysis and temptation.

Although we all have our own particular biases we all tend to overestimate the influence of the *person* in a situation and underestimate the influence of the *environment*. This is why it's known as the *fundamental* error. (The term Fundamental Attribution Error itself was first used in 1977 by Lee Ross, who developed the original 1967 research of Edward Jones and Victor Harris.) This is even more pronounced when something has gone wrong and it's one of the reasons why reactive investigations can be so poor and why injustices proliferate. Even on a day-to-day basis it's easy to imagine why a hard-pressed supervisor might respond to an unsafe act with a shout of "idiot!" when faced with a person behaving unsafely.

For example, imagine that as you exit your drive a strange car nearly runs into the side of you. Your response is most probably annoyance and aggression ("idiot!") but then you realise it's your long time neighbour and friend. How many of us would laugh say "oh, it's only you!" and calm down instantly?

Further along the journey you nearly run someone off the road. They react furiously and your thinking will probably be along the lines of "sorry, but there's no need to react like *that* as I'm really tired and/or stressed and/or you were in my blind-spot and besides, I'm really late for a really important meeting". This illustrates an interesting aspect of the attribution error, which is that the person involved is very aware of all the environmental factors and (depending on how defensive they are) will likely throw in a few excuses, along with the reasons.

A little later and a car nearly runs you off the road with a risky and aggressive overtaking manoeuvre before skidding off the road and bursting into flames. Be honest now – how many of you would have the initial reaction of Serves you right, you moron! That's just natural selection in action, that is!"

And then we discover that it was a doctor rushing to attend to a heart attack victim...

In short, when it's *us* we are instinctively aware of all the environmental factors but when it's *them* they're just an idiot.

Inconvenience and discomfort are hugely important environmental factors and we need to keep this in mind when attempting to be objective in our analysis because, as we all know, the objectivity of our analysis puts an upper limit on the efficacy of our response.

# How to Use These Theories

Companies have found that systematically seeking to *design out temptations* proves far more effective than increasing punitive action – especially because design solutions are *permanent*. Therefore, the comments "I can't be bothered", or "it's too time consuming" should be understood as "some people are tempted not to do X because it's inconvenient, but we can make it more convenient by. . ." As well as being effective it sets the right tone because it's also an adult way of interacting with the workforce.

We can use this principle to our advantage, both reactively and proactively.

**Reactively – 'Five Whys' Analysis.** To simply recall that 90 per cent of all issues are caused by the environment and that despite our instinctive response to blame the individual, we should always ask the question "why?" about an issue we've seen.

The vital distinction is to ask *curiously*, not aggressively.

# Case Study

A famous example of this occurred at Manchester United football club a month after Alex Ferguson took charge. He called in the youth team boss, Eric Harrison, and asked him why the number and quality of youth team players coming through to the first team was poor. Harrison assumed he was about to be sacked but Ferguson's tone was *curious*, not accusatory and when Harrison replied: "Well, Manchester City have 10 times as many scouts as we do for a start. . ." Ferguson's response was: "Really? Well, I'll get that sorted straight away".

Within weeks, Harrison reported: "We suddenly had loads more scouts, and *good* ones, too." A few years later, the United team that Alan Hanson famously dismissed with You'll win nothing with kids" won the English league and a few years after that, the European Champions league, with home-grown ex-youth players to the fore. (Even if you loathe football you've heard of one or two of them!)

'Five whys' analysis simply stresses that we continue to ask "why" curiously until we reach an end point where the question *can* be asked but it makes little sense to do so. Often, it takes five steps but it could be one, two or seven. There may also be several answers so that that several streams of analysis are started, as in figure X. They usually converge back into a key aspect of the organisation, however.

For example, the question "Why did we choose PPE supplier X over Y?" makes sense to ask. But if the answer is "To save money" then asking "but why do we want to save money?" is rather unnecessary. The better question would be "but is that proving a false economy?"

We have an exercise where we ask if anyone has been burgled, or had their car broken into recently. We ask: "How did you feel about that?" and write the answer on a flipchart, along with the answer to "What did that make you want to do?" The answers are often quite intemperate, if not alarmingly graphic.

We then ask delegates to undertake a 'five whys' of youth crime in the UK and they work through issues like lack of money, drug addiction, poor parenting, poor schooling, and so on. They'll also come up with answers like "unlikely to get caught", "current punishments are no deterrent", and so on until they (invariably) present back something thoughtful, comprehensive, progressive and practical that might have come straight from a Labour Party think tank and called "tough on crime and tough on the causes of crime".

We point out that although they have only been talking for 15 minutes these answers are a long way, in terms of depth and long-term sustainability, from the initial and instinctive violence based responses they originally came out with.

The point of the exercise is that 15 minutes of thought can get you a long way, and the practical implications for the time poor, exasperated and 'blaming' supervisor are obvious.

### Proactive Use – Anything Slow, Inconvenient or Uncomfortable?

If you haven't seen anything to discuss you can simply ask the question "Anything slow, inconvenient, or uncomfortable about doing this job safely?" If the answer is yes then you know you have a problem. As above, you simply need to empathise rather than blame.

The good news is that this technique works equally well with peripatetic workers in vans. People will very happily tell you what frustrates them about their work and about conflicting goals and outcomes. They don't need to tell you what they or their colleagues do when those goals conflict!

It can also be used with front-line **supervisors**, who can be asked if there is anything slow, inconvenient, or uncomfortable about leading safety?

This proactive approach to anticipating issues could be called 'advanced situational awareness'.

### Formal ABC Analysis

There is not space in this book for really detailed notes on the approach – but it is covered in great detail in the freely available 2002 HSE article *Strategies to Improve Safe Behaviour*. Briefly, however, the approach:

Identifies the **unsafe** behaviour and its **safe** counterpart;

Makes a list of all the antecedents (i.e. triggers and relevant contextual issues) to both those behaviours – for example: warning signs, training, rules, the need for a piece of PPE, etc. – or even the fact that the worker is tired, hungover, or drunk;

Makes a list of all the potential consequences for **both** of those behaviours, safe and unsafe – for example: speed, comfort, increased risk, decreased risk, and so on);

Look in particular for consequences that are **soon, certain and positive**.

On training courses we encourage delegates to think of this in terms of a football score, where a 3:1 is a clear win and points in the bank. For example, stretching from a ladder that's *nearly* in the right place but not quite, rather than coming down to reposition it, saves times but runs a small risk of falling. Rounding up a one in 1000 chance of falling we can say this is a soon, certain and positive – a score of 3. The negative consequence would at least be soon but it's unlikely, so that's a score of 1. What that means in English is that most of us, when in a situation like that, would be tempted to stretch, and if we're tempted to stretch. . .

Once we understand the temptations at play we are best placed to understand what we need to do to change the design of the job or task to ensure the consequences for safe behaviour are at least as powerful as those for unsafe behaviour.

**The Rationale**

Importantly, 'scoring' the consequences helps us concentrate on the driver in the situation and helps us identify high and low impact solutions. I would argue strongly that a high impact solution has to address the temptation *directly* and, if it doesn't, then it isn't high impact. For example, knowing you will be fired if caught committing a certain unsafe act (like reaching from a ladder) only reduces the temptation but doesn't entirely design it out. Making the unsafe act impossible, unnecessary, or no more time consuming than the unsafe way *does* directly address the temptation – in this case, by moving frequently required items to ground level, or installing a mezzanine deck so that ladders aren't required, for example.

In addition, by listing the triggers/antecedents *systematically* we often suggest a creative engineering solution that would have been missed, had we jumped straight to some 'obvious' solutions. To repeat the James Reason quote, this is because "if you solved a problem with a hammer yesterday, then today everything looks like a nail". For example, in the ladder case above, someone might have commented: "I saw this at my last job. We need a mezzanine deck here." However, using the 'five whys' technique on the antecedents we might ask "*Why* does a person need goggles?" and get the answer that a machine they work on spits out swarf. When we ask why isn't this machine guarded we might be told that when it was installed years ago, lightweight Perspex guards weren't available as they are now. . .and we have a design solution further up the safety hierarchy that takes away the need for goggles entirely.

**Using ABC Analysis – a bullish guarantee.** If an organisation can double the number of times it asks these 'curious why' and 'anything slow, inconvenient or uncomfortable' questions (while having the commitment to do something with the answers) I absolutely guarantee that the safety culture will be transformed. This shouldn't be difficult, as few organisations I have seen ask why curiously anywhere near as often as they could and, in most organisations, proactively asking 'anything slow. . .' probably isn't being undertaken at all.

## A Simple but Tragic Case Study – Combining 'Five Whys' and ABC

I was involved in a fatality investigation in Glasgow many years ago. A workman had been crushed to death by a two-ton slab of metal in a hole in the ground. The safe system of work was for him to secure the slab at the top with a colleague and only then secure it at the bottom. They chose to do both simultaneously and it slipped and killed the chap in the hole.

Why were they tempted to cut a corner like this? Because they wanted to save time and get themselves to the pub to watch the football. Celtic and Rangers were playing that day in an important fixture. Why were they able to do this? Because the supervisor had gone on ahead to get the beers in and secure a good table and had left them to 'job and knock' (i.e. follow him on as soon as they had finished).

He'd presented them with a classic temptation and, as stated above, what we so often do with temptation is to yield to it. Just as the base of Heinrich's Triangle is full of unsafe acts and conditions, it should also be considered to be full of *temptation*. The more temptation to cut corners, the bigger the top of the triangle.

## Some Illustrative Case Studies

**Texas City** is a case study that can irk. Following an internal investigation based on 'Just Culture' principles six workers involved at the front end of the explosion were sacked. But this was based on yes/no questions about actions, with hindsight looming large. Had they applied the 'in their shoes at that time' rationale they would have seen that most people would have acted exactly as they did. They should have passed the substitution test, not failed it. Yes, violations occurred but they were *routine* violations. As ever, 'junior heads must roll' and what should be a tool that delivers objectivity skewed in favour of the senior staff and against the front line.

At the other end of the scale, following the Texas City explosion, John Browne's lawyers were able to ensure that he wasn't even cross-questioned. (Browne's internal review was headed up by someone who worked *for* him. That's the way to ensure hindsight bias can't colour an objective analysis of events!) In the real world he was never going to be convicted, despite what I would argue is a clear and direct link between his ambitions to please shareholders, the company culture he presided over/created, and what happened at Texas City in 1986. Lawyers made a fortune as the sessions debated the definitions and practicalities of 'accountability' and 'responsibility'. Hopkins says with some exasperation that "This debate could have continued indefinitely". Just reading a summary of key exchanges gave me a headache and a desperate need for an energetic session with a heavy punch-bag in my gym.

John Browne is now a lord, technically, and remains a very influential and rich man. Like many, I feel that with great power comes great responsibility and, clearly, I have some very ambiguous feelings about all this. In its final report, the Baker panel even noted that management's role deserved further investigation but that, in effect, its hands were tied by the parameters Browne set in ensuring the scope of the inquiry was limited to refining operations only.

Hopkins suggests that the experience of being vigorously cross-questioned in public might have given them a 'harrowing experience' that could have shifted his mindset more than it *was* shifted. Having watched Rupert Murdoch and his brood squirm in front of the Levinson inquiry, I have to agree. In the real world, that's perhaps the best we can achieve. The cheap line would be to comment that, following such an experience, "Macondo wouldn't have happened" but that might well not be true as, rather ironically, one of the case studies that follow illustrates that BP's reputation rather preceded it.

It wouldn't have hurt, though.

Two quotes from the Texas Consumer Advocacy Association summarise this well:

"The decisions made by corporate CEOs in boardrooms around the world threaten the safety of communities here in Texas... we all face a greater danger when CEOs are allowed to avoid accountability for the decisions they took."

"In Texas (we're taught) that if we hurt anybody, whether on purpose or by accident, then we have to face the consequences. The same principle applies to Browne and his band of CEOs."

The counter argument was a concern that too robust an approach would make companies 'reluctant to shift business operations to Texas'. One person commented: "We must think about the progress Texas has made in creating an environment hospitable to economic growth". I don't believe it. There will always be a queue to run businesses in Texas, if there are profits to be made. Ironic how inhospitable the coast of Texas was to become to birds, plants and fish a few years later.

**East Midlands.** The plane crash at Kegworth near the UK's East Midlands airport in 1989 is another excellent example. If you only read the newspapers you'd know that the crash was caused by an engine fire and blamed on human error. The pilots – *who survived and who turned off the one working engine, for pity's sake* – were sacked. I mean, really? That's about as open-and-shut a case of individual error as you'll ever see, surely?

When I watched the BBC film about the crash to see if it was worthy of inclusion in the box set I paused it, made myself a coffee, then sharpened my pencil. This certainty that the film would be interesting coming when one of the pilots commented: "Do you know, no one ever really asked me *why* I made the mistake I did. . ." It was clear he felt it was a question well worth asking and, as the film unfolded, it was also clear he was right.

The answer, of course, is that the control panels were confusing, the training inadequate and the whole situation was an accident waiting to happen. For example, the presence of a burning smell and fumes in the passenger cabin led them to believe there was a problem with the right engine, as there was a connection between the cabin air-conditioning and the right engine on the earlier types of B737, with which the pilots were familiar. However, on the 737-400 they were flying this had been changed to the left engine, and the pilots were unaware of this change. The pilot was not reinstated, so either the excellent BBC film about the incident is libellous, or it's an excellent case study with which to kick off a training course on 'blame'.

Again, I want to quote Andrew Hopkins when he suggests we can see clearly that "there's nothing natural about natural justice... we have seen over the various inquires and commissions that intelligent and well-meaning people often flout it". If we want more genuine justice we need more key people conversant with Dekker's principle.

Similarly, headlines lambasting 'stupid engineers' were generated when, on an Airbus A319 flying from London to Oslo in May 2013, a maintenance panel flap opened, severed a fuel pipe and caused an engine fire shortly after take-off. This was because BA maintenance staff failed to secure an engine covering after routine servicing. However, it transpired that the only way to check that the work was secure was to physically lie on the ground. Not entirely unpredictably, this wasn't always done effectively, and it transpired a cover had blown loose 32 times previously; this was just the first one to cause a fire. David Learmount, safety editor of *Flightglobal*, commented: "This is an accident waiting to happen. It is a design inviting people not to see a fault." Incidentally, this '32' is a figure I'll delight in quoting the next time I hear a 'Heinrich knew nothing' comment. (And of course I'll add that I have *hard proof* that the number of times the flap wasn't properly secured and *nearly* opened was exactly 330!)

On a rather less frivolous note, who knows what might have happened to the maintenance team if the plane had crashed? Or maybe crashed into a school?

**The rail crash at Great Heck:** The Politics of Negative Consequences. Clearly, the whole area of reacting to bad outcomes is hugely complicated and subjective. Another example from the UK involves the rail crash at Great Heck (Selby) in 2001. A car driver fell asleep at the wheel and crashed on to a train line. He was unable to free the car from the track and it derailed a high-speed train heading south for London at 120 mph. This train then derailed a freight train heading north on the opposite track. Ten people were killed and 120 seriously injured. It transpired that one of the reasons the motorist was tired was that he'd stayed up until the early hours chatting to a potential sexual partner online. He was sentenced to five years in jail.

Not long after this, a similar situation occurred but this time the person who fell asleep was able to get the vehicle off the track just in time. He was hailed a hero and I'm not sure if anyone even asked him why he was tired.

A key question is: how many of us have fallen asleep at the wheel (if only briefly?) I know I have, and I'm sure when I did it was as likely to have been caused by late-night revelry as working too hard. (Campaigners have suggested that the metal barriers protecting the line in question were far too short and the wooden fence barely any barrier to the motorist's out-of-control vehicle.)

As ever, the trick is to be discussing and reducing risk factors at the bottom of the triangle, not at the top. A recent high profile fatality occurred at Liverpool railway station, as a result of which a station guard was sent to prison for signalling a train to move off when a recently alighted passenger was still leaning drunkenly against it. (She was a 16-year-old girl called Georgia, who had been out with friends and was three times the drink-drive limit. She fell under the train and was killed.) This case was summarised in the January 2013 issue of SHP magazine by Michael Appleby, who said the judge concluded that:

"The CCTV footage is unequivocal. Georgia was not moving away and was not showing any signs of moving away. . .I am satisfied that you merely hoped and assumed she would get out of the way when the train began to move and on that wholly inadequate basis, you took a terrible risk."

He was sentenced to five years in jail.

The Rail Accident Investigation Branch has inspectors with specialist investigative training but was asked to delay publication of its report into the incident until after the trial, so the jury was therefore unaware of its findings. The RAIB found that it wasn't certain in which direction the guard was looking at the time of signalling, or what his line of sight was at key times. His version of events was found to be unreliable but, according to medical opinion, it was possibly or even *probably* due to psychological shock and distress. The report suggests three possible explanations for his actions:

He saw her and simply expected her to move (as convicted);

He looked briefly in her direction but did not see her (a known phenomenon associated with repetitive tasks is 'looked but failed to see');

He did not see her at all because his attention was on the control panel and a large group of people on the platform.

It was argued that he failed to follow procedure but there was discussion of the efficacy of the procedure and, following a review, changes made to the procedure since the incident have moved it closer to what he did on the night.

The standard of proof in a criminal case is to be 'beyond reasonable doubt'. As ever, the only people who come out of this well are the lawyers. It may well be that the station guard has been released on appeal by the time you read this (some more lawyers' fees accrued). Forgive the sneering at lawyers but as I write this, my friend still cannot bury his son, who was stabbed to death some weeks ago in an unprovoked attack in Manchester in broad daylight. The body can't be released, as the defence counsel has opted to exercise its right to a second autopsy – presumably in the hope that they'll find that, in an extreme coincidence, this perfectly healthy 18-year-old actually died of a heart attack just seconds before someone with previous convictions for violence and who should have been in hospital because of a known personality disorder plunged a knife into his chest.

**Two Personal Case Studies to Ponder:** To lighten the tone (now I've got that off my chest) I'd like to describe two alcohol-related incidents in which I feel the outcome and the behaviour are not necessarily in accord.

I once ran a one-day and one-night pre-launch session for an oil rig crew. During the evening session the night before, some of the crew were drunk enough to heckle the Scottish dancing/sword-fighting demonstration. It certainly wasn't very sensible of one chap to creep up behind and lift the kilt of the 6ft bearded Scot with a 5ft broadsword who'd been an extra in the film *Braveheart*. That nearly ended very badly!

The next day, a table at the back was swigging away from a large jug of orange juice as my team and I presented away at the front about the key lessons of Heinrich's Triangle, or some such. I have to say that the group was very well behaved, considering that the jug was *half vodka* and none of them had slept a wink yet. Unfortunately, they'd acquired the vodka from the hotel bar at 5am in clear view of the CCTV camera when, technically, the bar was closed at the time. The Police quite literally tapped them on the shoulder and took them away from the back of the room, mid-session! (It's the closest I'll ever come to being the piano player in a wild west bar urged to 'keep playing!')

They were all summarily sacked, of course, but it's worth mentioning that they'd enjoyed the benefits of a free bar from 7pm until 2am, and platform management were up until 4am themselves. These managers were reprimanded but I wonder how many of us would have passed the Elvis test, had we been part of this tight-knit team. Being the *first* to be sensible and say "I've had enough" isn't easy – especially if you've been drinking at a free bar for nine hours.

Similarly, I once attended a two-day session to plot a worldwide safety strategy for a large company in a high hazard industry. We all flew in to Delhi the night before but one wide awake director had a late night and drank until 2am. Unfortunately, this was 2am *where he'd come from* – so, 7am **local** time. Naturally, he was too drunk to attend the first day's session, which started at 8am. In fact, he was still too hungover and embarrassed to attend the second day and flew back out without me ever even meeting him, or him contributing at all! All very amusing, of course, but this really wasn't an unimportant planning session. In the five years since, I'm extremely pleased to announce that the company in question has taken the international fatality rate from an average of 5.5 to 0.66 per annum. In short, what we planned in that room over two days has saved a couple of dozen lives to date, and prevented an even greater number of life-changing injuries.

The consequences of the behaviours described above were, respectively, dismissal, official reprimand, and 'quiet words' had. But you'll note that the severity of consequence is perfectly (reverse) correlated with seniority. That's just the way it is but again, if you can see any moral or objective *consistency* in the two stories above, then you're doing better than me.

## Summary

There will be politics, subjectivity and unfairness wherever we go. In the real world, it's always going to be 50 shades of grey, rather than black and white. However, to paraphrase that rather less-than-great 21st century philosopher, Donald Rumsfeld: "*Known* unknowns are better than unknown unknowns."

# 3.5 Leading and Lagging Measures

Finally in this section on risk literacy we need to consider how we can assure ourselves that the excellent training we rolled out and thoroughly followed up and embedded has actually worked and changed our organisation for the better. We need to consider objective measurement. In particular, I'd like to educate the line manager to be hugely sceptical of the dangers of being reassured by that colourful pie-chart or bar-graph headline figure.

(I have a wonderful little book on my shelf called *How to Lie With Statistics*, by Darrell Huff. The main way, it suggests simply, is to "use a bar graph or pie chart"!)

Although a pedant might argue that 'lead' measures are badly named because they are still a measure of events that have already occurred, all measures must be such. Personally, I think of them as 'bottom of Heinrich's Triangle behaviours' – basically, measures of things more plentiful than near misses.

The use of lagging measures is inevitable; lost-time injury cases, first aid cases and the like will always be the headline figures. The weaknesses in this approach are that:

an organisation can have apparently excellent figures and be just about to blow up anyway – for example, Deepwater Horizon and Texas City;

most organisations don't have enough accidents for data comparisons to be statistically meaningful – ideally, you need more than 30 data points. As well as Rosenthal and Rosnow's classic textbook on statistical analysis it's worth referencing Scottish football teams, which need to play each other three times to make a league of 30 plus matches; and

Official incident rates can be inaccurate. Without getting into the whole debate about the suppression of data to give 'management what they want' and/or to secure bonuses for peers it is true that first aid cases, near-misses and minor incidents often *increase* as the culture strengthens

We need something more **risk literate** and, at a glance, lead measures promise that.

The good thing about lead measures is that they are more proactive than the likes of lost-time injuries, or first aid cases. The bad thing, in my experience, is that many of them aren't telling us very much at all. For example, a 'classic' lead measure would be percentage of training courses run compared with percentage intended to be run, as per the training matrix. Now, an improvement up to 90 per cent from last year's 80 per cent might make for a nice bar graph or pie chart, with a 'halved the problem!' feel to it. If I were a head of training that's certainly how I'd want to spin it. However, there is a list of questions and observations that we might like to consider before getting too bullish about the nice bar graph:

We have trained nine out of the ten intended rather than eight (isn't that actually a 12-per-cent improvement?)

Those targeted for training might only reflect 10 per cent of the population. (In such a case, this would mean that of the whole workforce only an extra 1.2 per cent received training relative to last year).

In all cases:

> We'd like to look at the appropriateness of the training (to what extent was it based on a systematic and scientific gap analysis?)

> We'd also like to look at the quality of the training delivery (what do the happy-sheet scores tell us?)

> And, of course, we need to follow up the outcome of the training for the reasons described above...

> To what extent were the new behaviours requested on the course implemented on site over the weeks after the course?

> If they were, did we follow them up and embed them to ensure they have become 'part of the way we do things around here'?

And finally:

Did we follow that up to ensure these embedded new behaviours actually delivered something positive for the organisation in terms of key indicators? Or do we merely have a slightly different set of behaviours delivering the same key outcomes and the same levels of risk?

Clearly, our highly-positive lead measures, which looked so fine at a glance on our boldly-coloured bar graph, might not look so impressive if we find ourselves with less than ideal answers to the questions above.

Recently, there has been a push to assess competence as a lead measure – Robin Stowell argues the case well in the September 2013 issue of SHP magazine. In particular, the competence of individuals can be mapped on to the risk profile of the specific area of an organisation. Again, this is excellent, as far as it goes, and will add much useful data to the safety management process, especially in times of change, but still begs the question: just because they *can* do it does it always follow that they actually *do* do it? It's also difficult to find reference to competence in soft skills, a lack of which is often the biggest problem.

I do think that good quality *behavioural* lead measures avoid many of these pitfalls, as there is a direct point-to-point correspondence with actual risk.

## Cultural Assessment is a Good Measure

If you have measured the organisation with a suitable cultural model like Parker and Hudson's, as described in Chapter 1, then revisiting the organisation to see if things have improved is a useful measure.

If the culture is stronger then fewer people will be getting hurt, though, ironically, you may know about more of them so your lagging figures may not reflect this!

### Behavioural Lead Indicators

Behavioural lead measures are better than standard lead measures simply because they have a more direct relationship with key outputs. For example, we can measure the number of people wearing safety glasses when working outside, where airborne debris is a risk. If more people are wearing their glasses then fewer will get things in their eyes. If more people are lifting kinetically, or sitting correctly in chairs then fewer will develop bad backs. The relationship with the key outcome sought is simply more direct than with such events as lifting and/or posture training.

The confounding variable, of course, is the key focus of this whole book: the working environment. It doesn't matter how well trained you are – if the environment you return to isn't supportive to applying the training then you will have a problem.

### If You Can Measure It You Can Manage It, and What Gets Measured Gets Done

Behavioural lead indicators do two things only: first, they can deliver the benefit of 'what gets measured gets done' and second, they can deliver the benefits of 'if you can measure it you can manage it'. The latter is far more difficult than most companies appreciate but for the former you just need to be there making notes in a way that looks authentic! A journalist friend once smuggled me into the press box at Manchester United. It was the deciding match of the 2002 Premiership season. My job was to diligently note the time of all fouls, corners and shots, complete with the player's name. I was happy to help him in this way in exchange for a prime seat about 10 feet from where Posh Spice (at she was known at the time) was sitting watching her husband David Beckham.

Sadly, Arsenal played very well that night – Patrick Viera, in particular, I seem to remember. After the game my friend just threw my notes away! As I complained he explained: "Sorry about that but I needed you to *look* like you were working and not totally caught up in the game!"

If a good sample strategy is used then just watching and noting items will deliver the benefits of 'what gets measured gets done', regardless of the quality of the data. However, you need *accurate* lead indicators to get the benefit of 'if we can measure it we can manage it'.

It must be stressed, though, that at the very least companies need to implement a process of actively monitoring behaviours with a *good* sample strategy to achieve the benefit of *either*. Developing accurate percentage measures takes quite a lot of work, using techniques similar to those used to check product quality. This is just like quality assurance itself – hard work, but achievable.

The biggest **problem** is companies that collect data from badly-defined items,

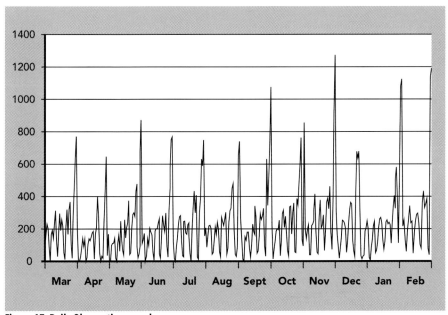

**Figure 17. Daily Observations graph**

with no proactive sample strategy to ensure the site is scored when it's busy and dangerous. These companies simply end up analysing sexy-looking pie charts that tell them (*inaccurately*) how safe the organisation is when it's nice and quiet. Worse, badly-managed quotas for, say, '10 observations by the end of the month' might mean scores for nine are made up in the van on the way home on the 30th.

The fascinating graph in figure 17 is taken from a major utilities organisation that had 'number of walk and talks' as an item on the appraisal. It shows clearly that the quota was achieved but nearly always at the end of the month. I've no idea how many were simply made up but from talking to the workforce it is clear that many *were* and that many others were of poor quality and tended to focus on issues within the comfort zone of the person (whether people were wearing or not wearing PPE outside of their window, for example).

## Ensuring Accurate Behavioural Lead Measures

To generate consistency you simply need to ensure that items are defined well. Basically, if you see a pie chart with 'Inappropriate PPE' on it, it's worth asking "What do you mean by *inappropriate*, exactly?" The response should be something like:

"Well, we have a map that shows were job specific PPE should be worn and also list of mandatory PPE. Boots should be worn at all times, so that's easy to score, but with splash overalls, for example, if the person is in a *designated* area we look for the following:

> that the overalls are done up to the neck;

> the sleeves rolled down and outside of gauntlet gloves (in case of splashing);

> the trousers are outside of boots (ditto);

> tears are no greater than 2cm (so little nicks are allowed); and

> they are not overly impregnated with oily waste.

'It's difficult to define 'overly impregnated', of course, so we have this borderline photograph that sets the standard. Anything worse than this (shows small encapsulated photo) and we fail them! The tricky bit is making sure we get out and score when it's busy, but we have a system where the supervisor covers me for half an hour while I do my observations if I need it."

If the response is something like that then the team collecting lead data *can* tell you pretty accurately how much risk the workforce is running in relation to inappropriate PPE use. You now know where the problems are and can measure how much better you're doing when you implement, analyse and action plan as you would with any issue.

## Two Lead Measure Case Studies

**From a factory in Europe.** In Figure 18 you can see that a simple behavioural benchmarking exercise led to a significant improvement in standards (12 basic behaviours were measured, relating to housekeeping, lifting, manual handling and plant/people interaction, followed by a simple root cause analysis). The objective scores underlined and validated the subsequent observations and suggestions.

I'm hoping the scores themselves illustrate how effective this simple exercise can be but the point I want to make is that, if you look closely, you will see that things started to improve not when the findings were presented but *just after the phone call* from head office warning this site that is was going to be visited in a few weeks.

So, what is *about to* be measured gets done, too, for the same reason. It identifies what's important to management, and what's clearly important to management from HQ is just *fascinating* to local management!

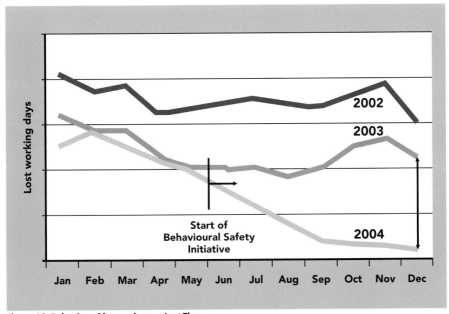

**Figure 18. Behaviour Observations vs Lost Time**

**Photo 3A & 3B. Walkway Before and After**

**From a large utility company in the UK.** In this case study we were given five men full-time, who were on light duties because of heart problems. The photos show a typical walkway, where we gave a mark for each 30 yards or so. This length of walkway would get one mark, something three times its length would get three marks, with something like a pipe, a gate, or a post marking the point and identified on the map.

We collected some 2000 housekeeping data points for the whole company, with some very small unmanned sites only scoring 1 or 2 marks and the larger sites up to 100, or more. When we showed this borderline photograph 3A to the board the first question to the lawyer in the room was "if someone trips on that are we paying?" and when the answer was "yes", we had their attention – especially when the collated figures showed a pass rate of less than 20 per cent.

We were asked "but why aren't these issues addressed?" and it was explained that getting three local quotes for the work was difficult, and then getting the contactor back in to do it was even more difficult, so it was suggested "why not get a major contractor to quote for the job lot?" We did and, some months later, it all looked like photo 3B. The key element here is that the data allowed the management to see exactly what levels of risk they were running.

Good lead measures increase risk literacy.

# Training Is Not Even Half the Story . . .

Hopefully, you'll have found the above material interesting and will think that having employees trained in some of the techniques mentioned just the thing. Unfortunately, that might achieve nothing but lots of disruption and a large bill from a consultant.

## The Vital Importance of Embedding Learning and Change

You may well have asked yourself over the years why so many excellent 'happy sheet' scores from well targeted training courses fail to turn into any sort of meaningful improvement in culture in the medium to long-term. This section seeks to explain the psychology behind that. It's very simple, very powerful, and often very poorly understood – even by the best companies.

For example, Prof Eduardo Salas of the University of Central Florida, interviewed by the Wall St Journal in October 2012, points out that US firms spent about $156 billion on employee learning in 2011 alone, according to the American Society for Training and Development. But with little practical follow-up or meaningful assessments, "some 90 per cent of new skills are lost within a year".

He stated: "As well as poorly designed and delivered training] the major problem is many organisations don't evaluate how well employees have learned. Or, if they do, they usually stop at the first level of evaluation – the reaction data. Companies think that if there is a positive reaction to the training, people will learn. But what we know is that the correlation is very weak between reaction to training and actual learning."

An article in the magazine Business Wire in 2001, quoting the training and development journal as above, reported that Xerox Corporation had carried out several studies on the effectiveness of coaching. They determined that in the absence of follow-up coaching to their training classes, 87 per cent of the skills change brought about by the programme was lost. A safety-specific study by Komaki et al of behavioural safety training concluded that "whereas employees showed only slight improvements during the training-only phase, their performance increased substantially during the training and feedback phase."

Effective ***training*** is about far more than simply briefing people in what needs to be done. Basic education is merely about knowledge, but training should be about genuinely embedding a change of behaviour. The world renowned US safety culture expert Scott Geller uses the same jokey illustration of this point in every presentation he gives, when he asks: "How would you feel if your teenage kids' school announced that, next week, they weren't going to be doing sex education but sex training?" Quite! It really isn't the same thing at all.

Geller also suggests that we focus on the willing first, and not the resisters: "First work with the willing, then let them loose on the unwilling." I'd agree, and the shop-floor-focused methodologies that follow later in this book certainly reflect that, but so often we have to work with *everyone* from the start. Safety leadership training, in particular, will be for all.

My experience is that a small band of delegates on a standard leadership training course will be keen. They are proactive by nature, perhaps, and keen to implement anything you suggest if it sounds as if it will improve things. Then there is a small number of out-and-out cynics. Some people call them 'cave dwellers' – as in, 'citizens against virtually everything'. Their attitude rather mirrors the UK's infamous TV interviewer, Jeremy Paxman, who is reputed to always first ask himself when prepping for an interview with a politician: "Why is this lying bastard lying to me this time?" (Of course, in some organisations, most of the audience will be asking themselves that too, and often not without reason.)

On a normal day, however, most are in the middle. These people will be *sceptical* – not cynical – and their scepticism is often for good reason. Their view might be "Well, I've seen them come and I've seen them go and I don't suppose you'll prove any different to anyone else who's come down here with a safety initiative, but I'll listen". Then, after they've listened, they will think "fair enough, I'll give it a try and I'll make management blink first but I really don't expect this one to be followed up any better than the last time." These are the people I'm talking to and it's this 'I'll call your bluff and give it a go' mindset that so important to address directly, without follow-up procedures.

Specifically, I argue that the Vroom model of individual motivation (see figure 19 below) clearly explains why so many well designed and delivered training courses fail to achieve any long-term benefit for the organisation. As above, this is often despite some really excellent 'happy sheet' scores. Our adaptation of this model says that in order to understand an individual's motivation level to do anything we need to multiply four factors. (Please note that the fact it's a *multiplication* is key; it's not an addition, where you can 'bank' a score, like on *Who wants to be a millionaire?* It's a multiplication, so a low score anywhere means a low score overall.)

Before we talk further about embedding let's imagine two young safety professionals making their way through the industry. They are about to have what is, from their point of view, one of the year's most important conversations. This needs to be a cold 'walk and talk' conversation, with an unknown pair of potentially hostile and unresponsive individuals. The least experienced one leaves it to his more confident colleague to approach the pair in question and raise the issues that need to be raised. Luckily, he's skilled at the techniques required and the girls in the club in the Spanish holiday resort respond well.

Let's call the confident one Terry (are you old enough to remember The Likely Lads?) He raises his glass to the girls as he returns and they raise theirs back, twinkling and smiling at him. "How did you do that?" asks his friend (let's call him Bob). Terry explains some basic techniques about being confident and friendly, but not overdoing it, about the importance of eye contact and showing positive interest in what's said, even if you have to pretend ("but you've always hated Bristol and you haven't even got a sister, let alone one who's a hairdresser, too!"), about the importance of complimenting the plain one on how stunning she looks tonight and the pretty one on her wit and perception – then backing off in good time while the going is good.

"I explained you had to ring your brother, who's ill, which is a big worry given his important TV audition coming up, and also to check on your cat. Worried sick about that poorly cat, you are." "But I haven't got a cat!" "Well, no, but the one on the left has a small Cats Protection League pin on her blouse, so let's try that club down the road and we can always come back if that doesn't work out. But this time *you're* doing the talking!"

Please forgive the slightly sexist 80s sitcom reprise to try to colour this section in a gentle way. However, it's intended to lead to two very important questions. First, when the young safety advisors reach the next bar, how likely is young 'Bob' to enjoy similar success, despite his recent crash course in technique? Can I suggest that – outside of Hollywood films, where the stunner with a heart finds a timid and gauche approach endearing – he's unlikely to get very far?

The even more important second question brings us to the heart of the section: in the absence of coaching, practice and the confidence of having achieved some success when trying these techniques out, how likely is Bob to be any better at this on the *following* year's holiday?

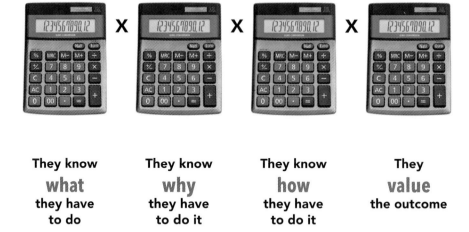

**Figure 19. Vroom / Marsh model**

To return to Vroom's theory and to reiterate: to embed the change we need to consider four factors:

- 'What do you want me to do?' (of course);

- 'Why do you want me to do it?';

- 'Do I feel I have the skills to do competently what has been requested?';

- 'Do I value the outcomes these behaviours are aimed at achieving?'

## What Do you want me to do?

Clearly, if a workforce is confused about what they are supposed to do, then a range of different behaviours will occur. If you want me to lift safely, don't tell me to "Make sure you don't put your back out" but show me the principles of kinetic lifting. Likewise, "Make sure you step down safely" will simply mean "Jump if you want but just don't trip" to many people.

We need to be concise, precise and clear in our instructions and then, with a mindful mindset, use active listening techniques to confirm genuine understanding. Confirming they've signed the attendance sheet isn't the same thing.

I recently came across an example of a simple communication that led to two very different behavioural outcomes, owing to culture and the subtle nuance of language. Following a merger, a client company has two broadly similar operations – one in the UK and one in Germany. Following a basic risk management review, it was strongly recommended that senior teams not fly to meetings on the same plane. Now, in the UK, we tend to view recommendations as something to do *if we can*, which, in practice, means *if not too inconvenient*. In Germany, however, the translation essentially means 'directions' and these are nearly always followed. At the senior management session I ran it transpired that none of the dozen, or so Germans had caught the same flight – but the same certainly wasn't true of the UK-based managers!

Cue Bob and Terry (and quoting directly from a classic episode!): "You want me to go and talk to those two?" *"Yes!"* "And ask if they'll join us for a drink?" *"Yes!"* "You want me to do it *now*?" *"Yes, now!"* "Oh hell, do I have to?"

## Why Do you want me to do it?

In his Allan St John Holt Memorial Lecture in 2011 Paul Thomas referred to the vital importance of all submariners on his nuclear subs knowing not just *what* to do but also being crystal-clear as to *why* they are doing it. In this extremely challenging environment, it is vital that all personnel can respond as effectively as humanly possible to any unforeseen event. Fully understanding the rationale behind any specific task is key to this. Likewise, Scott Geller is adamant that safety champions must be taught the relevant method and the theory behind it, if they are to embrace it fully.

The same is true in any other environment and is a key element of the 'mindful' mindset discussed above. Harvesting ticks and signatures is all very well but not if they become an end in themselves. The 'why' should always be explained clearly at training, and we need to train employees to always ask the question "What exactly am I trying to achieve with this task?" Again, we are talking about genuine risk literacy here.

The review of almost all major incidents is littered with examples of audits and checks that had been undertaken apparently effectively just prior to the incident but without picking up what they were supposed to be looking for. For example, reviewing the paper work and insurance audits on the permit-to-work and deluge systems on Piper Alpha would have been erroneously reassuring the day before it exploded.

As well as intellectual understanding, subjective motivation is also vital here. When was the last time you did anything with a glad heart when told "because I say so"?

So, the use of data and illustration is vital. (Useful coaching *techniques* are covered in more detail in the later section of that name). We simply mustn't send employees off half-cocked and resentful. Here's an example: some recent research from the US shows clearly why the line management 'safety walk and talk' can achieve little if it is done badly. The research shows that four things correlate with these interactions:

The greater the number of conversations undertaken proactively, the fewer the injuries;

The greater the breadth of individuals involved, the fewer the injuries (as they increase manpower, offer the insight of fresh eyes, and enhance shared understanding);

The greater the number of '100 per cent safe' reports, the greater the number of injuries! (There is *always* something to find, so 'all fine' means you just weren't looking hard enough, or perhaps not asking the right questions);

The greater the number of repeat items found, the greater the number of injuries (because we're just generating symptom-level 'crap lists' and doing nothing about it at a root-cause level, so they recur, or, *even worse*, not getting the lists closed out at all).

This is a really useful piece of research to quote when training a group of supervisors in the mechanics of undertaking a learning-focused walk and talk. We need to be able to say to our trainees: "That's why you all need to do them – head office staff, too – and why you need to do them well. If you don't do them, then we will hurt more people. End of story."

Followed by: "So now we've got that straight, lets practise. . ."

This is especially true of the ones who walked in to the training room resentful and bemused as to why they were there at all.

## Case Study

When training people in the use of face masks and/or extraction devices it is best practice to use a dust lamp, which makes the normally invisible micro-particles visible to the naked eye. Saying "There are harmful particles" simply isn't as powerful as **showing** delegates the harmful particles. It's the reverse of the old coal miner's joke that "I like to be able to see what crap it is I'm breathing!"

## Can I Do it without Embarrassing Myself?

Back to Bob and Terry! When they reach the next bar and Terry pushes Bob forward, is he primarily thinking: "This is a good opportunity to meet a girl!" Or even: "It won't work but it's a good learning opportunity?" It's far more likely he's thinking: "Oh hell, I'm going to make a right fool of myself here!" and suddenly a game of darts, pool, or even an early night becomes hugely attractive. In ABC analysis terms, Bob will almost certainly have in mind a consequence that is likely to be soon and negative, as well as uncertain. In flight-or-fight terms, he'll be highly motivated to flee to the safety of a pool table.

The same is true in work, of course. Most people will avoid tasks that they're wary of, if at all possible. It's just human nature. In a former life, I had a job I hated in financial services before I retrained as a psychologist. I remember a supervisor once saying: "Tim, I really don't need another coffee and can I remind you that coffee making isn't an item on the appraisal you're getting from me next month!"

On a behavioural analysis course, for example, we need to cover 'Five Whys' analysis, ABC analysis and other Just Culture based techniques but these aren't often the problem as delegates can see clearly that a Just Culture based conversation will nearly always be an opportunity to learn, empower and empathise. Trainees will nearly always be pretty comfortable having a go at something with a 'win:win' feel to it. Where they more often struggle is with the soft skills, such as ice-breaking and assertion techniques, which underpin such uncomfortable acts as challenging people.

The prospect of giving a toolbox talk to a group of hard faced contractors is another example. It isn't all that scary if you're an experienced and competent presenter but, technically expert or not, it can be utterly petrifying if you're not – and we've all seen these vital communication events reduced to a mumbled shambles. The classic *Book of Lists* by Wallace *et al* has speaking in public as the number-one fear (greater, even, than dying). In 1984, a *New York Times* survey on social anxiety placed death third in the list of people's biggest fears. The top two responses were walking into a room full of strangers and speaking in public!

I'm not sure how scientific either reference is but it is a certainty that many people are terrified of speaking in public, and the less experienced and/or prepared they are, the worse it's likely to be.

I absolutely guarantee that the vast majority of readers of this book who have a 'walk and talk' process find that, even though the time is available (*if* it is – but that's another matter) they aren't done as frequently as they should be. Similarly, that even if these walk and talks *are* done, many are done as *quickly* as possible. In the section on ABC above, we discussed the vital importance of proactively looking for where the safe way is uncomfortable as, where it is, many will try to work around it.

The same principle applies where supervisors are uncomfortable about talking to colleagues – many will simply work around it, if they can.

So we know what to do and we know why it's important. Better than that, we've had a chance to practise the skills we're not comfortable with in a safe environment. We have some fabulous happy sheet scores for the files. Unfortunately, everything is still up for grabs, as we still have to **multiply** what we now have by a final factor – which is: does the individual value the outcome?

As discussed above, the bad news is that when looked at two years from now we will be on safe ground to assert that 80 per cent, or *more* of the efficacy of any training course is determined by this fourth factor, regardless of how well designed and delivered the course was. It's worth restating that the figures quoted from such as the *Wall St Journal* reflect *general* training courses, not safety specific training, and it's fair to assume that, if anything, a course aimed at enhancing productivity is of course less likely to be run as a simple 'tick box' affair.

## Do I Value the Outcome?

I value safety. If you're reading this out of choice, then it's highly likely that you do, too. We're a self-selecting sample. Unfortunately, many supervisors are influenced by the "'elf and safety gone bonkers" media coverage and think of the "'elf and safety Gestapo". As above, the default setting for most delegates will be deep scepticism. Let's empathise and agree that this might be perfectly understandable when the typical supervisor doesn't appreciate the genuine cost of accidents, the laws of Heinrich's Triangle, the principles of Just Culture or ABC analysis, and the mechanics behind blaming the victim in hindsight.

They need to be systematically taught in an ongoing way to value the behaviours we request on our training courses.

Safety items need to form part of the formal appraisal process – and this doesn't just mean ensuring they are included; they must be given the same *weight* as productivity items. (Here's an exercise to try: record an appraisal and watch out for the body language and voice tone when the individuals get to the safety items – it often looks like a half-time kick about rather than the real thing.) This, of course, will directly reflect the participants' perception of the importance of safety to the organisation

The ad-hoc follow-up is arguably even more vital, and this means we need to make the effort to watch out on a daily basis and note when these behaviours are done well, so that we can praise them. We also need to watch out for opportunities that weren't taken and follow that up with some timely and constructive feedback.

This fourth factor is summarised by an experienced safety manager, who states that: "If the behaviours requested on the course are not considered career enhancing in the smoke shack three months after the course, then you've wasted your money!"

An illustration of just how important this support and feedback is to ongoing improvement comes from the general world of health, from a classic paper by Alan Deutschman. He discusses how some 90 per cent of heart surgery patients fail to maintain the lifestyle changes recommended as key to their survival unless provided with group support sessions that include meditation, yoga and exercise. Among those who do receive such support, 77 per cent were able to maintain the changes, and Deutschman, referencing a study by Dr Dean Ormish of the University of California, feels two elements are key.

First, it's important to 'frame' the targets positively rather than negatively, as a fear of dying seems to have limited shelf life, especially for patients whose initial bad habits reflected their way of coping with emotional pain. (Who wants to live longer when you're miserable?) Therefore, instead warning patients that 'backsliding will probably lead to death' they stress 'maintain these changes for just a few months and you'll be able to walk the hills, enjoy a kick about with the grandchildren and have sex again!'

Ideally, these messages will be emotionally resonant, simple, easy to identify with and positive, and, directly or indirectly, many a CEO has reflected this approach when articulating a vision of an injury and illness-free workplace.

Incredibly, and showing just how powerful the ABC model is, some 66 per cent of patients will cease to take their statin drugs (which reduce cholesterol) within a year, and what could be easier than taking a simple pill once a day? Ormish feels it's the lack of feedback that's key. In short, vital though it is, taking the drug doesn't make you feel any better.

## Conclusion

If we equate an individual's heart attack with a traumatic fatality at an organisation we can see just how easily heartfelt promises and intentions can dissipate. If a person whose life depends on them taking a simple pill can get into the habit of not taking it then it's not hard to imagine a supervisor letting safety drift off his or her radar.

Training experts point out that we need to practise something around 30 times to achieve a basic mastery of the behaviour. Think of any sport or hobby: how many times do you need to practise it before you stop saying "I am learning to be. . ." and start saying "I am a golfer, Samaritan, piano-player..." The experts point out that genuinely embedding something as a refined skill takes *hundreds* of times, so two or three timid attempts don't even get you to base one!

Therefore, to recap, it isn't just being taught what to do – it's just as important that we know *why* and *how* to do it competently and that the organisation systemically ensures, through appropriate feedback, that we practise these behaviours enough to make them an embedded part of what we do and who we are. Obviously, we can conclude here with reference to Geller's thoughts on individual and organisational 'DNA' and 'the way we do things around here'. But let's talk about Terry and Bob instead, with, in the analogy, the frequencies, timescales and transferable skills entirely *intentional*!

Imagine Terry takes Bob out most weekends in the year between holidays. He encourages him to practise, coaches him and gives him timely and constructive feedback. Now, how much more likely is it that, next time, the first holiday 'walk and talk' is something that Terry can safely leave to Bob?

Great Britain will probably continue to bask in the glow of the London 2012 Olympics for some time, so a final thought in this regard: how many of the competitors made it to the Games simply because they were inspired by watching the film *Chariots of Fire*? It might have inspired the sweat, hard work and years of commitment required to reach a world-class level, but inspiring you to dig out the running shoes is all it can do.

Effective training has never been a one-off event but in safety it's often treated that way. Knowing what to do is barely first base. Ongoing feedback and facilitation are far more important in the medium-to-long-term.

## Two Infamous Case Studies and a Very Difficult Behavioural Challenge Indeed

I'd like to cover a couple of well-known case studies here with these 'risk literate' principles in mind. I hope you'll see that the concepts discussed have a lot to add to the objective analysis of the events that occurred.

## The Challenger Disaster

An excellent example of just how important underlying causes are is the explosion of the space shuttle Challenger in 1986. Engineers had found erosion problems with the O rings that held the joins of the sections of the solid rocket boosters. The design did not expect erosion and the engineers were adamant that "this is a sign that something is wrong". Though data were limited and the correlation not perfect it was clear that erosion was generally worse the colder the weather. For example, the worst erosion was at the second-worst temperature. Line management were originally supportive of their engineers' no-fly recommendation, despite push back from NASA management, who added comments to the discussion such as: "I mean, *come on* Thiokol – when are we going to fly? August?!" (Morton-Thiokol was the manufacturer of the solid rocket boosters.)

However, when George Harding – 'a strong-minded and powerful NASA figure', who was listening to the debate on conference call – was called on to comment, he observed: "I won't overrule the contractor's decision but, frankly, I'm appalled by their no-fly position."

A furious debate ensued, with Thiokol management suddenly wondering if perhaps they were being over-cautious after all. Dissenting voices of the engineers were ignored as the management team closed ranks. This included the head of engineering, who was infamously told that "it's time to take off your engineering hat and put on your management hat." It is inconceivable that this recommendation review wasn't strongly influenced by the upcoming contract negotiations – worth the small matter of US$2 billion. Effectively, Harding overruled the contractor.

At the inquiry, the main NASA representative at the meeting, Larry Malloy, said there had been a debate but it was agreed that the cold wasn't an issue and that he had a document from the management of Morton-Thiokol confirming this. At this point, Allan McDonald (the Morton-Thiokol boss who later co-wrote the book *Truth, Lies and O-Rings*) jumped to his feet and interjected that he'd refused to sign the internal document. He was allowed to make his point but was ejected suspiciously quickly from the commission, despite the one independent person on it (the famously strong minded physicist and Nobel Prize-winning Richard Fennyman) demanding he be questioned at greater length. Figures were quoted at the inquiry suggesting that the likelihood of losing a flight was around one in a million. Fennyman scoffed at the figures, suggested the scientists were trying to make the commission 'snow blind' and that it was more like one in 200.

As the BBC film *Challenger* makes clear, the commission had all the makings of a classic whitewash. (The maverick Fennyman was added to the commission presumably to give it credibility but proved a real handful.) The film makes clear that, in simple terms, NASA had pushed a contractor in a vulnerable position too hard and, in the end, the truth did come out, which was as high-level in terms of context as it ever gets.

It transpired that a secret deal had been struck for space shuttles to kill two birds with one stone and carry military equipment in order to secure funding that would have gone direct to an exclusively 'spy in the sky' programme. Guaranteed *regular* flights were key to this strategy and seen as hugely important in securing NASA's continued existence.

Though key individuals continue to insist this wasn't a conscious cover-up, or conscious pressure to fly against the engineers' advice, "they would, wouldn't they?" (as the woman at the centre of the 1960s Profumo affair, Mandy Rice-Davies, famously said about some lying politicians). They may even believe it themselves. However, the two films I've quoted are utterly damning and no one has been sued, you'll note. The sad postscript is that, 17 years later, the Columbia shuttle was also lost. This was one of 110 flights that followed Challenger (itself the 25th shuttle flight) before the programme was discontinued after a total of 135 missions. Therefore, either Fennyman himself was optimistic or NASA was unlucky. Either way, it's safe to say that NASA needed a lot more luck than it would publicly admit to.

An organisation that makes such mistakes, is bullish in its defensiveness about those mistakes, and then covers them up definitely has a in which such mistakes are likely to be *repeated*. (There goes my chance of ever working with NASA!)

## Macondo (Deepwater Horizon)

Huge amounts have been written about Macondo and I have chaired several conferences where is has been described as a 'game changer'. This is because it was, in the words of Andrew Hopkins, not so much a BP accident as a "drilling industry accident".

This short overview of some of the key themes isn't intended to be all-inclusive – rather it picks out some of the issues that illustrate a strong cultural component. To stick with my simple 'learning: leadership' model the opportunities to learn where there in abundance. The safety leadership was strong in many respects but continued to lack balance and perspective regarding process-safety issues.

Like Challenger it was suggested as a defence that the cause of the Macondo blow-out was that companies were operating at the edges of their technological capabilities, so error was almost inevitable. However, as with Challenger, it wasn't the technology that failed so much as the organisation of the work. With hindsight we can see that the technological failures could have easily been avoided if some simple errors of *perception* had been avoided.

Indeed, as well as BP both the other associated organisations could have avoided the accident if they had acted differently. Transocean had suffered a similar blow-out on one of its rigs (in the North Sea) just four months earlier. Had it learned the lessons from that, the incident could have been avoided. Certainly, the VIP visit the day before the explosion might have had more of a process safety focus. This didn't stop President Obama referring to just the one company and pointedly referring to BP as *British* Petroleum – the first time its old name had been used for decades!

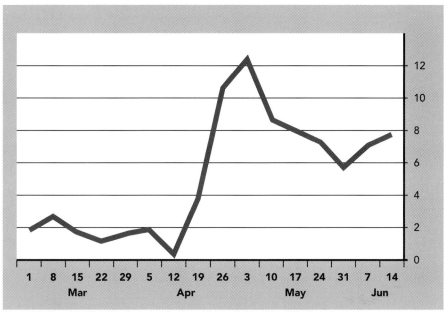

**Figure 20. Use of 'British Petroleum' as % of mentions of BP in US publications** Source: Dow Jones Factiva

This criticism wasn't fair but it was 'coming', perhaps, because of the legacy of Texas City. The above graph, published in The Economist, illustrates the subjective and political nature of responses once things have gone wrong. BP had been BP since 2001.

**BP and Texas City.** The accusation of the Baker report – and as so clearly documented by Andrew Hopkins in the book *Failure to Learn* – was that BP was too focused on personal safety and not focused enough on process safety because of a drive to maximise profits. Boiled down, the accusation is that the company was not at all mindful of safety (except regarding slips trips and falls) and confused low lost-time injury rates with actual risk management. Assuring themselves that safety around BP was good because LTI rates were low and there was little bad news is the very definition of a lack of risk literacy.

Effectively, John Browne is accused of heading a culture that asked "Any problems with that? No? Good!" when the latest round of cuts were requested. Browne presided over an organisation that only wanted to hear good news. This meant that the management at Texas City were very popular in the UK for a while, as they complained the least.

In particular, this 'tell me good news' culture meant that when site visits were undertaken reassurances would be given and passively accepted (usually in a discussion over a table) that any problems that might exist were under control. The protestation from the CE level that "We never knew how bad it was" jarred with reports in 2002 in which "serious concerns about the potential for a major incident" were expressed, and in 2004, when there was "an exceptional fear of a catastrophic incident" and the situation was described as "horrifying" and "completely unacceptable". Hopkins sums this up as 'fortress refining'.

I'm not very interested in who was most culpable but it's clear that this was an accident waiting to happen to a major and well respected organisation. A lot of experienced people knew just how likely it was to happen, but, because of its culture and lack of risk literacy, that didn't include the people who ran the company. When they did ask questions they asked the wrong ones, or they asked them in the wrong way.

To recap the definition of mindfulness introduced above, BP was guilty of:

    failing to be wary, which led to overconfidence;

    not carrying out audits for learning (but rather 'crap-list' critical or 'back-pat' celebratory);

    ignoring ambiguous and intermittent warning signs;

    normalising ambiguous and intermittent warning signs; and

    putting the onus on the safety department to *prove* failure would happen.

All of these are themes revisited in Andrew Hopkins' book about Macondo, *Disastrous Decisions*, which looks rather damning at a glance. The true story is rather more complex and subtle, however – and, I'd argue, illustrative.

**Macondo.** By the time the incident occurred many commentators felt that BP's commitment to personal safety was exemplary. On the rig itself, just a few days before the blow-out, a minor injury caused by a lifting operation led to BP instigating a time-out of an hour or two. This, as Hopkins puts it, "where time is money... that an injury requiring only a first-aid treatment could trigger such a response is an indication of how seriously BP took personal safety". Similarly, the TOFS process (Time Out for Safety – a dynamic risk-assessment tool) was working well for personal safety – but no one called a TOFS on the day despite, as detailed above, all sorts of warning signs. In short, the measures and recommendations from the Baker report were being implemented and embedded – very well on production but less so on drilling platforms, for which the lead indicators still needed to be tailored but weren't fully completed yet.

All wells will work to production deadlines and, prior to drilling, the 'technical limit' will be identified (based on the quickest each element of the task can be completed). There is, of course, huge commercial and professional interest in keeping as close to this perfect score as possible, with the ongoing monitoring of progress hugely impactful. (For example, the head of drilling for the Gulf had been challenged twice about the expensive coffee used in HQ as part of an 'every dollar counts' culture.)

In contrast, though personal safety was being very well monitored nobody was really monitoring the likelihood of a blow-out. No one even reacted effectively when it started to actually happen (the 'kick', as explained on page 59).

I described above that Reason's overstretched elastic band model provides a frame on which to hang an overall safety strategy. The speed with which a well recognises that a kick has occurred and the efficacy of its response would be a perfect example of that. Sidney Dekker says "measure what matters" and this clearly matters. But it wasn't being measured.

## Specific Issues at Macondo

Much focus was put on the failure of the blow-out preventer (BOP) but this was merely the last line of defence and arguably not the most important. As well as this a holistic overview would consider such organisational issues as the bonus system, the decentralised organisational structure, the over-emphasis on personal safety at the expense of process safety, the lack of understanding that defence in depth requires independent maintenance of each layer, and that organisational flaws can undermine all layers simultaneously. so that what we assume is a 1% x 1% x 1% possibility simply becomes a 1% chance of failure.

It's known that BP had made great efforts to improve safety since the John Browne led aggressive profit-chasing days that led to Texas City. Macondo was different. It wasn't hopelessly under resourced, incident rates (as measured) were world class, and during the high level visit the day before the incident the visitors had praised local management for the way they stopped a lifting job because of a potential incident. Indeed, they had some specific safety issues they planned to praise when on board in exactly the way we suggest embedding occurs.

In short, they wouldn't have got a poor score from a safety culture survey and they weren't at a glance an overstretched elastic band. Except that they *were* overstretched and were utterly blind to it. They would have described themselves as in balance but with lots of weight on both ends. A big emphasis on safety but with a very strong focus on cost, profits and speed. (In a later section we'll discuss nudges and subconscious messages.) The visiting party will have inadvertently emphasised the importance of production by treating process issues as 'out of bounds unless something obviously dangerous is seen', because they didn't want to be disruptive.

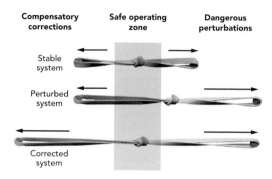

**Figure 21. Rubber Band Model revisited**

This is an organisation with no *leeway* so that when some simple and well understood problems happened they would have devastating consequences.

Macondo managers were answerable to local operations managers, which led them to focus on cost-cutting and speed rather than engineering excellence. (A criticism is that the impressive-sounding job titles and experience actually meant men without a university education were in charge. Their common sense isn't doubted – what was needed were high scores on such as the Watson-Glaser critical-thinking tests.) Therefore, at core the problem was that if the cement job succeeded then they could 'crack on' but if it failed then the job would be delayed, at a cost of millions of dollars. The commercial risk was foremost in their minds when they reviewed its success. They weren't as analytical as they should have been and they'd have realised it had failed if they had been.

What happened was a combination of confirmation bias, normalisation of deviation from accepted practice, inadequate situational awareness sand Group think.

Hopkins summarises this very clearly:

"The team opened the valve to bleed off water and reduce the pressure to zero. But as soon as they closed the valve the pressure began to rise. This was a clear indication that the well had failed the test (i.e. the cement job had failed) and was not in fact sealed. (The team) did not draw that conclusion and tried the test a second time and again, the same thing happened. [However] the group could not accept what this was telling them."

**Confirmation Bias.** Confirmation bias (also called confirmatory bias), first studied in the 1960s, is the tendency of people to favour information that confirms their beliefs or hypotheses. Jason Zweig, in the *Wall St Journal* in 2009, referred to it as "an internal yes-man", which sums it up rather well.

It was very rare for a well to fail a test of this type, and the people involved were in essence not *investigating whether it had succeeded or not* but *confirming that it had*. Therefore, the mindset is that if the answer is wrong, ask the question again. Hopkins makes the point with an illustration of a decision tree used by engineers at head office. Instead of a diamond-shaped box (i.e. one with a yes or no? *fork*) it is a rectangular box (i.e. one in a line of similar shaped boxes). Clearly there is already an assumption that it is merely a task in a *list* of tasks. Indeed, the test was only performed at all on the day at the request of a Transocean manager. It simply wasn't top of the agenda for the BP engineers on the day.

This was the famous 'Spot the Gorilla' exercise writ as large as it ever will be. (In this exercise, delegates are challenged to count passes between intermingling basketball players, some dressed in yellow, some in black. The question is whether the large gorilla that walks across the scene in the middle of the game blows a kiss or beats his chest. The majority of delegates, distracted by the players, will ask "What gorilla?" The science behind the clip is explained in an article by two scientists from Harvard, called Daniel Simons and Christopher Chabris.) Though the 'gorilla' was clearly there the BP engineers didn't see it because they weren't looking for it. As far as they 'knew' the gorilla had been caged and their attention was on the next job and their paperwork.

**Normalisation of Warning Signs.** To my mind, this is the most noteworthy factor. As with the O-ring erosion on the Challenger Space Shuttle, which should have set alarms ringing because it wasn't what the design expected, the benign-sounding 'bladder effect' was put forward to explain the rise in drill pressure. (The theory suggests that a rubber seal is slightly flexible so is able to transmit pressure from the 'mud' above to the water below, which, in turn, transmits additional pressure up the drill pipe.)

Ironically, it was the Transocean employees who put this forward as something not uncommon. Of course, the 'bladder effect' makes no sense at all to experts and could not possibly account for the findings. However, with this plausible explanation for the test readings the faulty assumption that all was well remained. Similarly, when readings at the top and bottom of the drill pipe contradicted each other they went instead with the reassuring zero-pressure reading from the bottom. They should have said "What?!" but didn't. They went with the data that assured them that all was well.

This is, at this point, entirely a mindset issue.

Hopkins suggests that for all their experience the individuals involved were not as senior and well-educated as they might have been (as mentioned above). A position described as 'well site leader' had previously been known as 'drilling foreman'. This wasn't ideal when abstract thinking was required.

**Group Think.** A William H Whyte Jr. coined this term in March 1952, in *Fortune* magazine, suggesting that it is not just mere instinctive conformity but rather a rationalised conformity – an open, articulate philosophy, which holds that group values are not only expedient but right and good as well.

Technically, the team offshore could have escalated the problem to the shore-based well team leader but, in practice, the team was empowered to decide locally. This is as it should be, in many respects, and it was a team decision, with "all parties needing to be comfortable with the decision". Again, this is as it should be – books like *The wisdom of crowds* show that a group decision is often better than an individual's. (Except that other studies show that it's not better than the *best* individual in the group. This is important if they then become the subject of Group think.)

However, in this situation a classic 'risky shift' occurred. A risky shift is where a group will make a more risky decision than an individual would make. In small groups, the norm is for decisions to be unanimous, as any one who has ever been the dissenting voice in a group of five children will remember! The dynamic is similar, with good-humoured pressure applied to the dissenter. In this case, the BP employee who was worried about the 'bladder effect' explanation found himself the object of amusement among the others.

You're a long way off shore, there are time pressures, there are 'data' confirming things are alright, you're surrounded by hard bitten experienced men, who find your caution amusing. The majority of us would say "Oh, OK..." We address this by having the expert individual consult with the team - which will explicitly involve someone playing devil's advocate – before withdrawing to make the final decision for which *they* are responsible (which, following the learning from Macondo, is what BP now does).

**Defence in Depth.** Related to the above is the issue of defence in depth, as described by the Cheese model. This only works if each individual barrier (the tests, the BOP) is treated as an *individual* barriers in its own right. Once assumptions are made upstream they can all fail for the same reason, and what should be 1% x 1% (i.e.

one in 1000) simply stays as 1%. Again, on Macondo, this appreciation was held to be missing.

This time BP can't really be accused of being a rogue company, cruising for a fall. This was a lack of risk literacy about human error specifically, in a key place at a key time.

## A Very Hard Behavioural Challenge

I recently spoke with a company that makes highly effective cancer-fighting chemicals. These drugs are hugely powerful even though the active element of the drug in question is so diluted its concentration levels are close to that claimed for homeopathy. (Except that this is the real deal – there's no placebo effect here). The problem is that as well as not being visible to the naked eye we haven't got the technology to swab and screen. (The company scientists joked, in classic Monty Python style: "*Radiation*? Ha – how *easy* is radiation?! We can make radiation click loudly and set off alarms at levels not even all that dangerous! I wouldn't even get out of *bed* for radiation!").

Worse, the lag time between exposure and illness is years (usually decades) and, of course, there's a **huge** financial imperative. This isn't the Atomic Weapons Establishment, run by a government department, which will still be here, accountable and able to be sued 30 years from now. The 'suits' – who aren't scientists, let alone hygienists – running this company now will be long retired to the golf courses of Spain and Florida (or in the Lords) when any crap hits the fan.

Being faced with this 'perfect storm' of a behavioural problem inspired me to go back to first principles. How exactly *do* we get the technicians in these labs to follow protocols that will keep them safe?

Starting with **control** we have to ask from a Just Culture perspective whether or not the technicians have the tools to implement the training they have been given and understand the risks. (Actually, yes they do.) Next, we can ask if it is possible to follow the protocols given the time constraints, i.e. a 'situational' violation (again, yes it is). Finally, is there unspoken pressure to finish up and turn to something the organisation values and rewards even more than hygiene – what Reason would call an 'optimising' violation? (Here it gets interesting, and we'll return to this.)

What there is most obviously, it seems, is an 'individual violation' – a classic ABC situation, where there are no short-term consequences at all for a little corner cutting, or lack of thoroughness. (They can't even set off alarms and 'beep' as they are screened. The work surfaces look spotless even if they aren't, and no one looks or feels the slightest bit ill – not even after working there for years.)

My analysis of the problem is that although the workers are 'fully' trained and therefore worried about their health they aren't as *out-and-out paranoid and scared* as they should be! Thus, a two-pronged attack was suggested. The first was to deliver some very intense and visceral training, illustrated with the effects of contamination that they could never forget. In other words, to completely maximise the 'why' element of training as well as the 'what' and 'how', as described in my article on training excellence in the August 2012 issue of SHP magazine. The second element is to follow this up with a series of intense observation and feedback sessions regarding the decontamination protocols and using trained coaches to fully embed the behaviours requested. In other words, to treat the health protocols with the same intensity as a key set of behaviours that could cause a catastrophic crash in share prices next week.

This intensity of follow-up needs to be maintained long enough for the protocols to genuinely become the **norm** – 'part of the way we do things around here' and therefore, in part, self-sustaining. However, they must still be followed up often enough for this standard not to degrade. This investment is vital and is where management's long-term commitment comes in. The point I want to make is that since this *is*, under the current circumstances, exactly what is required to tackle this health issue effectively then **anything less than this** is indeed the 'optimising' violation I alluded to above.

Chapter 4.
# The Financial Benefits of HS&E Excellence

## Context

Gareth Morgan, in the classic text *Images of Organisation,* says that all organisations have limited funds and unlimited demands on those funds. Therefore, different elements of an organisation will have to compete for those resources and that, suggests Morgan, "*organisational politics is absolutely inevitable.*"

It's difficult to argue with that observation. Therefore, when we talk about risk with people whose definition is based almost entirely on risk to organisational viability or profit, we need to talk to them in their own language. If nothing else you get much better service in France when you make an effort to speak a little French (well, outside of Paris anyway). This chapter considers how best to articulate the *first* 'win' in what really is a 'win:win' proposal.

### The figures

It is calculated that the UK lost 26.4 million days to illness and injury in 2010/11 (HSE). Estimates of the financial cost of this to the UK economy vary but it is certainly several billion pounds.

The International Labour Organisation estimates that a worker dies from occupational illness or injury every 15 seconds, with 6300 killed daily and 2.3 million annually. When we add in work-related road deaths it means we are losing the population of my home country of Wales (or a New Zealand) every year. The ILO estimated that the cost to the global economy is adjacent to 1.25 *trillion* dollars.

These figures are simply too big for me to comprehend. This is especially so when I watch an awareness raising film about *one* serious accident, where, often, the parent, child, or partner of just one worker is giving heartbroken testimony. The concept of the collective misery generated by the figures above is overwhelming and it would be very easy to get disheartened and fatalistic.

I'm reminded, however, of the Buddhist story about the man on the beach throwing back starfish that had recently been washed ashore and were stranded. A passer-by asks him: "What are you doing? There are thousands of starfish washed up on this beach and you can't possibly save more than a dozen. What you are doing is utterly pointless!" The man replies: "Well, it makes a big difference to *this* one. . .and *this* one..." In a similar vein, there is a very moving line at the end of the Stephen Spielberg film *Schindler's List*: "If you save one life you save the world entire."

Finally, there is also a wonderful African proverb. It says that in the morning, if you are an antelope, you'd better be running faster than the fastest lion. If you are a lion then you'd better be running faster than the slowest antelope. Either way, *you'd better wake up running*. To stretch the analogy here to breaking point, this book is an attempt to help organisations know in which direction to run. Certainly, we can all agree that there's often much running around like headless chickens *after* an incident!

## Financial costs to *individual* companies

The Outtakes film *The Secret Siphon* describes the costs of an accident, starting with an increase in insurance premium rates. Other uninsured costs can include:

Lost time due to illness or injury to the worker;

Direct disruption to production, which may directly lead to loss of contracts and good will;

Indirect disruption to production through investigation time;

Sick pay;

Damage to product or raw material;

Damage to plant and equipment;

Extra wage costs in the form of overtime, or temporary labour;

Legal costs;

Fines;

Consultancy costs;

Bad publicity, which can affect how attractive the company is to potential clients and potential employees.

The Health and Safety Executive in the UK have estimated that the ratio of insured to uninsured costs is between 1:8 and 1:36. Even taking the most modest of these ratios that means a major accident that, at a glance, 'costs' £10,000 is likely to *actually* cost the organisation a cool £100,000 and may actually cost more than £250,000.

Describing the costs and benefits in terms the CFO and the CEO understand, Martin Carter of the energy firm EON says that when talking to the board we must always consider the classic trinity:

- Obligation;
- Reputation; and
- Numeration

In other words: what they need to be doing to keep out of *court*, what they need to be doing to keep out of the *newspapers*; and what they need to be doing to keep the *shareholders* happy. This certainly isn't to suggest that all board members are indifferent to the moral argument but it's a theme of this book that we are all well advised to consider the basic drivers of the specific group we are working with.

Here's a simple technique that clarifies things for 'bean counters', as it turns the cost into units of production. Imagine that a production operator at a soft-drink canning factory has driven a forklift into some machinery and badly injured a colleague. The direct costs, as above, are around £10,000, so the actual costs are at least £100,000 (as above, possibly more). Imagine that this company makes a healthy 5p profit on every can of drink it sells; to get back to square one they need to manufacture and sell *at least two million* cans of soda to break even, and possibly **five million.**

One of the DuPont philosophies is that "safety isn't a cost, it's an *investment*" and to quote the Outtakes film *Secret Weapon*, "like any other investment you'll be looking for a return." At an international symposium in Rome in 2012, Neil Budworth of EON reported estimates that for every £1 invested in a proactive health programme the company had saved £5. The London Olympics build team suggested even better returns (at around £9). Collated research of 300 companies by Braunig and Kohstall for the International Social Security Association and published in 2012 put the figure at £2.2. Of course, there can be no definitive figure because it very much depends on how well funds are invested, but it can be said with absolute certainty that a well thought-through and targeted investment in safety will prove profitable in the medium to long-term.

I wish I had a pound for every time I've heard the expression "If you think safety is expensive, try having an accident!" This short section has been specifically for any line manager who has heard that expression and scoffed a bit. Or perhaps for any safety professional who works with such a manager.

In short, if you work with a truly hard-hearted S.o.B who thinks *only* of money and 'pallets departing on trucks' then it makes sense to talk to them in those terms.

**There must always be a moral case, too**

On the other hand, Lawrence Waterman, the man lauded for delivering such a safe Olympic Games build in 2012, sounds a warning. He argues that we must never lose sight of the moral case and, specifically, that the neo-liberal view that has dominated British politics for the past 30 years is a flawed model. It argues that deregulation (combined with lower taxes in the economic model) will create rewards that will 'trickle down' to benefit all of us. The trouble is that capitalism, especially as seen in the finance industry, may well seek short-term rewards that cannot be obtained without inordinate risk.

We saw, for example, what happened when the sub-prime loan issue exploded in the USA. Similarly, despite being the richest country on the planet, health policies in the US have left the country 38th in the world, in terms of best health statistics. This was only just behind Costa Rica in the WHO rankings but some way off Columbia. 'Trickle down' is clearly not working very well here.

Waterman points out that if we fight safety on the 'financial' ground only, then we may back ourselves into a corner. The response at the very highest levels may be to take this argument to extremes, and these 'powers that be' will use it to justify cuts. The plausible-sounding argument Waterman is so wary of goes like this:

"Yes, we agree that safety is good for business. That argument is over! What this means is that there is indeed a genuine commercial imperative here – and because of this the markets will self regulate. Companies with strong safety cultures will thrive and companies with weak safety cultures will wither and die off. Now admittedly, these massive cuts to the HSE budget will lead to fewer inspections and will mean a smaller safety net but, through the process of natural selection, this will actually *accelerate* the improvement process. So these cuts are actually *good* for safety, when you think about it..."

At this point it's worth remembering that satirical UK TV programmes like the *The Thick of It* are so funny because they are based more on reality than we'd care to admit!

Sticking with politics, Professor Ragnar Löfstedt produced a report on the state of the health and safety system in the UK in 2011 that was seen by many as scientific, data-based and balanced. Löfstedt's thoughtful conclusion, that the balance is just about right, was met with thin smiles and thanks. These thanks were not for the conclusions, of course, but for the 'thoroughness' of the report. ("Thank you for the thoroughness" arguably translates as "Thanks a lot for that … I'm not sure you quite understood what was required here. . .we really wish we hadn't bothered asking you now!").

Waterman's view therefore is that we must refer to historical data that show what actually happens to accident rates when regulation is eased and spending on inspections is decreased. For him, the balance is just about right and it's very likely that any change will make things worse. He is a man who has had a lot of discussions that started with someone very powerful asking him "Do we *really* need to...", won most of them and was proved *right* on the biggest of stages. Or we could consider some words from the late Bobby Kennedy about wellbeing:

"The gross national product does not allow for the health of our children, the quality of their education, or the joy of their play. It does not include the beauty of our poetry, or the strength of our marriages; the intelligence of our public debate, or the integrity of our public officials. It measures neither our wit nor our courage; neither our wisdom nor our learning; neither our compassion nor our devotion to our country; it measures everything, in short, except that which makes life worthwhile..."

What a beautiful piece of prose, reminding us that we are supposed to be working to live.

## Indirect Financial Benefits of Excellence

Better news is that a strong safety culture has benefits over and above avoiding the aforementioned financial costs. To a great extent the behaviours required for cultural excellence are generic and as much about productivity as they are about safety. Even the most safety specific principle in the book – Heinrich's Triangle – can be used as a metaphor for life itself, not just for workplace excellence. The non-technical skills certainly generalise.

It's worth reiterating that the proactive safety organisation is characterised by:

a learning focus;

mindfulness and objectivity;

trust, openness, transparency and consistency;

clearly articulated goals;

leading by example;

coaching, not telling;

involving and empowering; and

praising, not criticising.

It's very simple: you simply can't have a world-class safety culture without the majority of the management and supervisors undertaking these behaviours the majority of the time. If they are in the habit of thinking and behaving this way, then they will apply this to **everything** in work, not just safety.

This can work the other way, too. In 2012, British Gypsum was able to boast a reduction in accidents from an average of 20 a year across its three UK sites to none at all in the three years to the end of 2012. This wasn't delivered by an explicitly safety focused approach but, arguably, by a more quality focused approach that saw unplanned factory stops down from around 650 a month to single figures. It's considerably less risky to simply monitor an efficiently running machine than to have to gain access to repair it. Key to this success is that no matter how clear and sincere the 'don't rush' message to engineers is, workers will undertake this ad-hoc work as quickly as they can to get the line back on. In short, this is a huge amount of highly predictable risk designed out at source.

We've suggested bluntly that productivity and quality are always going to be at least equal in importance to a commercial organisation as safety is. It's impossible to imagine a set of managers delivering world class safety who didn't also apply these principles and behaviours to quality and productivity. Show me an organisation with a world class safety culture and I'll show you a world class organisation. End of (as the youth here in Manchester so succinctly put it).

**An 'unintended consequences' warning:**

Here's a red flag, however, about management commitment and 'unintended consequences'. Imagine a company with a traditionally weak safety focus that has a strong need to show that it is 'doing something about safety' (let's say because of an HSE enforcement notice). Consequently, it sends some largely untrained managers on a course that covers the techniques of communication, empowerment, coaching and analysis discussed in detail in this book. To what areas of work do you think they will *most readily* apply what they have learnt on their return to the workplace? We might have a situation where, before, they were weak at management all round but now we've simply given them better tools to cue the workforce to address what's *really* important!

# Additional Benefits – Organisational Citizenship Behaviours

Dennis Organ (1988) defines OCB as "Individual behavior that is discretionary, not directly or explicitly recognised by the formal reward system, and that, in the aggregate, promotes the effective functioning of the organisation". Other writers have dubbed this 'pro-social behaviour', or 'above the line' behaviour and debate the finer points. but Organ's definition makes clear what we are discussing and also that OCBs are a positive thing.

Collectively, this concept encompasses reduced turnover, reduced absenteeism, reduced 'presenteeism' (present in body but not in spirit), greater likelihood of volunteering and more readily helping new starts – all of which should be highly attractive to any executive board, with its eye on profits, and the frontline supervisor, with his eye on Friday's shipment of goods. (See Jones 2010 for an overview of literature on presenteeism).

Later sections of this book go into detail regarding the importance of subtle cues to behaviour. Ideally, in some respects, this section would come after a description of the likes of nudge theory and the power of subconscious drivers in determining behaviour, but first I'll continue to try to establish 'why bother?' before moving on to 'how?'

I'd like to consider one important and politically sensitive benefit of a healthy safety culture – claiming for injury. At a macro level, claims are influenced by factors such as the national psyche. I was once told by a proud Scandinavian oil worker that Finnish workers do not often claim for injury, as the national culture is for injury to be considered as part of the job, and claiming is seen as rather unmanly. This, if true, is excellent for the claims department but it isn't a great mindset for the behavioural safety expert to deal with.

The proliferation of adverts for 'Where there's pain, there's a claim' or 'No win, no fee' isn't always helpful either of course. However, workforce empowerment advocates like Nigel Bryson would say they are merely an overreaction to a considerable historical injustice. I'm not sure big business would be in loss if we could objectively balance spurious claims that have succeeded over the years – perhaps because they are cleverly pitched just below the 'fight it' threshold – and genuine claims denied over the *centuries* of blaming the victim.

At a micro, individual level, however, we respond very strongly to the notion of 'fairness'. It underpins the much studied concept of worker/employer exchange called the 'psychological contract' (A term coined by Denise Rousseau in 1995).

What this means in practice is that a person who may well have grounds to put in a legitimate claim doesn't, 'to be nice'. Though a rational view would be that no one notices and no one cares, either – it's not about rationality, it's about an internal balance. In this case, the individual rationalisation process is: 'I enjoy working here and, by and large, they are good to me so I won't make a fuss', and this works in favour of the organisation.

For example, in a series of programmes on Radio 4 in 2012 James Reason talked about hospitals taking a more transparent approach to their mistakes. Intuitively, the worry was that they would be simply giving ammunition to claims lawyers, but the figures show that wasn't the case; claims actually decreased.

Coming at this from the opposite direction an individual who isn't utterly amoral will have to justify a false claim to themselves in some way, in order to maintain their self image as 'an OK person'. (Books such as *The Psychopath Test*, by Jon Ronson, suggest that up to10 per cent of the population are, indeed, amoral and impervious to anyone's viewpoint but their own utterly self absorbed one – but that still leaves at least 90 per cent of the workforce to work on).

For most of us, perceptions of fairness and personal control are hugely central to our behaviour. Azjen's model mentions control in terms of 'Can I behave this way?' There is a second, under explored aspect, which considers an individual's need to kick back, which is very much about internal perceptions of fairness and self image. For example, I have a very upright and sensible looking friend who hates being kept waiting. In a supermarket, if the queue is what he would consider unreasonably long, he will often confidently pop something into his pocket to compensate himself for the inconvenience. If he thinks the item is too valuable, then he'll pop the equivalent amount of money into a charity tin by the door. A small victory for him over 'the man', and the balance of his universe is restored!

Similarly, Sidney Dekker recounts the story of a family that was put up in a hotel during formal legal proceedings. Angered by the organisation in question's lack of transparency they ordered as much room service as possible, then 'threw it all away'.

**I am a man not a number**. Similarly, the holistic model of culture I've introduced in this book talks explicitly about control. Azjen means control of the environment but, to me, it also refers to my friend in the queue. (Think of the classic TV series *'The Prisoner'*, where the titular character insists: "I am not a number I am a free **man**,!") There is a need in all of us to fight back against a world that seeks to emasculate us – male or female! For some, this will manifest itself as spurious claims, scratching the MD's car, or even sabotage. For most, it means leaving the company, 'presenteeism', or simply deciding not to perform 'organisational citizenship' behaviours when given the chance.

McGregor's classic 'Theory X and Theory Y' shows, for example, that, often, if we treat people badly then, often, they will act badly. Workers who are treated badly – or perhaps just indifferently – will feel that a response hurtful to the organisation is *fair* and restores balance. An organisation with a strong safety culture will, by necessity, be treating most people well and will consequently be likely to be full of adult behaviours and positive mindsets.

Spurious claims will always occur. There will always be a small minority of people who are entirely self-interested. However, spurious claims will only *proliferate* in a 'spurious claims' culture.

# Chapter 5.
# A Closer Look at Individuals

In the previous chapters I've tried to address some broad and important themes about organisations and the people who work for them; issues that we all need to understand if we are to become risk literate, because they are universal and widely influential. In this section I'd like to address some other issues about the variation among individuals.

The questions I'm most often asked as a safety psychologist are "Why do we do risky things?" and "Why do we make mistakes?" The answers start with our genetic residue from our evolution millions of years ago; ever since our early ancestors left Africa human beings have been hot wired to 'give it a go' and assume everything 'will be ok'. It is also necessary to take into account individual quirks of character, and, finally, that it's considered that a significant slice of the population will be sociopathic. (See Hare 1996).

This means sociopathic in the *social* rather than violent sense and refers to people who simply haven't taken on board many of societies' key values around sharing and caring and are instead almost entirely self serving. (Whether that's 1% or 10% of the population depends very much on the definition chosen). Films such as *Pay it Forward* illustrate the Beatle lyric "And in the end the love you get is equal to the love you give". Social psychopaths are utterly unmoved by such notions and don't see caring people as kind and enlightened and contributing to the greater collective good; they see them as soft minded easy targets. In other words a social psychopath may volunteer for a safety committee but only if they can see a personal opportunity in doing so!)

I'll try and suggest ways of addressing these mistakes as I go, as well as providing a SWOT analysis of some of the most well-used methodologies.

# Are Some Individuals Accident prone?

A frequently-asked question is "Are some people more accident prone than others?" It's a rather controversial subject because of the issues of blame and scapegoating, the importance of a Just Culture, and studies (as above) that show that it's the environment, not the person, that is the root cause of the vast majority of problems. Therefore, it is essential we focus on the individual only when all organisational factors have been systematically analysed.

While this 'person last, if at all' position is a central tenet of this book, we should take care not to dismiss the individual's importance. If you were flying off on holiday want your family to be in the hands of a pilot who was easily bored and distracted, low in conscientiousness, highly creative (so prone to daydreaming) hugely risk tolerant, unintelligent, easily tired, and given to mood swings?

Personally, I'd prefer my family to be in the hands of someone conscientious, focused, risk aware, emotionally stable, physically robust, and clever, thank you very much! As a chap once said to me in a smoke shack:

"Tim, this Just Culture stuff is all well and good, but there are a couple of muppets out there I wouldn't trust to walk my dog!"

I'd like to leave the minority to one side and concentrate on the typical worker and how individual variations within the 'normal' band can impact on safety. I will be talking about personality, intelligence (and its different types), and motivational drivers.

Firstly, some background theory. Individual differences can be categorised into three broad types:

Physical – size, etc;

Physiological – for example, health and fitness; and

Psychological – essentially intelligence, personality and motivation.

It's fair to say that large, clumsy and badly coordinated individuals undertaking complicated tasks are more likely to have bumps. It's also fair to say that unfit or unwell individuals will be more prone to tiredness and that tired people make more mistakes and have more slips. We certainly know that badly designed shift systems, or jobs with excessive physical or psychological strain can make people unnaturally tired and therefore accident prone, and I'll discuss this via a case study later in this chapter.

But there are many individual differences that little can be done about because they are innate to the individual in question; for example, different types of personality, motivation and intelligence can all interact to cause stress, poor performance and safety issues. And this is where things get complex, as intelligence, motivation and personality are multi-faceted and interact in any number of ways. Further, the relationship between a behaviour or trait and risk is not always linear, where it is the case that 'the more (or less) of a behaviour or trait the worse it is'. Sometimes, too little *or* too much of something can be an issue.

## Intelligence

As you can imagine, intelligent people usually make fewer mistakes than unintelligent ones, all else being equal. However, this isn't always the case and studies show how intelligent people can be more likely to switch off when faced with mundane tasks. Originally described by psychologists Robert Yerkes and John Dodson back in 1908, the 'Yerkes–Dodson law' suggests that performance increases with physiological or mental arousal, but only up to a certain point.

It's said that peak performance is achieved between 40 and 70 per cent emotional arousal. It depends on the task itself, the duration of the task and the individual's relish of the task but, rather like Heinrich and his ratios, it's the basic principle rather than the exact percentages that is important. If we are working at too low a level of arousal we are likely to become bored and therefore prone to distraction; if we are working at too high a level we are likely to become stressed. Hence the old adage: "Brain surgeons make for lousy taxi drivers."

# Case Study

A transport company client employed ex-pilots who were looking to top up their pension pots and keep active as train drivers. The problem was they clearly weren't any better than typical drivers; in fact, although numbers were small and statistical analysis was tentative, they were *worse*. The reason is that it's likely that the job simply couldn't get them up to that fabled 40 per cent arousal.

By contrast, I once had the delightful job of conducting an on stage interview with a group of bus drivers who'd won awards for working for the company for 20 years without a single incident. When we passed the questions to the audience one was asked: "What's the most enjoyable aspect of the job after all these years?" He stumbled over his answer a few times (it was a very large audience of several hundred senior managers) before announcing boldly and clearly: "Actually, *all* of it. I still love it after all these years. I just bloody well love driving buses me … always have!"

This was a man clearly suited to driving buses and on the day in question he nearly got a standing ovation!

## Personality

Although this short section has one foot in the field of personality theory it has long been agreed that outside of illness and trauma the typical person's personality is a broad balance of social experience and learning and our genetic inheritance.

There are many models of personality based on everything from Freud's id and ego through to the Simpsons characters. (Simpsons' profiles can be surprisingly astute, as well as interesting – though you really don't want to be Homer!) Collated research, however, has focused on the 'big five' factors:

Extroversion;
Anxiety;
Conscientiousness;
Open-mindedness; and
Agreeableness.

In a substantial piece of research collating the findings of dozens of studies and based on the 'big five' factors, Clarke and Robertson found that personality factors such as conscientiousness and aggression did, indeed, correlate significantly with accident rates.

The actual figures are interesting, and illustrate the point. Though careless, overconfident, sloppy people have more accidents than careful, cautious people it's just a statistically significant correlation – not a perfect correlation by any means. The reason, of course, is that the environment is far more important.

My PhD used these factors to predict suicidal behaviour in army recruits. Unsurprisingly, I found that the Army took anyone half sensible who would give basic training a go and then let that basic training sort out the ones who wanted to stay. The problem wasn't just that those low in conscientiousness made more mistakes but also that those who were naturally anxious really worried about it. On top of this, the introverts hated barrack life, so anyone low in conscientiousness, as well as anxious and introverted tended to be having a horrible time. (As I said, it was a study into suicidal behaviour).

## Personality and Safety

We know that some people are naturally physically extrovert and tolerant of physical risk so are much more likely to be up for rugby, driving fast, taking experimental drugs and bungee jumping. Obviously, this inborn 'risk tolerance' can dramatically influence day-to-day behaviour and the neurobiological basis of this is that these people tend to have slow-firing synapses that basically need more 'oomph' to get a satisfying charge. (The self confessed 'adrenalin junkie' characters in the Keanu Reeves and Patrick Swayze film *Point Break* would be a perfect illustration).

As you can imagine naturally liberal types are more tolerant of innovation and change whereas naturally conservative types are instinctively more anxious. The latter are wired to prefer order, consistency and certainty; in other words, they simply see far more risk in the world around them than liberal people do.

The practical implication is that we need a mix of both in any organisation or a team tasked with strategy, or its decisions will be apt to skew one way or another.

Incidentally, the research suggested that naturally 'conservative' types might actually be less dogmatic in their thinking than naturally liberal types. This counterintuitive finding is rather alarming for those of us who consider ourselves liberal and therefore, by definition, the very model of open-minded and tolerant. Basically, conservatives are apt to say things like: "I can see why you want to have a go; it does look quite exciting but it's not really for me" whereas a liberal is apt to say things like: "Oh for God's sake. What is your problem? I just don't understand that attitude at all."

The world champion rally driver Colin McRae was a much loved and lauded Scottish sportsman. His catchphrase was "if in doubt, go flat out". Though this attitude certainly stood him in good stead on many occasions when he was 'at work', experts in the field have said that had he not been quite so aggressive he'd actually have won more races and titles.

Sadly, McRae died in 2007 when the helicopter he was piloting crashed near his home. The accident also claimed the lives of his son and two family friends. Helicopter pilots operate under strict regulations. Under Civil Aviation Authority rules, they are expected to undertake a competency test every year, and to renew their licenses every five years; not to do so is illegal. It emerged that McRae had not undertaken a competency check as required in March 2006 and that, effectively, his licence had expired in February 2005. A report into the accident was published on 12 February 2009. In it, the Air Accidents Investigation Branch (AAIB) stated:

> "The helicopter crashed in a wooded valley while manovering at high speed and low height … it is likely that the pilot attempted a turning manoeuvre at low height and crashed … whether due to the pilot encountering handling difficulties, misjudgement, spatial disorientation, distraction, or a combination of such events. There were indications that the pilot had started a recovery but, with insufficient height in which to complete it, the helicopter struck trees in the valley and crashed, killing all four occupants."

A fatal accident inquiry into the incident concluded on 6 September 2011 that McRae was at fault for the avoidable helicopter crash. Sheriff Nikola Stewart stated that McRae had been engaged in "unnecessary and unsafe" low-level flying at the time of the crash, and that, for a private pilot such as McRae, low-level flying in that terrain was "very imprudent".

Basically, McRae was a man very tolerant of risk indeed. On the day he died he was just rolling the dice again, as he had so many times before. This time his luck ran out and he died – but taking his son, his friend and his friend's son with him.

## A More Prosaic Case Study

To illustrate how all these psychological factors can interact with a specific job and lead to error I'd like to relate the case of 'Steve', who was disciplined as an incompetent manager over a lack of containment at a chemical company.

Before describing what actually happened to Steve, however, here is a simplified list of some individual differences relating to task, personality and intelligence (as above) and my estimate of Steve's rating on these differences, based on a scale of one to five.

### Intelligence

| | |
|---|---|
| Spatial intelligence (working out how objects interact) | ***** |
| Numerical intelligence | *** |
| Verbal intelligence | *** |
| Musical intelligence | ***** |

### Natural ability/personality/preference for

| | |
|---|---|
| Being in charge | * |
| Working in a team | **** |
| Task clarity | ***** |
| Job security | ***** |
| Power, influence and money | ** |

From this, it can be deduced that Steve was ideally suited to solving engineering problems as part of a team on a day-to-day basis: 'Today's engineering problem is this…' and off he'd go. Afterwards, he went home, spent some time with the kids and played his music. He was a fulfilled, highly competent and contented man. Then, because he was the best engineer in the team, he was promoted and felt he couldn't say no as the family could use the extra money. (As you can see from the profile though he's a bit timid, hates confrontation and doesn't like to say no.)

After a swift round of 'rightsizing' he was promoted again. He was now effectively in charge of process safety for a large and dangerous plant and was, of course, liaising with HR on a whole raft of training courses identified as relevant to his needs.

The task was difficult and vague and all about budgets, strategy and man management, and, despite having the right technical qualifications, he was just not very good at it. Indeed, his emotional arousal was a long way north of the 70 per cent maximum described above and you won't be surprised to learn that he got very stressed, very quickly, and started making mistakes. In fact, he made lots of them. A month or so later, the incident occurred.

Similarly, there is a train operating company that gives its best guards the opportunity to train to be drivers, thus acquiring more prestige and more money. Except that the sociability required of the best guards walking up and down the aisle chatting to passengers is of little use when they find themselves sitting *alone* in the driver's cab.

## Individuals Accident Prone? - Summary

We all know that adding people to the workplace is a minefield (as if you didn't know!) and that it's all about person job fit. But is there a generally accident prone personality? The short answer is that despite some recent controversy surrounding the subject, yes there is. Of course there is!

However, it has to be stressed that outside of hugely safety critical tasks, like flying jets, it's not really viable to use measures of these traits to influence the selection process. Further, focusing too much on the individual may well distract us from the bigger picture, which is that for the vast majority of tasks the environment is far more important than the person.

Most jobs are undertaken by average people, so any job should be designed in the first place to minimise the likelihood or problems caused by individual variation, and maximise the likelihood of any errors being spotted and quickly controlled when they do. Though complex psychological assessment is beyond the resources of most companies there are basic steps that can be taken to ensure a decent fit between task and person. For most situations, this will just involve task analysis and training. This is the basics or ergonomics of course and many excellent books have been written on the subject.

This isn't a book about ergonomics, so all I'll say here are two things: it's unwise to design a task that's difficult to do error free; and if a qualified ergonomist suggests something needs changing it's wise to listen. It's best to do this at the design stage rather than have to go through the expense of a retrofit, but it's also something that very much falls under the 'risk literate' mindset proposed in this book.

A couple of infamous, but essentially very simple, examples illustrate this point:

## Case Study: Three Mile Island

At the Three Mile Island nuclear plant a criticism of the control panels was that they had been designed to 'look nice'. However, the 'nice' symmetry and uniformity made it an ergonomic nightmare to the extent that the workers had actually taken to putting certain beer cans on important levers to make them more user-friendly. (Coors for important levers and Michelob for unimportant ones, I believe, but don't quote me on that!) When the infamous trip happened, this symmetrical design contributed to the poor response, as did the alarms that couldn't be overridden and which made thinking straight difficult. Considering this from a 'mindful' mindset, it's difficult not to wince.

## Case Study: Ladbroke Grove Rail Crash

The initial response to the train crash at Ladbroke Grove was to blame the driver for inattention, as he had unequivocally driven straight through a red light. However, the investigation found this to be the second worst signal in all of the UK for being passed at danger (called a SPAD). There was an ongoing problem with seeing the light that made it quite possible – if not probable – that the driver was paying full attention but simply couldn't see it. It had been passed many times at red in the past.

Rail industry experts assure me that, traditionally, tracks were laid first, then signals installed, and finally the drivers were left to get on with it as best they could. Of course, lesson one from the field of participatory ergonomics is "start with the user". We could, alternatively, try and select only drivers with superb eyesight and high concentration levels in the very upper percentiles. Better to make the signals easier to see!

Both these case studies reflect physiological issues, which are very much the domain of mainstream human error and ergonomic disciplines. I'd now like to turn to some psychological errors that can affect our daily judgement. You'll see that many have very subtle physiological causes. But before these, consider this less than subtle example of worst practice from one country in which I worked: a signal that became difficult to see because of a newly erected glass building, which reflected light towards drivers, momentarily blinding them. No one would take any ownership of the issue (not the owners of the building, the builders, the track operators, or the consultation team). One bright spark did suggest, however, that maybe the drivers could be issued with sunglasses!

# Some Mistakes of Judgement

This section is about some of the other errors to which we're prone and which are most relevant to a health and safety process. In the section on risk literacy I discussed the 'fundamental attribution error', which leads us to give too much weight to the person and not enough weight to the environment – especially when something has gone wrong. This concept is central to any discussion of Just Culture and Hindsight Bias, though, logically, it could also have been discussed at this point.

Almost all of these mistakes of judgement are more likely when we're tired and/or stressed so I'd like to cover this underlying issue first.

### Fatigue

This is a subject that has been covered in great detail and no one needs telling that tired people make more mistakes both physically and intellectually. However, from a risk literate mindful perspective there are two key facts of physiology I'd like to include because, while not always taken into account, they are so important.

Firstly, we can only adjust our body clock by an hour a day. Regardless of what the working time directive regulations say is legally acceptable, where shift systems require us to do this more quickly we are going to be working when our biorhythms think we should be asleep. Secondly, once we have been awake for 17 hours our attention levels fall off a cliff. Studies (Colten and Altevogt; Williamson) show that those who have been driving for between 17 and 19 hours have concentration levels on a par with most countries' drink-drive limits. What this means is that if you get up extra early (say 5am) to drive somewhere, you really do not want to be trying to drive home after 10 o'clock at night no matter what! A strong coffee, caffeine tablets and/or a high energy drink like Red Bull may offer a short-term solution, though these are far from ideal and come with all sorts of potential consequences unless their consumption is an infrequent event).

I worked with the board of a major UK organisation with their workforce travelling the country in vehicles 24 hours a day, and they had shift systems that didn't fully allow for the above. (The schedules were legal I should stress). When I quoted these figures they admitted that, in two of the four recent incidents we were together to discuss, fatigue had been claimed as an 'excuse'. They labelled it an 'excuse' because they'd double-checked that they were legally compliant. It made for an interesting discussion where their (genuine) commitment to best practice and the safety of their employees clashed head on with operational demands.

Similarly, in the UK, we are currently debating the increased use of night-time lorry

**Photo 4. Cyclist HGV interaction** Source: Photo by CrazyD, reproduced under licence from Getty Images International

deliveries (as used successfully during the 2012 Olympics, where complaints were there were far fewer complaints than predicted. This is, in part, to reduce congestion and also to reduce danger to commuters, especially those on bikes. (There is also a big push in the UK at this time to get people out of cars and trains and on to bikes). At a glance it seems a sensible part of a holistic health and safety approach. But it also means, inevitably, more 22-ton lorries on the road being driven by people whose bodies think they should be asleep. Please refer to the photograph above as a graphic reminder as to why that's not ideal.

The golden rule of risk assessment is to say what you're worried will happen, why you're worried it might happen, and what the consequence would be if it did. With that in mind, take the example of a driver who falls asleep as he returns to his depot and collides with, let's say, a school bus. What do you imagine the consequences will be for the people who agreed this approach? Just a question.

## The Buncefield Explosion and Fire: The Human Factors Element

At Buncefield, there were several indications that the organisation didn't appreciate just how potentially highly dangerous the plant was. As well as the fatigue issue, I'll address presently how there were other warning signs that layers of defence were being undermined. It was regular practice, for example, to use the alarms to tell them the tanks were full, which didn't help when there was confusion on the night regarding the overfilled tanks involved in the explosion.

Specifically, from a fatigue perspective:

workers were undertaking three-day 12-hour shifts, then switching to four days of 12-hour night shifts. (As above, that simply can't be adjusted for physiologically);

Overtime could be up to 120 hours a month and averaged between 50 and 60 hours;

Workers were eating meals at their desks because of pressures of work; and

After the incident, witnesses were confused and (genuinely) saying "I just can't have got that wrong" and "I just can't see what went wrong there", as well as other signs of being oblivious to risk, or of being in genuine denial. (Both are very typical of a confused and/or fatigued mind).

In summary, a member of the Buncefield Major Incident Board, Richard Scaife, presenting at Safety & Health Expo 2013, concluded that he "couldn't say how much the human factor element contributed" but "was certain that it did". He explained "we had to phrase it tentatively like that for legal reasons with regard to being cross-examined!" Nitpicking lawyers aside, I really don't think anyone would take too much issue with his assertion.

What is really quite shocking, given that they were about to deliver the biggest explosion in Europe since World War Two, is that the site had no fatigue policy or procedures! This situation I've described above wasn't illegal, which suggests strongly that our understanding and regulation of the human factors element of safety management is often completely inadequate. It also illustrates, yet again, that compliance is 'first base', if that. Certainly, this case is a very clear example of risk *illiteracy* with fatigue playing a central role.

So far, in this section on individuals, we've covered two things. First, don't put people into jobs to which they aren't suited, and second, don't have people do safety-critical tasks when they are tired. The generous among you will be thinking that that's a useful reminder of the basics. The less generous will be thinking that moving on to some causes of error that are not 'bleeding obvious' is overdue.

# Some Psychosocial and Environmental Causes of Error

## Inevitable Fatigue

To paraphrase the material above under Just Culture/Error, we live complex lives doing complex stressful things. We get tired and distracted and no matter how interesting and stimulating the task a certain amount of 'zombie' time is unavoidable. Hardly any planes crash because the pilot falls asleep during the adrenalin charged take-off or landing; they fall asleep when they're driving home 50 minutes after they set off from the airport.

Basically, although (or perhaps because) our brains are the most complex things on the planet they need lots of recharging. This means it's inevitable that for five minutes an hour minimum you'll be experiencing what is technically known as 'presenteeism' or, as we all know it, ' being away with the fairies' – present in body but not in spirit. If you are stressed, tired, ill or hungover from the night before then it's likely to be much worse.

This is vital when we find a residue of accidents apparently caused by lack of attention (slips, trips, and other incidents described in simplistic accident investigations as 'easily avoidable if only they'd been paying attention'). Faced with this, it's very easy to slip into blame and conclude that 'paying more attention' is all that's required, so what we need is a nice blend of colourful posters, inspiring toolbox talks, and shouting at people.

Unfortunately, if you have a workforce of 5,000 it is inevitable and unavoidable that it will spend around 16,000 hours a week 'away with the fairies' if we use the figure of zoning out for five minutes every hour. Many organisations will employ 120,000 employees worldwide – that's a lot of unavoidable zombie risk.

One tactic is to mechanise but a better tactic in the short-term (and in terms of job retention) is to ensure we spot the likes of housekeeping issues in the 55 minutes of alertness and tidy them up. That way, when we come back around the corner 30 minutes later in zombie mode there's nothing there to trip over.

## The 'Availability Heuristic' and Unintended Consequences

The availability heuristic (Tversky and Kahneman) says that we'll give more weight to something at the forefront of our minds, or which can be most easily recalled. Previously, I referred to the amount of publicity given to shark attacks. In his bestselling book *Inevitable Illusions*, Piatelli-Palmarinini refers to this as 'ease of representation' in his list of 'seven deadly sins of reason'.

Similarly, SARS and bird flu are oft-quoted examples of this phenomenon, where the public panic had a lot of people walking through airports in face masks but where fatalities worldwide were utterly insignificant compared to the road traffic accidents in any country in the world on any given day. (A little known fact is that the Spanish Flu pandemic killed more people in the years following World War One than were killed in the fighting. This was just 100 years ago, so maybe this apparently irrational fear is also, to an extent, a subconscious reaction to something that was incredibly dangerous just a very short time ago in evolutionary terms).

On the other hand, we have to put up with all sorts of intrusive searches and security whenever we travel through these airports, as the trauma of 9/11 lives on and governments will do almost anything to prevent something similar. In truth, however, the only terrorist incidents that have occurred in aviation since 9/11 have involved someone burning his own toes in a failed attempt to set a shoe bomb off, and some others burning themselves quite badly in the arrivals lounge of Glasgow airport – before getting a severe thumping from a couple of locals for their troubles.

As I write this, however, some 15 million people worldwide have been killed on the roads since the September 11 attacks in New York (about 1.2 million a year). However, even though the UK enjoys some of the safest roads in the world and takes driving safely very seriously no one in the UK has ever been prosecuted for driving less than two seconds behind the car in front – not even at 70mph in heavy rain – unless there is a negative outcome, in which case this would fall under 'careless driving'. Yet this is an incredibly unsafe behaviour, with a hugely steep Heinrich's Triangle. (There was talk last year of beginning to take prosecutions over such behaviour as advances in technology make it easier to do so – and the sooner the better!)

## Emotional Reasoning

A good example of the subjectivity of safety is neatly summed up by the observation that anyone driving more slowly than me is boring and timid and anyone driving more quickly is reckless and dangerous.

Emotional reasoning is basically "Because I believe it to be true it is true". There are clear links here with a failure to validate opinion with objective data, which could be caused by Freudian denial, overconfidence, or plain foolishness. For example, I have a friend who's a bit of a new age hippy, whose pregnant wife and he only picked out names of girls because they *knew* the child was a girl. "I just knew on the night that we'd just made a girl and a few weeks later the pregnancy test was positive …" he offered as proof, with all the confidence in the world. They eschewed a scan, which would have told them the sex of the baby, and some months later they had a lovely, healthy … *boy*! My friend remains utterly bemused to how he can have been wrong pointing out that, in defence of his beliefs, he was "100 per cent right" about his first child. You may note a very simple statistical explanation there. (As an aside if any reader is interested in a wonderful debunking of all sorts of new age ideas can I strongly recommend Ben Goldacre's *Bad Science* - A wonderful, rational, book).

Basically, there are simply some people convinced that the laws of nature and statistics simply do not apply to them and, specifically, that health and safety laws are all nonsense and an inconvenient nonsense at that. Let other fools act on these rules and regulations because nothing bad will ever happen to me. I just *know*. And maybe nothing bad will ever happen to them. It might never, of course, but it is almost certainly true that with such a fatalistic attitude they'll need more luck than someone a little more logical!

## Preferring to Learn from the Positive

An element of this subjectivity is that we are all hotwired to learn from positive experiences. We'll ignore several excellent learning opportunities until we come across a positive one that 'is clearly more applicable' to us or, perhaps, puts us in a better light. (Hallinan calls this 'wearing rose-coloured glasses'). This is an example of where we come to a general conclusion on limited data. As the most creative and innovative species on the planet this optimism has served us very well over the years as we learn from trial and error. Certainly, if we were as a species not hotwired to learn from the negative, I'd be writing this in a cave somewhere in North Africa – on the wall!

But though at times it can be useful, it can also be dangerous, especially when we ignore hard data. For example, we all know people who maintain a smoking habit because "My aunt smoked 40 a day and lived to be 92!" Or the driver who doesn't like to wear a seatbelt because they read a report in the paper that says a driver would have survived a crash had he been thrown from the car – just like the other passenger in the vehicle who wasn't wearing a belt. And they will quote this at volume whenever challenged, regardless of the overall research evidence or other examples covered by the media, such as the Princess Diana car crash in Paris – where the only survivor was the passenger wearing a seatbelt.

An infamous example of following the training *not* being appropriate is, again, the Piper Alpha oil and gas platform explosion and fire. Most of those who tried to follow the rules and reach the muster point, as they'd been trained to do, were killed. Many of those who survived did so because they ignored these rules and got into the sea by any means possible. From a risk literacy perspective this is a good example to spark a debate about "Rules being for the blind obedience of fools and the guidance of the wise – discuss". It really should not, however, be used as *carte blanche* to ignore any training not considered convenient to follow.

## Expectation

We often see what we expect to see. Obviously we can be biased against certain individuals or groups because we hold animosity towards them whether based on past behaviour or blind prejudice. As well as obvious examples such as ethnic groups, personality types and unreliable subcontractors, this can include triggers such as merely looking like someone you don't like.

In school I sat next to a friend who always had a particularly hard time from a teacher who would berate him unfairly on frequent occasions; every time he did it would be "Jones!... *Jones!*" with this exasperated scream giving a strong clue as to why my friend was so often singled out. My friend's name was Thomas, with it clear that he reminded this teacher of someone called Jones, of whom he clearly had less than fond memories. (Around 20 years later this very same lad Thomas emigrated to California and briefly married the Hollywood actress Drew Barrymore – but that's a whole other story!)

There is a wonderful experiment that illustrates this phenomenon based on the fact that a touch of balsamic vinegar in beer makes it taste a little better. Told that an expensive flavour enhancer has been added to the beer most people do indeed agree that it tastes better. (Balsamic vinegar is far more expensive than beer before you ask!) Told, however, that someone has accidentally spilled some vinegar into a person's beer, but don't worry, as "I took a sip and I think it actually tastes rather nice", most people take one sip and spray the beer around the room in grand cartoon style. "Ugghh! That's horrible."

What's really interesting is that research on the price and perceived quality of wine shows that this bias is actually physical. Joseph Hallinan reports researchers from Stanford universities who gave students wine with a variety of prices from $5 to $90 and found that the more expensive the wine, the better the quality the students reported it as being. But this wasn't just simple snobbery at work. Brain scans showed that the pleasure centre in the brain (the medial frontal cortex) actually showed more activity when the 'expensive' wine was drunk. And this held true when the wines were switched!

In a variation of this experiment, at the same university small electric shocks were given in conjunction with no pain relief, a cheap pain relief pill, or an expensive pain relief pill. The results were clear, with 61 per cent reporting pain relief on the cheaper pill but 85 per cent reporting pain relief on the more expensive pill. Again, both pills were placebos with no pain relieving properties whatsoever.

So it's not so much that we see what we expect to see because we're biased; we often actually do genuinely experience physically what we expect to experience.

## Group Think

A concept briefly discussed in a previous chapter in relation to the Challenger and Macondo/ Deepwater Horizon disasters, it was first applied to the Bay of Pigs fiasco when the CIA persuaded the Kennedy administration to send a doomed cadre of Cuban exiles to try and overthrow Fidel Castro. It's where a group gets together and, because they are like-minded and self-supporting, can charge off a long way from objectivity. In the world of extremists 'This isn't fair, we should do something!' becomes 'We should take direct action they can't ignore' and so often begets something ugly and illegal. The mechanism is very simple. The people in your group are often the people whose opinion matters most to you and we all learned in the playground that dissenting from the peer group has negative consequences. First, they'll try and win you around with good-natured banter (which worked on Macondo, for example). Then they'll lean on you psychologically with implied threats of exclusion. Then they will indeed exclude you and then it can get genuinely ugly, or perhaps bemusing and amusing to an outsider. The wonderful film *Four Lions*, and the 'People's Front of Judea' scene from *Life of Brian* illustrate the issue perfectly.

On a similarly lighter note, anyone who remembers ringing a friend before an exam to find that they haven't done much revision either will recognise the real relief and camaraderie that flows from that – especially when we find out that our friend has just spoken to a couple of others from the group who haven't done much revision either! The relief and feeling that 'We're all in it together' will be genuine. Until someone remembers that there are 20,000 students due to take the exam the next day and not just you four!

## Leadership and Group think

A strong or charismatic leader can create an apparent 'Group think' by genuinely swaying the rest of the team by their force of argument and/or force of personality. (In the *Challenger* films, NASA's Larry Malloy tries to do this but with mixed results; however, the more powerful figure of George Harding achieves it with a comment). Margaret Thatcher's chairing of cabinet debates about the 'poll tax' as related in several books and portrayed in the Meryl Streep film *Iron Lady* show both how this works and how destructive it can be. As previously discussed, John Browne of BP was accused of presiding over a culture that only allowed good news to travel upwards.

If you recall, the proposed solution BP implemented post-Macondo was to have one person withdraw from the group and make a decision on their own for which they are accountable – i.e. no comfort in numbers.

## 'Not Invented Here' Syndrome

This phenomenon does exactly what it says on the tin. Logic and rationale are put to one side and 'who thought of it first' becomes the defining logic. "It wasn't my idea so I'm not interested because I have a large ego." Or, perhaps, "I feel that I won't get on within this organisation if I'm seen to be the sort that follows others no matter how successful they seem to be, so I'll come up with my own initiative. It doesn't matter what I do, just so long as it's something different and original."

This is driven by pride and political ambition, or even spite. It doesn't help if this is congruent with the prevailing culture of the organisation and no one else will share! I'd suggest that the Milliken approach of giving extra credit to managers who copy someone else's good idea to save time addresses this directly and should itself be copied by all.

For example, I remember a group exercise in which we went through the parable of the long forks (if you don't cooperate then no one can eat). We went through some of the errors above and quite clearly set up an exercise that could *only* be achieved successfully in full with the cooperation of two teams. We sent them to separate rooms and then watched as they instantly took to working competitively in silos, as they so often do.

Eventually, one team approached the other for help, commenting that they would all fail if they didn't swallow their pride and acknowledge it was impossible to succeed on their own, just as the trainer had predicted. So far, this 'experiential learning' was just as we wanted. However, the team that had just completed an element of the task refused to share the solution; "you can work it out for yourselves, losers!" was the observation from the team leader.

This meant the learning point had appeared to pass him completely and, though team one succeeded at the first task, they all failed the main task and therefore no one could collect their prize (a round of beer at dinner). He commented bullishly: "I don't care, I'll buy the beer. As far as I see it we won and it's worth it to see those morons choke my exhaust fumes!"

He was, of course, the managing director! You can't win them all.

In *Thinking, Fast and Slow*, Kahneman gives an excellent example that addresses this issue. He points out that if a risky innovation has a 70 per cent chance of success but a 30 per cent chance of failing completely then no sane local manager would ever risk it. However, if at corporate level, the order is given to all of the, say, 20 regions that they should attempt the innovation, then overall, the corporation will be far better off. Again, objective analysis, data and leadership are key.

# Some Physical Causes of Error

In his bestselling book *The Power of Habit* Charles Duhigg gives the example of a US Army captain in Iraq who thought he'd noticed a definitive pattern leading up to a riot. First, young people would congregate, then grow in number getting more and more agitated and hostile. Then there would be a temporary lull where the crowd would fuel up with kebabs from the local mobile kebab stalls that would be appear at the outskirts of the crowd. Soon after this the riot would commence.

### Habits and Maslow's Hierarchy of Needs

Duhigg describes the captain saying he broke this habit pattern by preventing the kebab stalls reaching the crowd. (This fascinating book is flawed by the author's insistence on referring to every type of behaviour as a habit). However, I'd like to offer a more individual and physiological explanation, which refers directly to Maslow's famous Hierarchy of Needs: he says that first we must satisfy our basic physiological needs, then our need to belong and be valued, and then our need to grow and self-actualise as a person).

In this case it's likely that the would-be rioters are not motivated by habits but by hunger! Can you not imagine a would-be insurgent saying (quite possibly in a voice not unlike Eric Idle): "Well we need a bit of insurrection. I agree, brother, these oppressive fascist occupying forces of mammon do need putting down and driving out for sure. But I'm really starving and my mum does a lovely spicy couscous on a Wednesday. Maybe we could directly contribute to the overthrow of the running dogs of oppression tomorrow?"

Risk literacy is about always first considering the basics. In this case, that hunger is likely to come before more esoteric motivations. In the world of safety culture we need to look always at the environmental causes of unsafe acts and how we can address these through the safety hierarchy before we look at individuals.

### Risk Assessment – 'Gut Feel' Gets it Wrong

Putting individual differences of personality aside, we are all moderated by naturally occurring chemicals, such as testosterone and cortisol. Testosterone, which is found in women as well as men, is hugely useful in many respects, as it drives us forward to take risks and we simply wouldn't have ever evolved from the caves without it. However, every testosterone-fuelled success is followed by a rewarding and incremental boost in testosterone levels. For example, there will be a mini baby boom after any national sporting success.

Consequently, we are a little more bullish next time we have a decision to make and this can build to a level of overconfidence and even recklessness. In the animal kingdom this leads to more time spent in open country, so more fights and, whoops, more mortality. In the corporate jungle it's often been suggested that the senior managers at places such as Enron and BP could have done with reading the books that advocate that, ideally, we'll just aim for second or third best!

We know that adrenalin's effects are short-term and designed by nature to get us through an individual battle but it's cortisol that takes over if the 'risk' that triggered the adrenalin lingers for a while. For example, it could be caused by a lengthy military battle or a prolonged period of job insecurity. On the plus side, this cortisol increases arousal and sharpens attention, so is adaptive, but if it stays in the blood too long it can cause perception problems and a sense that danger lurks where there is none. What follows is inaction, excessive caution, and stressed individuals who become pathologically risk averse or who overcompensate in their panic and are blindly reckless. You've all seen the films. It's rather like a car with fuel problems where we keep the foot hard to the accelerator because it's so sluggish, but then the block clears for a moment and we lurch forwards alarmingly. (Coates, 2012).

## More Positively

Any systemic bias is going to weaken a safety culture because it reduces objectivity. It may help entrench the existing culture through its impact on homogeneity but that's hardly ever going to be a positive thing. There is good news, however, and that is that some of these subconscious drivers are positive. To start this discussion off, let's all go to a party.

## Love (well, Trust) is the Drug I'm Thinking of

Some recent research has shown that many of these perceptual issues are caused by naturally occurring chemical changes in the body not unlike the perceptual changes that can occur rather less naturally on a Saturday night!

Some years ago my family raised money for charity by holding a casino night in the local Irish club. (With reference to the heading, I'm sure we played some Roxy Music tracks). On the night in question, circumstances conspired to cause me to undertake all sorts of risky behaviour but also to demonstrate the neuroscience behind why workforce involvement is utterly essential if any degree of Bradley Curve 'interdependence' is to be achieved.

A 'charity casino night' involves a hall full of people playing roulette, blackjack and the like for monopoly money, which can be exchanged at the end of the night for real (donated) prizes. Everyone dresses up in tuxedos and posh frocks and has a great time. Several kind people came to me as I manned the 'bank' on the night in question and said: "This is brilliant fun and, feeling sorry for you stuck here, I've got you this pint of beer" –typically as they came back to the table to put hard cash down to buy more 'funny money' and plunge back in, having sworn earlier they definitely wouldn't do that!

After a few hours of this I found myself staggering back home across several busy roads, tuxedo pockets stuffed full of notes and looking like a posh Michelin man. "Everyone's having a great time but I'd better get this lot put away somewhere safe!" I thought to myself. I survived the cars, and the fact that this was south Manchester and I must have looked like the most obvious mugging victim of all time. When I woke the next day it took me two hours to remember where I'd hidden the cash. I'd had the bright idea to put it in a bin bag and then hide it in the bottom of the real bin!

At the real cash auction for the very best prizes at the end of the evening, people were bidding many times what they'd promised themselves they'd donate and were happy to do so. Even the next day the feedback was: "I winced when I woke up but it was all in a great cause after all – and I had just the most fantastic night. When's the next one?" Basically, even when the alcohol had worn off (for those who drank) the 'buzz' remained.

We've all had nights like this where you'd have thought the drinks were spiked with a drug that had made everyone happy, cooperative, generous and empathic – and in a way, we had. However, it was not just the alcohol (a big help of course) or MDMA (aka 'ecstasy') in the punch that caused the behaviours. It was, to a great extent, naturally occurring oxytocin in the brain.

Scientists (Haidt, *The Righteous Mind*) have found that when something nice happens to us we produce this chemical and it makes us less likely to hold back, less likely to cheat, less likely to take shortcuts and more likely to engage in the 'organisational citizenship' behaviours described in previous sections, including volunteering, intervening, praising and helping) This is nature creating a virtuous circle where everyone just seems at their very best; "It's still you, but on a really *good* day" as the advert has it. All of which is clearly hugely useful in building a strong culture and/or minimising a 'blame and claim' culture.

We all have experience of these being true and oxytocin is the chemical mechanism by which this works. Indeed in his book *The Moral Molecule*, Paul Zak has suggested that the most important element in whether entire societies do well or not is not natural resources, education, healthcare, or even the work ethic of its people. It's actually the level of trustworthiness in that society that correlates best with success. If his analysis is true it certainly helps explain why the concept of the Bradley Curve has proved so influential despite its lack of scientific heritage.

At a debate on behavioural safety at the Safety and Health Expo 2012, Bud Huspith of Unite the union and workforce involvement champion Nigel Bryson passionately extolled the virtues of workforce involvement as very much a 'win-win' opportunity. McGregor's Theory X and Theory Y has long been known as perhaps the most famous self-fulfilling prophecy, where if you treat people like adults they'll most likely act like adults. There is an entirely social element to this based on the societal adaptive norms of fairness and reciprocity, but it nevertheless seems that nature is, as ever, giving this process an unseen helping hand.

## "It's Good to Talk" – Because We Used to Live in Caves

We are all instinctively wary of 'others'. Even the most politically correct will show an unconscious negative physical response when presented with people of colour if they are not used to actually mixing with them. This holds true even if they are the same colour as you but you've been adopted. (The evidence from electrodes measuring galvanic skin response and negative areas of the brain firing is irrefutable). We simply can't help it and this is hot-wired from millennia ago when any 'other' we bumped into when out gathering berries may well have proved highly dangerous. The only way to reduce this instinctive response is through repeated exposure – getting out and spending time with different people. (Paul Zak, as above, suggests clearly that "Exposure to those outside our geographic tribe is vital if we are to have an oxytocin driven and more prosperous society").

Clearly, this is hugely important when we consider wider cultural integration and harmony issues but leaving that to the politicians and community leaders, it is also of vital importance when discussing organisational cultural improvement. Lots of research, for example, Zohar (2003) and a Predictive Solutions 'white paper', shows that the greater the number of 'walk and talk' conversations undertaken proactively the fewer the injuries, and the greater the breadth of individuals involved the fewer the injuries.

But at a molecular level another benefit of these interactions is that (so long as they are done well and the person who is talked to feels valued, not patronised) the corporate level of oxytocin increases and our instinctive fear of others decreases.

In the UK, for years we had a famous advert for telephone use with the punch-line: "It's good to talk". Taking this further and suggesting that talking face to face is even better, British Airways had an advert that starts with the conclusion of a positive phone call where the salesman puts down the phone and says to his colleagues gathered around a conference call: "I think we're going to get this contract!" But then we cut back to the businessman ushering in a delegation that has flown to meet him in person and, as the advert fades, it's made very clear who's going to get the business. Similarly, all politicians will try and physically meet as many people as humanly possible.

The point is that there is more to a walk and talk than the exchange of information and the opportunity to coach and praise. It turns the manager from a stranger into a casual acquaintance and that can make all the difference in the world, as studies have shown that we respond behaviourally to casual acquaintances as strongly as we respond to friends; for example, when asked to endorse someone on a networking site such as LinkedIn. This isn't the book to go into the depths of altruism theory and the Rosa Parks case study outlined in the introduction illustrates the point well.

Similarly, a famous study by Francis Flynn showed that when a person lies 'injured' in the football shirt of a team that a person doesn't support they are far less likely to stop and help than if the 'injured' person is wearing the football top of the team the passer by supports. What's interesting though is that helping is significantly increased if the person has just come from a lecture on what a wonderful sport football is. The injured person is now seen as from an in group not an out group. Self-policing rugby crowds were described above when the concept of taboo was discussed. One key element of this is that broadly anyone who plays (or supports) rugby is seen as part of one big rugby family.

It's difficult to know exactly how the social and physiological start, end and intertwine, but the key point is irrefutable and indisputable. One simple way to strengthen the organisation's culture (safety and generally) is simply to get out among the workforce and turn a few strangers into casual acquaintances! The less colleagues are seen as 'other' the better.

**Positive Feedback**

Obviously, these conversations need to be done properly. Just going through the motions won't achieve much except to alienate the workforce (though they are unlikely to call it that in the canteen!) and this links to the effective use of praise and reward…

It's often stated that praise is 10 times as effective as criticism in changing behaviour and, again, there's physiological explanation for this, which is that the parts of our brain that deal with praise are much more responsive than the parts that deal with criticism. As discussed above, we're hotwired for optimism. For example, some studies (Alloy and Abramson) show the only people walking around with a realistic self-image are the depressed! Piatelli-Palmarini lists overconfidence as the first of his 'seven deadly sins of reason'. Again, we see that there is a scientific imperative why we need to train ourselves to actively seek out the bad news that is inevitably out there, as stressed by Hopkins' 'mindful' safety concept.

I'll address the theory and practicalities of this in depth in the section on praise, under specific leadership skills. It's enough to say here that in 20 years of consultancy work, I have yet to undertake a culture survey in which the workforce didn't state that there was considerable scope to improve the use of praise – and, as above, to enhance workforce involvement. (Dominic Cooper, for example, has always clearly articulated the vital importance of good and varied feedback as part of a behavioural approach).

## The Stress of Change

A useful exercise is to ask a room of delegates to name 10 reasons for opening a bottle of champagne to celebrate something major. They will inevitably come up with a list of events such as a major birthday, starting a new job, moving to a new house, the birth of a child, retirement, and so on. All would also feature on a list of the most stressful thing they've ever done… because the champagne is opened to celebrate a major change.

This instinctive response, which impacts on so many safety processes, also has a very simple neurobiological explanation. Basically, learning and doing new things requires the use of new (or weak) neural pathways. This is more uncomfortable and tiring than acting by habit (using well established and strong neural pathways) and therefore instinctively to be avoided. So the answer to the question "Why do we behave by habit even if it's potentially harmful?" is because at a neurological level it's just easier. However, with repetition, these neural pathways become stronger just like any other muscle, and using them becomes less tiring and stressful. We'll come back to this when we discuss person-focused initiatives that actually work.

Of course, this links directly with the vital importance of following up training courses and ensure the behaviours requested are repeated until they become embedded and easy-to-do habits. Any cognitive behavioural therapist (or Buddhist teacher) will explain that the way to become a 'glass half full' rather than 'half empty' person is simply to force yourself to practise focusing on the positives and to keep doing that until it becomes habit and second nature.

## Risk Assessment – Gut Feel Gets it Right

A little earlier we discussed the weakness of going with 'gut feel' so obviously, then, we should never ever use gut feel to determine our actions. Except this is when we really *should*.

For example, have you ever walked into a pub with a sign over the door saying "A warm Irish welcome guaranteed here" and left straight away, even though no one as much as looked at you, because the 'feeling' you have of the place is all wrong? Then, next door, in a far rougher pub full of bigger, tougher men you feel instantly safe and at ease. In his multi-million selling book *Blink*, Malcolm Gladwell explains that such experiences are our instincts working at a subconscious level. (As stated in Chapter 3, but worth a repeat as it's wonderful advice, he suggests that anyone who ever feels uncomfortable should try and work out why from near a door!)

In part, the physiological explanation for this is that the gut has its own 'brain', which connects it to the brain in the head by the Vagas nerve. Described by Gladwell as "A hotline between two superpowers", this nerve controls much of our 'fight-or-flight' response including blood flow to the eyes and muscles. I always struggled with my physiology exams and find the idea of a 'brain in the stomach' rather alarming and peculiar, so perhaps it's best to give a couple of practical examples of how this 'instinctive brain' works.

In the 'Iowa gambling task' experiment it was shown that subjects switch to the statistically most productive of two gambling options (small gambles, low odds) and away from more obvious and sexy options (bigger odds, bigger amounts) before they are conscious as to why. Fascinatingly, the electrodes to which the subjects are wired up confirm there's nothing going on in the brain, but the machines show spikes of electrical activity coming from the body! So 'gut feel' is a real thing based on millions of years of evolution and not just an expression.

A second example is perhaps the most useful, unconscious risk assessment ability of them all – for men at least. A study by Aaron Sell from the University of Santa Barbara suggested that men can tell another man's strength simply from the tone of their voice. 'Well yes, of course!' you may think, but it's not related to how *deep* the voice is – it's just something about the tone. Mike Tyson, for example, infamously squeaks – but in an alarmingly intimidating way, don't you think? But although we *can* tell strength from tone scientists can't say exactly *how* we do it. It's an extremely useful skill, though, when you literally bump into someone on a night out.

## Unintended Consequences

As with so many of these causes of error the way to deal with them is to maintain a commitment to be driven by the data and objective analysis. Knee-jerk responses lead to unintended consequences. For example, an initiative to confiscate as many needles as possible from heroin users in Edinburgh meant that those that were left were shared around and the city found itself with Europe's worst AIDS epidemic. On a similar drug related theme, a few deaths were reported in the UK media where the (then) legal drug known as 'meow meow' was used. (In nearly all cases it was as one of a cocktail of other more harmful drugs so causality wasn't proven). Something had to be done, however, in the light of a media panic, and so it was banned. Consequently, overdose deaths from taking illegal drugs such as cocaine, which had fallen in the years when 'meow meow' was popular, returned to historical levels. This became yet another example of a titillating little moral panic, driven by the need to sell tabloid newspapers, leading to the morgue.

On an international level, Francis Wheen has described the *realpolitik* of countries around the world in their pursuit of national interests, suggesting that they are governed by the maxim that "There is no such thing as a permanent friend or principle, merely a permanent interest". He describes, with reference to Kissinger, the Oliver North/Iran-Contra scandal, the Taliban and the Middle East, how this can leave us fighting an enemy one week who we actually armed only last week when they were the enemy of an enemy (and therefore our friend). Often, when organisations such as America's CIA, proactively attempt to align current events with these 'permanent interests', it can become very Orwellian and confusing. It often goes spectacularly wrong. The trial of Oliver North is a good example and empowering Bin Laden when he was fighting the Russians in Afghanistan wasn't without later consequence.

The CIA has a name for this. They call it 'blowback', which is a nice, soft innocuous word that rather makes it all the more sinister. There are parallels to be drawn between this geo-political principle and when the chief finance officer sits down with the head of HR and plans for change are made with the concerns of the safety department 'noted' or rationalised. When such plans are hatched, minimising unintended consequences requires high levels of risk literacy.

A tragic example of an unintended consequence was the deaths of Ollie Pain and his passenger Harry Smith in a car accident in 2012. The black box gyro technology in Ollie Pain's car allowed him to receive reduced insurance costs if he drove well – for example, by not breaking or accelerating sharply. Automatic 'fines' kicked in on his premium should he speed at greater than 50 per cent above the speed limit or miss his curfew time of 11pm. One evening, in danger of missing the curfew, he drove down a country lane at a speed above the official limit but of course below the 50 per cent he was 'allowed'. On some country lanes in the UK even the official speed limit is far too risky, especially at night or in bad weather and, in this instance, the young man crashed his vehicle and was killed. This was an apparently sensible and creative approach to risk management at a glance, but it was one that failed to see the world from the point of view of the individual.

On a more mundane level, labelling something 'low fat' or a 'healthy option' seems to lead to people eating twice as much of it, or perhaps having it for a desert when they wouldn't have had a desert at all otherwise.

Instinctive reactions are not always correct and it's always worth thinking issues through with data and human nature in mind. If someone wrote a book about this with a catchy title like 'Thinking, Fast and Slow' they'd probably win a Nobel Prize!

## Error – Conclusion

Human factors specialists are often asked: "Why do people make mistakes?" Often, we'll talk about poor ergonomic design, lack of data, biases, physical misperceptions, prejudices and the like. Above, we've covered ABC analysis, the soon, certain and positive consequences of temptation, and the social psychology of peer pressure. We've also addressed organisational culture at great length, and in Chapter 8 (on leadership) we'll look at how we communicate what we *really* want, rather than what we *say* we want, through subtle cues of body language, voice tone, and symbolic acts.

Underneath all this social science, however, we are a swirling soup of hormones, chemicals, and weak and tiring synapses causing a variety of entirely subconscious perceptions. We assume that when we're alert the mind is logical and rational – separate from the body – but it's not. So to the question: "Why did they do that?", the answer may be that we're under the influence of nature's valium, nature's cocaine, nature's ecstasy, or nature's dope. Or, perhaps, our head brain was overriding our gut brain when it shouldn't have. Or vice-versa. Or both.

You get the idea, I'm sure.

However, we can use our understanding of this science to our advantage. We can learn to listen to gut feel but always follow that up with some objective analysis, so that instinct is properly validated. We can realise that embedding change is always going to be difficult and lack of concentration utterly inevitable – so we must design and plan for both. We can ensure that all important decisions are taken by teams balanced with youthful drive and hard-won experience. sFinally, we should always make time to get out and about and talk to people proactively, involving them and praising them so as to maximise the amount of the one entirely helpful natural chemical – oxytocin! Safety culture set to a *Pulp* soundtrack, perhaps?

# Chapter 6.
# 'Cognitive Dissonance' - The Interaction of Perception and Behaviour

We've considered how our utterly inevitable lack of objectivity can influence perception and behaviour. This short chapter considers, in a little more detail, something hugely important, which is the reciprocal relationship between behaviour, attitude and perception because, in many instances, the way we behave influences the way we perceive even more strongly than the way we perceive influences our behaviour. This is, to put it mildly, both a threat and an opportunity, with several important and practical implications for safety management.

Previously we've discussed a number of ways in which we can be pulled away from objectivity. We can imagine that if we were in the same situation we might well make the same errors. However, sometimes people's subjectivity seems excessive, if not unreasonable. I'd like to address issues of distortion, denial and rationalisation.

Imagine a wedding table at which one of the guests suggests that women can't get pregnant when raped (to justify a fundamentalist anti-abortion view). Then a rich guest, who notoriously made his money asset stripping, keeps nipping to the toilet when it's his round. Finally, someone joins you and regales the table with a story of how someone tried to mug them in the car park on the way in but they fought them off with a karate chop. The only thing is that you were outside taking some fresh air when they arrived and saw that no such thing happened. Leaving aside some tempting direct action options, would you give any of these individuals "House room for five minutes", as my old mother would say?

In the US elections in 2011, however, Senator Todd Akin, to whom I was alluding in scenario one above, almost kept his seat. The swing was decisive but minor – just one out of 10 people switched to an alternative candidate, meaning that nine out of 10 didn't. Mitt Romney's refusal to disclose his tax returns didn't prove completely fatal to his presidential chances, even though that money was made on the back of some business many would consider the unacceptable face of capitalism (scenario two). On the other side of the Democrat/Republican divide, Hilary Clinton's career sails on very successfully after she explained that she didn't tell a big fat lie to try put herself in a good light and win power but merely 'misspoke' about exiting that helicopter under enemy fire (scenario three).

What this means is that tens of millions of Americans have rationalised these events as what a football referee would call 'yellow card' behaviours at worst. Best keep the red card in the pocket for when they do or say something *really* unacceptable.

Obviously, we don't have to say something as off-the-scale scientifically nonsensical and offensive as Todd Akin to impact on safety, but you may be wondering how does that work, psychologically speaking? And what relevance does that have for the management of health and safety?

# Cognitive Dissonance

The phrase 'cognitive dissonance' was first coined by Leon Festinger in his 1956 book *When Prophecy Fails*. It describes a state in which several of a person's stated beliefs and values are contradictory, or at odds with their actual behaviour. Clearly, we can address this by changing our dissonant behaviour or beliefs to be in line with our stated values and principles. Certainly, studies show that people have an inherent motivation to reduce this dissonance, which they can do by altering existing cognitions, adding new cognitions, or by reducing the importance of a dissonant element. In other words it is, in many respects, much easier and more convenient to fudge certain attitudes than to align them all or change our behaviour!

For example, I might say that I'm a fan of good rugby but I support Newport Gwent Dragons. This is a difficult one to reconcile but I'm able to do that by noting that the Dragons' fans have a wonderful sense of humour and some of the wittiest songs you'll hear. (Singing "He's knocked it on, he's knocked it on… heee's knocked it on! He's knocked it on, he's knocked it on!" to the tune of the French national anthem, for example). In this case, that little bit of mental gymnastics allows me to remain a fan of my hometown team.

This is important, as that integrity and consistency are more important to most people than a winning team, and it is why many people would instinctively sneer at people from Brighton who support Manchester United. Again, it's that unspoken norm of behaviour that drives the perception. The original work of Festinger and others raised a similar smile with descriptions of doomsday prophets who said "The world definitely ends on Thursday, so this is goodbye" and how they then had to explain the need for a Friday press conference.

At work, for example, instead of accepting that our frequent risky behaviour makes us a 'risk taker' we can decide "These rules are over-cautious; it's not actually that dangerous", or "I only take the risks I really have to and still get a day's work done! It's just that I'm both safety-conscious *and* pragmatic." At this point we need someone to step in and say we're deluding ourselves. A supervisor is a good start, but it would be much better from a peer who we trust, or better still from a group of peers.

## The Proactive Use of the Dissonance Principle in Safety Challenges

We can to use the inherent motivation to reduce dissonance to our advantage by systemically using rational data and challenging techniques during coaching sessions. In more general use these techniques have been shown to successfully promote positive health and safety behaviours, such as increasing condom use (Stone *et al*, 1994) and reducing speeding on the roads (Fointiat, 2004).

Indeed, the celebrated child psychologist Jean Piaget's concept of 'cognitive disequilibrium' explains how the inevitable conflict a growing child experiences between their current beliefs and new information received leads to a disequilibrium, which motivates the child's progress through the various stages of mental development. To an extent I'd argue that good safety coaching through the stages of cultural safety maturity rather mirrors this learning process. (For some reason, every time I read Piaget I can't help recalling a very young godson who, having announced he was interested in motor racing, said he thought the world champion that year would be "Either Schumacher or Alonso". As my jaw hit the floor at this stunningly unexpected sophistication from a five-year-old, he added "Though I think Noddy has a good chance, too!")

As well as the general need to challenge rationalisations as they arise, there are several important applications of the principle, as well as coaching and education, that can be proactively applied to the health and safety field.

The 'effort justification' paradigm shows how we can justify an activity required to achieve a goal by increasing the importance of that goal. Anyone who has ever trained for a fun run with the loose aim of "Under an hour would be nice" will notice how the goal can become all-consuming during training in the build-up to the run and during the pain of the run itself, as we find ourselves risking injury and heart attack to beat this entirely arbitrary goal that is of significance to no one but ourselves!

A variation on this theme is that, given a choice between two options, we will tend to become more bullish about the chosen option and more negative about the option rejected, just after the choice has been made and is irrevocable. Rather tautologically, this is known as 'minimising the regret of the irrevocable choice' though 'choice justification' would be snappier perhaps. (See Knox and Inkster). Regardless, it explains a large amount of subjectivity and denial in the face of mounting evidence to the contrary. It is frequently seen in politics and commerce, of course, and is certainly a topic worth covering on any objective teamwork or problem-solving training course. It's also worth remembering when we discuss workforce involvement and giving people a choice of PPE, for example.

Indeed, cults and conmen use the technique of asking for "Just five minutes of your time", as they know that any time invested will most probably be rationalised later as being of some use, rather than written off as a complete waste. And, of course, the more time invested the harder it becomes to walk away. In everyday life, however, it's very much a case of 'Just say no' straight away (Lieberman, 2001).

From a safety perspective there can't be a person reading this book that hasn't been on the butt end of the 'not invented here' syndrome discussed above. Dissonance theory helps explain why so many people are so intractable in the face of overwhelming evidence that there is – and perhaps always was – a better alternative.

## The Free Choice Paradigm

Related to an active choice of PPE, Scott Geller and others have shown how individuals who take an active role in a safety process, particularly if they genuinely volunteered to take part, will show a meaningful shift in self perception to a more safety conscious person and often then adjust their behaviour to suit. For example, workers who are undertaking a checklist voluntarily are most often complying with all the items on it – even if they wouldn't have been before they volunteered. Most readers will have seen examples of workers becoming vociferous champions of a process only after active involvement in it (as above) and it's worth stressing again that this change in behaviour can lead to a sustainable change in attitude.

Coaches who use 'positive labelling' are also tapping into this phenomenon when commenting "and it's vital that the more mature and responsible workers such as yourself buy into this process".

It seems to me that the whole area reflects the 'reactive' versus 'proactive' debate and the famous example of the piece of string that can be pulled in a straight line but never pushed.

I'd suggest it can be summarised as "Push me, and I may well rationalise, but pull me, and I may well change."

## Dissonance and Incentives

Finally in this section, I'd like to discuss the 'induced compliance' paradigm, which is related to the highly contentious issue of incentives for safety. In a classic experiment, it was shown how a small bribe to vote for a disliked political candidate causes a shift in attitude in favour of that candidate, whereas a large bribe leads to no such change in attitude. This, Festinger and Carlsmith suggested, is because in the latter case the behaviour can be entirely explained by a large external factor with no dissonance ("I'm a penniless US student in the 1960s and, frankly, I need that $30"). However, in the case of the small bribe, there was an element of needing to internalise the belief they were induced to express, so as to make themselves feel less easily 'bought'!

It has long been known that substantial rewards for excellent safety standards in terms of lagging indicators can induce under-reporting of figures, and that these rewards are better targeted at leading indicators and/or, indeed, process indicators. Aubrey Daniels (one of the pioneers of behavioural safety in the USA) summarises this whole debate very well in his 2011 book *Safe by Accident?* Scott Geller gives an example of a well-known chemical plant where workers were happy to admit, off the record, that incidents were buried whenever possible.

Another well-documented side effect of incentives is that, often, the reward becomes the sole reason for valuing safety. Consequently, taking away the 'temporary reward' can feel like a punishment and cause a slump in performance. The very best inducements, concludes Daniels, are small and symbolic and supported by rational coaching techniques using questions, data and illustration – all of which are explicitly aimed at getting individuals to genuinely internalise the value. Glendon *et al* (2004), among many other studies, have shown that the use of hard data and illustration is a key element of what they term 'transformational leadership'.

I'd like to suggest one exception to this 'symbolic is best' rule, which relates to the high impact, low cost solutions discussed in the chapter on analysis.

## A case study illustrates why

I once worked with a chemical plant that achieved a step change in safety performance through the use of the methodologies detailed in the final section. We convened to agree how to push on further still and the issue of rewards was discussed. One of the senior managers made the point that the thing that most excited him was when someone comes up with a high impact but low cost solution to an issue and they'd had several come through over the 10 months of the project. The manager then said something I wasn't expecting. He said:

"OK, let's get the safety committee to ratify every suggestion that comes through. Anything we agree is genuinely a high impact solution gets £200 cash even if we can't use it at this time. A high impact but low cost solution gets £1000!"

The finance director nearly choked at this but the manager continued:

"Calm down, Bob, it's those ideas that have really driven our success isn't it? We've done most of the low hanging fruit so the next batch will require some real effort. There won't be that many great ideas left so it can't get that expensive, but if we could get another 10 that would be wonderful. Get this straight: if you had another 10 in an envelope now, I'd pay you £10,000 for that in a heartbeat!"

Though the importance of the psychological aspects of safety culture cannot be overestimated, the symbolic importance of hard cash shouldn't be discounted if used at the right time and in the right way. Alternatively, we could give that much-valued promotion to the manager with the best safety record. As Bob Dylan nearly said, "Money doesn't talk it swears … but it swears loudly".

## A Case Study of Error and Defensiveness – Hillsborough

I'd like to use a simple case study to conclude this chapter because it is written through with extreme subjectivity. Firstly, there were erroneous assumptions about the people hurt and their motives. These assumptions led directly to the catastrophic actions of the organisations involved, and finally to attempts to cover up the truth itself as the people involved become evermore defensive even in the face of overwhelming evidence. Though it's an utterly sickening case study, it does at least conclude with a positive in that long after many thought the chance had passed, the long-term persistence of a group of people – and one individual who stood up and said something on one day – eventually ensured that justice was done.

The Hillsborough story is over now, in broad terms. There are further investigations and, hopefully, prosecutions to follow, but the story itself is at a conclusion. Though the support group is currently claiming that the speed of prosecutions is pitiful, we at least know what happened and we know why it happened.

For any readers unfamiliar with events; 96 people were killed at the Hillsborough football ground in Sheffield in 1989 when a standing pen become overcrowded by fans pushing into it from behind and crushing those at the front. Those killed could not escape because the way out was blocked by security fences erected to prevent pitch invasions and opposing fans from getting to each other. Ironically, these were Liverpool fans; the security and perception of football fans generally at that time had been significantly shaped by the tragedy at Heysel in 1985, when Liverpool fans did indeed riot and the weight of fleeing Juventus supporters resulted in the collapse of a wall.

Worse, Liverpool was viewed as a city that liked to blame everyone else for any misfortunes that befell it, which contributed to the scapegoating. (For historical reasons, the city has struggled badly economically since its heyday as a major port, and the 'cheeky' Liverpudlian personality isn't to everyone's taste. Not everyone in authority at the time thought it funny when John Lennon suggested at a Royal Variety show in 1963 that "Those at the back clap along and the ones in the posh seats just rattle their jewellery".)

Except that at Hillsborough, the fans were blameless. Not mostly blameless but *entirely* blameless. The following is a summary that seeks to pick out some of the key elements of what went wrong.

Firstly, the selection of the ground itself was poor as it was old and simply not fit for purpose. The organisers weren't thinking about fans' comfort and safety; they were thinking of security only. Crowd and emergency management planning were inadequate and, worse, the implementation of that poor planning was inadequate, too. Manning levels were too low in key places, with one undercover policeman testifying that he was worried at one point that if he was spotted as an undercover policeman he was alone. He said: "I was asking myself, where are all the cops in uniform?"

Supporters who couldn't get in were beginning to get crushed at the turnstiles and the Police sensibly opened all the gates to minimise this risk but then contrived to steer all the late arrivals into the same, hopelessly over-crowded pen (with the pens to each side having space). In a book all about the nuance of environmental cues it's worth asking if the word 'steer' in the sentence above shouldn't be 'herd'. It's surely not entirely coincidental that the place behind the goal into which the supporters were heading was known as a 'pen'?

When it was obvious a terrible crush was occurring the police were wary of opening the (badly designed) crush gating, and some would-be escapees were actually pushed back into the pen when trying to climb over. When efforts were finally made to rescue people it was too late. Worse, the emergency response was pitiful, with ambulances slow to arrive and in very low numbers. Eventually it was estimated that 41 of those that died could have been saved if the emergency response had been effective.

Even as the drama unfolded, the Police at the ground briefed the BBC television reporters covering the game that the problem was caused by late and drunk fans arriving without tickets forcing their way into the ground, and this was relayed live on air before anyone realised fatalities had occurred. This was retracted within 24 hours, when the seriousness of the event was known, but that lie was a clear indication that blame would be put on the fans if at all possible.

Senior police meetings focused on damage limitation, and the victims were smeared as drunken yobs; hence, one root cause of the problem (that *some* fans were drunk and/or impatient) was used to mask the more important root causes of the disaster. Incredibly some 164 police reports were altered to ensure criticisms of the Police were taken out.

It was 'leaked' that some fans had gone through the pockets of the dying, urinated on them, and had attacked and hindered police and ambulance staff. (A headline in Britain's best-selling paper dutifully reported these allegations under the headline "The truth" and a city-wide boycott of the paper continues to this day).

The question is, how difficult is it to predict that some fans would be drunk, late and impatient? Fans turn up drunk, late and impatient to just about every major football match ever played anywhere in the world. It's entirely predictable – and should be especially so for people with experience of these events and who are paid to turn that experience into plans. I really do not mean to suggest by mentioning this factor that it was in any way the *fault* of the fans, or that they contributed to the disaster by arriving 'just in time' and some of them after drinking. That's their prerogative, and all part of the day out.

As it happens, a friend of mine was offered tickets for this game but turned them down. He'd been to the identical fixture the year before – at the same ground, with the exact same teams in the same semi-final round. My friend said that the year before he'd been "More scared for my safety than at any match I'd ever been to" because of the disorganisation and crushing at that game. No one was badly injured that year, but no one learned anything from this near miss because no one was thinking about the welfare of the fans. The game was held, tens of thousands of 'mindless yobs' arrived, were controlled, and went home, with no one badly hurt. Job done! What else is there to think about?

A key root cause here is a basic view of humanity, with clear and direct links to issues of empowerment and involvement. The Police viewed themselves as controllers. They just saw the supporters as a lawless mob of hooligans. They forgot that most were simply ordinary fans: fathers, children, women – even the young toughs who might have been up for a fight were someone's son, someone's brother, someone's lover, or dad. This is a classic 'deindividuation' of people and we are all aware of where this can end up when taken to extremes. (Watered down, this finds expression in the Theory X mindset that workers are not to be trusted and need constant supervision).

Britain is still basking in the glow of the wonderful Olympics of 2012, where friendship, excellence and humanity were to the fore. Is there a worse example of the polar opposite than to order a trawl through victims' records in a search for something that could be used to smear their name? Or to instruct medics to check blood for alcohol content before all the victims had actually died? Or to cover up many of the mistakes regarding the emergency services with a claim that all who died had done so by 3.15pm. This is the "But I'm not dead yet" scene from The Monty Python *Holy Grail* film enacted for real as macabre tragedy.

For me, however, a key element of the 23-year delay for justice can be found in a comment written in the margin of a briefing note by the woman at the very top at the time – Prime Minister Margaret Thatcher herself:

"What do we mean by 'welcoming the broad thrust of the report?' The broad thrust is a devastating criticism of the Police. Is that for us to welcome? Surely we welcome the thoroughness of the report… MT"

Thatcher was, perhaps understandably, very pro-Police at the time because of their efforts during the generation defining miners' strike some years earlier. It has to be said that she was nothing if not loyal. It's not exactly moral leadership with a commitment to truth, though, is it?

On a more positive note, at a service to commemorate 20 years since the disaster a local bishop led the service and was listened to respectfully. He was followed by a government representative (the then culture and sport minister Andrew Burnham, who began a talk with the words "The prime minister has asked me to share with you about the 96 victims…". There followed some kind but basic platitudes about them never being forgotten, which may well have been heartfelt but which didn't help matters in any way, especially as the same prime minister had, just the week before, confirmed there would be no more inquiries.

At this point, a lone voice in the crowd shouted out "Justice for the 96!" and this was followed after a short pause by another, then another, then another and within a manner of seconds, the whole crowd in unison was loudly chanting out "Justice for the 96 … Justice for the 96 …" over and over as football crowds do. They totally drowned out the politician, who had to stand there and wait for them to finish chanting and then the heartfelt applause that followed it. In footage, he doesn't look annoyed though. A local man, he instead seemed moved by the display of defiance and emotion. It's worth looking up the clip of the incident if you can. The expression on his face at the end when he nods his head says "I hear you". However, I see it as more an involuntary reflex and not for the crowd's benefit. It looks more like a private nod to himself.

He returned to Westminster and, contrary to what his prime minister had said the week before, was indeed able to set up another inquest. This one would be demonstrably open and fair. It was chaired by the Bishop of Liverpool and with a representative of the survivors' support group sitting on it. Its findings were thorough and objective and brought great relief and comfort not just to the families of the 96 who were killed but to an entire city. The new prime minister accepted the report and apologised unreservedly for the 'double injustice' that had been done to the families of the victims. He accepted that the individuals who were killed were blameless and that the initial investigations had sought to cover up organisational failings. After 23 years, this was closure for the families and pressure groups.

The Billy Bragg song commenting on the boycott of the *Sun* newspaper has ceased to be a rallying call and can be viewed now as a song of validation. After 23 years of demanding and pleading for justice, in the end it was one lone voice in a crowd of 30,000 that made all the difference. Had he stayed silent, it's very possible the politician would have finished his standard "It's terrible, but let's all move on" speech and the truth would never have been formally acknowledged.

The whole case raises an interesting point about prosecution. No one has yet been prosecuted for their failings on the day or the cover-up afterwards. In previous chapters we discussed how there had to be accountability to deter others from acting in a similar fashion, even though it might be counter-productive locally. Hillsborough was a case study I had in mind. What's interesting is that, echoing the findings of James Reason's study of patients harmed by hospitals, the fact that the (broad) truth came out seems to have given the survivors a certain sense of satisfaction and closure and the utter shame brought on the heads of those involved might be enough to deter others from acting in a similar way. Looking at events objectively it can be seen that the incompetence was broadly unintentional. (But the cover up was surely just *illegal* and the fact that no-one has yet been prosecuted continuing to be a source of great annoyance and frustration on Merseyside).

The other lessons don't really need restating but I'll state them anyway:

don't assume the worst of people as it might set off self-fulfilling prophecies;
make plans that fully allow for basic human nature;
acknowledge mistakes and learn from them; and finally,
shout out your truth no matter how pointless it may seem.

Chapter 7.
# Addressing Human Error with NLP-Based Initiatives and Other (So-Called) Advanced Behavioural Approaches

In the sections above we've discussed how 'try harder' and 'take more care' simply can't deliver a meaningful improvement in accident rates once they're half decent because of the upper limits of concentration. We also discussed how 'have a better attitude' methodologies work no better, because everyone thinks they already have a good attitude and attitude change is very difficult to achieve in the medium-to-long-term (except, perhaps, counter intuitively, though importantly, via behaviour change and cognitive dissonance).

In short, no combination of posters and/or inspirational speakers will ever deliver a meaningful improvement in safety culture and standards in the medium-to-long-term. To paraphrase Elvis: "They never have and uh, never will".

That said, an interesting strand of person-focused behavioural safety has proved successful in places in the short-to-medium term and this is based on neuro-linguistic programming (NLP) techniques. This is, in part, because the founders of NLP were, among many other peculiar things, very attracted to techniques that *worked* and were, to a great extent, behaviourists.

Their approach is that we can literally reprogramme the brain to react differently to situations. Specifically, they aim to programme individuals to see risk when previously they wouldn't have.

## The 'Person-Centred' Controversy

Before discussing the merits of NLP-influenced approaches in changing people it's worth stepping back and considering the full context in which they are used and, in particular, the ongoing 'person *versus* environment' debate, which has got quite heated in recent years.

The union view has been somewhere between scepticism and outright hostility in the UK, and especially in the USA, holding that person-centred approaches are somewhere between misguided (see Just Culture, above), or the work of the devil himself.

Some years ago, I chaired a conference that included a speaker who offered 'advanced behavioural safety'. At the end of a bizarre presentation that suggested walking on hot coals was the key to the safe mindset – "If you can do this you can do anything" – I challenged him from the chair, pointing out that, interesting though the talk was, nothing he said contradicted the union view outlined above that this type of approach puts all the onus on the individual.

We debated this for a bit and he said nothing to reduce my scepticism (or, I should point out, that of the audience), eventually leaving the stage with an indignant shout of "Throw me in a pit of snakes then … I'll show you what I can do!" His half-day workshop scheduled for the next day was subsequently cancelled.

A slightly less surreal and rather more informed debate occurred at the 2012 Safety & Health Expo with Bud Hudspith of the union Unite, workforce involvement champion Nigel Bryson OBE, Jim McKerron of Enterprise and myself forming the panel. Nigel kicked off by quoting one of the world's leading behavioural safety experts, Professor Dominic Cooper, as saying "99 per cent of all behavioural based safety (BBS) programmes fail because of lack of credibility". It was quickly pointed out that the full quote is actually "99 per cent of all those BBS programmes that fail do so because of lack of management credibility", which really isn't the same thing at all.

It illustrates a point made numerous times in the book that objective analysis and interpretation is vital. Nigel was just being deliberately irascible to get the debate going, but I've honestly seen union presenters suggesting from a stage that it's important to keep in mind that all behavioural safety approaches are based on the work of fascists.

I was rather taken aback and bemused when I first heard this but understand it to refer to the fact that Heinrich was rather right-wing in his day. (Unfortunately his day was America in the early 1900s). I instantly had an image of Mussolini doing a PPE audit. ("Helmet?" Tick. "Camouflage?" Tick. "Lovely boots …").

Though, with apologies to Mel Brooks, at least it might explain the goose-stepping marching style … "Now remember boys, there are trip hazards just everywhere, so let's really pick those feet *up*." With that effort to respond in kind to such a silly criticism out of the way, a quote from Heinrich's 1959 book suggests that, regardless of his politics, he did know his safety hierarchy:

> "No matter how strongly the statistical records emphasise personal faults, or how imperatively the need for educational activity is shown, no safety procedure is complete or satisfactory that does not provide for the . . . correction or elimination of . . . physical hazards."

Indeed, emphasising this aspect of workplace safety, Heinrich devoted a full 100 pages of his classic work to the subject of machine guarding.

The Expo debate came to a consensus to such an extent that we had to apologise to the chair for the lack of crowd-pleasing insult-throwing and arguing. What we agreed was that there is a large variety of methodologies labelled 'behavioural' and that the 'hot coal' merchants who run short-term awareness-raising initiatives with a behavioural tag are often guilty as charged. However, ongoing processes that are based on the principles of 'Just Culture' and workforce ownership and involvement are not.

More importantly, we agreed that this debate should be widely discussed and that perhaps it's actually time to stop using the word 'behaviour' itself. After all, when was the last time someone asked to 'Talk to you about your behaviour' in a good way!

Certainly, however, it is widely accepted that a safety culture is simply a collection of behaviours, whether undertaken by the shop floor, supervision, or senior management. I'm arguing that any world-class safety enhancement process must, by definition, have a behavioural element and that the debate about this is long over. Many unions undertake excellent safety work, of course, but I'd argue that it matters not *who* does it but *how* it is done. A good behavioural process is a process, not an initiative. It isn't about policing and 'try harder'; it's about analysis and facilitation. Focusing on the person should be the last thing we do, once everything else has been exhausted. If 80 per cent or more of the cause of unsafe behaviour is environmental, then the first 80 per cent of resources should be pointed that way. There's simply nothing to debate, outside of the politics of the thing.

The final word really should go to the fourth member of the Expo debate. When Enterprise's Jim McKerron was asked towards the end for a view from industry, he said: "I'd keep well away from this Just Culture, if I were you! A bloody nightmare, really", then, after pausing for dramatic effect, added "Because we thought we were doing well until we implemented a Just Culture based BBS system … then I had a very long list of things the workforce explained we could do better. We achieved fantastic results, but it was very hard work."

## The (Instinctive) Reason for Union Hostility to Person-Centred Approaches?

Dismissing some of the more extreme criticisms as silly or political is one thing. As we've discussed, too great an emphasis on the person is simply not risk literate, but it's worth empathising with an element of the debate that is more nuanced.

Proactively working the bottom of Heinrich's triangle means behaviour (traditionally workforce behaviour), and we all know that a conversation that starts: "Can I talk to you about your behaviour?" rarely ends well. Simplistic 'culture' programmes work from the principle that since our culture is, in essence, 'the way we do things around here', then a focus on behaviour is a culture change programme.

It's easy to think that, like the famous 'One minute manager', who stresses how we must get out and about and "Catch a person doing something right", we must therefore give praise to reinforce and embed the behaviour at hand. That's great as part of a holistic approach – systemically involving analysis, involvement, facilitation, design, coaching and the decisions and behaviour of management and supervisors *before* we focus on the person. However, get the tone slightly wrong and it's not hard to recall the roots of operant conditioning starting with Pavlov and his dogs: "Sit, wait, roll over ... gooood boy!"

Especially where this is a standalone methodology, a reasonable response to this approach is: "I can see you have my best interests at heart, but it's a little patronising at times." A more robust response is to accuse management indignantly of manipulation and 'mind games'. Add a few entirely person-focused 'hot coal' exponents to these approaches and it's very easy to see why a head of indignation has built up.

## Person-Centred Case Study – BP and High-Reliability Organisations

Andrew Hopkins' overview of BP's attempt to become a high reliability organisation (HRO) through training frontline staff is a good example of an attempt to create such an organisation through an individual focus. Quite reasonably, BP thought that becoming a HRO was something it should do. To this end it ran a series of training courses aimed at changing the way the workforce thought about themselves, their jobs, and the people with whom they worked. If their people can be trained to think mindfully, then BP will be transformed into a 'mindful' organisation, ran the thinking. The BP workforce was rather cynical about this, however, and one quote that Hopkins gives highlights the weakness of the approach.

"Warning signs are everywhere, the real ones are the lack of funding and the application of band aids on top of band aids."

Hopkins concluded that educational programmes have their place but they simply cannot be expected to move a culture on their own. What is required is a different set of organisational practices. However, the responsibility for implementing HRO lay with the refinery managers, which meant it had to be funded from refinery budgets. These refineries were already under pressure to cut maintenance, staffing and training costs. In simple terms, the front line of the organisation was never going to become a HRO before the top led the way, and the top was, and remained throughout the initiative in many respects, the very antithesis of a HRO.

I've seen examples where a workforce team was so inspired, determined and persistent that it achieved success in the short-to-medium term, despite senior management's lack of commitment and support. I have in mind a set of offshore workers from India, whose organisation and self-motivation in the face of senior management indifference were astounding. Even for them it was never sustainable in the long-term, however, and I'll say clearly that a bottom-up approach alone will hardly ever work in the long-term. To quote the American TV wrestling warnings, "Don't try this!"

The question remains, however: when we do turn our focus on individuals as part of a holistic approach, and do NLP-style approaches bring anything to the party?

# The History of NLP

The term itself is rumoured to have been made up by a Richard Bandler, when a traffic policeman asked what he did for a living. Certainly Bandler himself is a colourful, complex and charismatic character. In 1986, Corine Christensen, a prostitute and student of NLP, was shot and killed by Bandler's gun when he was present. Her boyfriend, James Marino, a cocaine dealer, was also present at the time. Bandler and Marino presented conflicting testimony at the trial, with Marino claiming that Bandler was angry at Christensen because she was having a lesbian affair with Bandler's live-in girlfriend, and because she owed him money. Bandler, on the other hand, claimed that Marino was convinced that Christensen had arranged to have him beaten up and killed. One can only imagine the facial expression of the charge sergeant when he heard all that! (Bandler was tried but acquitted of her murder, and the boyfriend was never charged. The crime remains unsolved).

There's nothing like that in the background of any of the mainstream psychologists though, as the film *"A Dangerous Method"* makes clear, both Freud and Jung had substantial egos and stubborn streaks, and Jung was partial to a bit of spanking – but it's not in the same league, really!

None of this necessarily invalidates any of Bandler's work but it does bring to mind the story of a young hustler called Ronald Hubbard, who reputedly announced one day, while winning again at the poker table, that this was great but the easiest way to get *really* rich was to start a religion. Certainly, many writers who like to uncover unscrupulous practices (Jon Ronson and Derren Brown, for example) have noted the cult style of training courses and the use of similar inspirational techniques.

**What is NLP?**  Bandler himself describes NLP as "The study of the structure of subjective experience and what can be calculated from that and is predicted upon the belief that all behaviour has structure". This means that it overlaps hugely with all sorts of other disciplines, up to and including Freudian psychology and Buddhism. Essentially, it is known as a training programme that deals with personal change and communication and is used to address both business and personal issues.

Crucially, it addresses the fact that often the world, as we see it, and the world, as it is, can often be very different things and influenced greatly by the language we use. As such, it overlaps not coincidentally with proven therapy techniques, such as Cognitive Behaviour Therapy. Specifically, Grindler and Bandler were influenced in their thinking by the work of Erickson and other person-focused therapists and it's important to bear in mind that NLP has its source in a 'person-centred' approach.

# Efficacy of NLP

The TV illusionist Derren Brown made a programme some years ago that was incredibly impressive and which clearly showed that, under the right circumstances, individuals could be influenced to undertake behaviours they would insist they would never undertake.

The programme was called *The Heist*, and Brown's set-up was meticulous. First, he selected volunteers who were susceptible to suggestion and then programmed them, via a combination of inspirational speaking and hypnotic techniques, to "Seize the day".

He then contrived to have them be present when a security van was unloading cash, with a realistic replica gun in their hands. (They were supposed to be delivering the 'gun' to a film set). The music playing in a passing car, the posters on the walls, and other cues were all deliberate subconscious reminders of the inspiration/hypnosis 'seize-the-day sessions'.

Unbelievably, three of the four subjects pulled out the 'gun' and went for the 'stick up'. Obviously, the situational factors are as enormous as they are contrived here, but it's certainly proof, despite the limited numbers, that we can use clever techniques to drastically influence the way individuals behave. All of them swore blind that they couldn't believe what they had done as they simply "Weren't that sort of person at all". Yet they did do it, so clearly they *were* that sort of person, or at least they could be in the right circumstances and with the right triggers.

It's all very clever stuff, which begs the question: where did techniques like these come from?

**Using NLP – Matching and Mirroring.** We tend to see the world predominantly in either an auditory, visual, or feeling way. Although we experience all of these when we think of something, one will be our preferred sense and will predominate. Hence, salespeople are encouraged to use visual words in response to someone saying "I can't see myself in this car" by suggesting "No, but I can see you in *this* one!" Likewise, in a deliberate attempt to develop a quick rapport with you and succeed in the sale they might "feel that way too", or, perhaps "hear what you're saying").

**Using Some of the Techniques Out of Context.** A trainer who once worked for me had the very good habit of reading a lot of interesting books and the very bad habit of then always incorporating large elements from the latest book into our training courses, whether this added to them or not. In particular, he was very keen on the concept of 'modelling' to develop rapport. After all, rapport is always a good thing but there are limitations to the approach.

You may have noticed that people in conversation almost 'dance' as they talk. Their body language, facial expressions and movements look almost choreographed. When one raises a glass or cup, then, soon after, so will the other. When this level of engagement occurs we are hugely tuned to nuance. For example, after a 20-minute conversation we often know instantly when it's at an end because of the flick of an eye, a subtle movement, or a tiny change in voice tone. On the other hand, some people can get up, put on their coat and grasp the door handle while someone delivering a monologue ploughs on without noticing these cues!

Decades ago, when I was young and footloose, a famous behavioural psychologist who was a colleague at the time took me to one side and warned me that he had spotted I was obviously romantically involved with a woman in the department with whom, perhaps, I shouldn't have been as these things are frowned upon. "I saw you walking back from the swimming pool laughing together" he remarked. "But everyone knows we swim together on a Wednesday and get on well – nothing wrong with that." I protested. He looked me straight in the eye and said: "But you weren't walking back Tim, you were dancing!"

As well as training delegates to look out for visual, kinaesthetic, or auditory preferences and use matching language as described above, we might encourage delegates to watch the body language of the person they are talking too and then replicate it. Such 'language' involves smoothing the hair, crossing the legs, leaning forwards and so on. However, while doing this very skilfully can indeed increase rapport, doing it badly can hugely disconcert the person to whom you're talking. For example, a colleague would use it in the office when trying to persuade us all to do something we didn't want to, such as change a training course to include some new material he'd come up with. He inevitably got the response "Will you please stop that modelling stuff; it's really annoying!"

These incidents clarified for me what I think of some of techniques of this type. Listening to people, valuing their input, learning from them and using interactive communication styles are key elements of any strong culture. Doing this sincerely is, however, vital. Using modelling techniques such as mirroring to convince people you're sincere when you're not doesn't seem to me to be worthwhile. Why go to all that time and trouble when it's no more effort to just engage with them and listen to them for real? If you're not sincere, it's just manipulation. Worse, there will be real consequences when they realise you were insincere.

On the other hand, engaging properly will almost certainly lead automatically to a natural mirroring style. Don't just *pretend* to engage. *Engage*! We like to say to clients that one way of tricking a sceptical workforce into thinking we are listening to them and taking them seriously is to genuinely listen to them and take them seriously. "The buggers don't see that one coming!" In short, the 'clever, clever' stuff adds little, but do watch out for it when you next engage with a salesperson. The experienced ones do it well and their underlying sincerity matters little!

One thing that stops people writing off NLP as a get-rich-quick bit of utter nonsense is that, often, the technique works very well, works quickly, and lasts a long time. This is because, at its best, it combines some excellent underpinning psychology with a dynamic showmanship, which maximises the power of the placebo effect. Both Derren Brown and Jon Ronson acknowledge this fact. In his book *The Psychopath Test*, Ronson describes how the UK TV star (and Bandler disciple) Paul McKenna spent a few minutes trying to cure him of his lifelong separation anxiety, which was worse now he had children. Whenever he took off in a plane for foreign work he couldn't stop himself imagining bad things happening to them, and it was threatening to derail his career. McKenna had him visualise his problems in bright colour then imagine them shrinking, fading and eventually being grabbed from near his ear and flung away in a dramatic, if not overly theatrical, denouement to the short session. "And that's it?" queried the incredulous and still skeptical Ronson. "Yes, you're cured" assured McKenna, which was utter nonsense, of course. Well, with the small exception that Ronson was indeed free from these troubling thoughts next time he flew, and apparently remains so.

# Changing People

Perhaps the most dramatic anecdote about the power of suggestion and positive thinking refers to a young soldier. He finished his first war "an awkward loner, who had never commanded a single other soldier", according to a book by historian Thomas Weber. Though able in later years to rewrite history, award himself all sorts of bravery awards, and kill anyone likely to contradict him, it seems he was the very definition of typical and unremarkable. He only made the nominal rank of corporal because of the attrition rate among his fellow soldiers.

After suffering some form of nervous breakdown that manifested itself as hysterical blindness his physician, recognising the problem as psychological, tried a new form of treatment. This involved assuring the patient he was special, "Chosen by God", and that he was destined to be a great leader for his country. The treatment worked spectacularly well. Inspired, he marched confidently into a political meeting soon after the war, impressed all assembled with his confidence, and enjoyed a quite meteoric rise to power. Meteoric and utterly tragic for mankind as the name of the young soldier, you've guessed, was indeed Adolf Hitler.

As well as the showmanship, Bandler and Grindler took a practical and admirably behavioural approach and readily incorporated any technique that seemed to work. They admitted they weren't very interested in how the therapies work or in the underlying mechanics. What they were most interested in were things that actually worked. Certainly, this is a mindset that will prick the ears of any behavioural safety practitioner! I think this need for speed and the limited time available for background research is clear, given certain lifestyle choices!

**Changing a Person's Response.** Perhaps the most useful element of the NLP arsenal, therefore, is this 'reprogramming' technique. This technique, although not unique to the NLP canon, can certainly be useful – especially when working one on one with individuals. There are several ways in which this may be used, in addition to a supervisor simply talking to a colleague about a worrying issue. This in-depth discussion will often be a last step before disciplinary action.

**Safety Coaches.** Increasingly, safety coaches are being embedded into organisations; for example by being sent to visit an oil platform for several weeks at a time. Alternatively, a safety coach might work one on one with a senior manager in the time-honoured way to challenge this manager's assumptions.

A warning, however: Legendary psychologist R.D. Laing's work on the damage parents can cause their children might be illustrated by a parent saying: "We love you so much; we've got you the best nanny we can" (while we go off and do something more important and/or interesting). Safety coaches must be there to augment a holistic approach to safety that includes the active and hands-on involvement of line management. It really shouldn't be seen as a substitute, or as something contracted out.

A clear example of the former approach is that, recently, some industries have run initiatives where a safety coach works with individuals who can neither be excluded from the industry, nor supervised when undertaking hazardous work. For example, the British Glass Federation found that although individuals might be sacked by small organisations they will almost inevitably pop up somewhere else in the area when another small company needs an experienced glazer. It's rather like the fairground game with pop-up heads and mallets.

The basic technique is to 'teach' ourselves to think of something in a way that is different to that which comes naturally (or, importantly, that has *become* natural, perhaps because of a series of experiences). This, in essence, is the core of what some people labelled 'advanced behavioural safety', which, for while, looked as though it would become widespread – but I haven't come across it for some time.

It's nothing new, of course, and any Buddhist will explain that positive thinking is about concentration and effort initially, until repetition strengthens the associations and neurological pathways so that it becomes natural and instinctive (if only because, as described above, the strongest pathways take the least energy to use, which is why bad habits are often difficult to break). For example, an experienced London taxi driver will have, on average, a significantly bigger posterior hippocampus than a new driver. This is the area of the brain that is involved in spatial navigation and clearly 'pumps up' as a muscle through use. (Syed, 2013).

A simple exercise is to ask an individual to consider a corner they cut, or a risk they took, or a bad habit they have got into. I'll go first!

I confess that I used to break one of the most important golden rules of proactive, defensive or advanced driving by driving too close to people in front. (I know well that it's "Two seconds minimum at all times and at least four in bad weather") I would not do this very often, of course, just when I'd left a full two second gap between me and the car in front and some moron has undertaken me on the inside and pulled into the gap. At this point, my anger would exceed my risk appreciation and I'd be apt to drive too close in an attempt to bully the other driver ("Two can play at that game, you idiot! Let's see how you like it!")

Dealing with this as a coach, first I'd have to challenge the rationale behind the response. This can be done with a series of sensible questions. Did I really think I was 'getting them back' in any meaningful way? Why was what this stranger thought about me important to me – especially since I didn't know them and was highly unlikely to ever meet them, or even know who they were? Was I really going to follow them into a service station and attack them, with all the physical and legal risks and implications that would entail?

Then, once the rationale is agreed, and I have to admit that what I'm doing doesn't make any rational sense and isn't going to achieve anything except increase my levels of risk, we can move on to the more emotive issues to try to give me tools to change my behaviour.

The coach might use a question such as: "What would my children be saying and feeling if they were watching a live broadcast of events?" Let's assume they are pre-teen and not glued to their iPhones and Xboxes and apt to simply throw the comment "Just chill out Dadz" over their shoulders! Then, I have to describe to the coach exactly how they'd respond in a detailed, colourful and vivid a way as possible to make it memorable. (In extreme versions of this exercise, I would have to picture them at my funeral. Indeed, several highly successful awareness DVDs and talks use this scenario as an emotional hook).

My personal 'hook of the last resort' comes from a presentation I saw by Mike Picknett of the Royal National Lifeboat Institution (RNLI). He showed the rescue of a father and his two sons, who had drifted out to sea. The terrified children were hauled safely aboard first but remained distraught imploring "Save my dad … please save my dad!" over and over. "In fact, he's safe by now, of course, with us right there – but they nearly always do that." commented Mike.

So far, this is good old-fashioned coaching and awareness raising. The key element here is to commit to substituting these images in place of the anger *every* time you get angry behind the wheel. Basically, don't think of the moron now ahead of you; think of the 'funeral' image and take deep breaths. You simply keep doing this until it becomes your natural and automatic response, so that you instinctively take a deep breath when provoked this way and the image pops into your mind automatically and when triggered by someone's poor driving. This is a form of Pavlovian conditioning. You can aid this by using a physical hook, too – pinching the back of your hand, tugging on an ear lobe, or sniffing a lemon skin that you carry with you for emergencies like this. You will have done this in the session. (If you look for it, you'll see examples like claustrophobics tapping their wrist on a crowded tube train, or footballers tugging an ear lobe while breathing deeply and checking their pulse before taking a penalty).

What's interesting is that you're still you. You'll still react exactly the same way to finding a burglar in the back garden, for example, as the behavioural change is largely situation specific. (Of course if you practise these techniques often enough and in a wide enough variety of situations or in the situations in which you most often find yourself then, in many ways, 'you' *have* been changed. But that's an area way outside the scope of this safety book!)

So individuals can change the amount of risk they expose themselves to, through using these techniques, but I'd still argue strongly that this shouldn't be the starting point of any safety intervention. If we have a problem with workers bypassing safety interlocks then we shouldn't focus on those individuals' neural pathways as a starting point. We should always focus first on designing out the temptation by making the interlocks impossible to bypass. Then we should consider, objectively, why they felt the need to bypass the safety feature. Is it a lack of risk awareness or is it the intense productivity pressure we put them under? Because if it's the latter then, more than likely, they'll soon enough find an ingenious way around that new failsafe system.

PPE is often very useful but it is at the very bottom of the safety hierarchy. It is the barrier of last resort, which is where person-focused coaching should be. I'd like to strongly suggest that it is never used as a standalone approach but only after a systematic attempt to understand and engineer the environment.

To an extent the anti behavioural safety position of many unions will be an instinctive dislike of the fact that many programmes have the person as an entry point. Even though it's for the workers' benefit and uses praise rather than criticism, the subconscious might be screaming: "I am not one of Pavlov's experimental subjects to be 'classically conditioned' like one of his salivating dogs. Leave me alone and go away and design out the risk" – or words to that effect perhaps. Again, analysis-based methodologies with Just Culture at their core avoid this.

# When a Person-Centred Approach is Appropriate

Using these techniques on the CEO, the CFO and the rest of the board can be extremely useful, especially in conjunction with good old-fashioned coaching, by explaining why a strong safety culture is a good thing financially, as well as morally, and illustrating this with hard data and case studies.

As the vastly experienced safety consultant Peter McKie quips to boards: "90 per cent of what I need to do to improve your organisation's safety culture I can do in this room", having first announced that he's: "Found the eight people causing all of the problems". Indeed, we know that a big push forward in an organisation's safety culture usually comes just after a funeral, and particularly so if the board members attend the funeral. The images they see there are seared into their consciousness and will be instantly recalled every time (the previously ignored) director of safety comments: "I see a potential safety issue here."

What is this if not one-off reprogramming, as described by NLP? (Though it's worth restating that this is reactive, and here we'd talk about education, legislation and effective monitoring and enforcement to engineer more proactivity. That's another book entirely, but an example was given above linking proactive or defensive driver training with the image of a family being rescued from the sea).

# Two Case Studies

A large mining company client is considered the leader in its field, though it wasn't always. A decade or so ago it was merely average. The story behind it is that a worker was killed and the CEO attended the funeral to pay his respects. At the funeral, he was approached by the widow who, he assumed, was about to abuse him, or even slap him. Instead, she thanked him humbly for taking time off work to show her husband the respect of attending the funeral, busy though he must be. Profoundly moved by this event, he vowed to make his company best in class. A decade later, and no one seriously doubts he achieved his aim.

A different mining company once lined us up to support a culture change programme. We talked about it and talked about it some more, but the project never took off. Then after (a second) three month hiatus, we took a phone call, in which everything was given the green light and the most advanced methodological options were requested, including individual top level leadership training, which we run as personal development sessions for senior managers.

I'm sure you don't need to be told what happened in the three months since we'd last spoken to them.

Are methodologies based on NLP 'advanced behavioural safety'? Clearly, I say no and argue that Just Culture based approaches achieve more. However, they can be very useful as part of a holistic approach. But when selecting someone to work with, beware of the fact that they will look very 'face valid' and will also look like the closest thing to a stress free 'magic bullet' there is. That will be very logistically attractive but please remember that there are no magic bullets. Their selection typically means that the 'behavioural issue' has been delegated to someone with a limited budget, and/or who is just seeking to 'tick a box' following a 'Do something behavioural' demand from head office. Their thinking will be that we need to do something, but we'll attempt to do it as painlessly as possible. Like sharks, many of these companies thrive in the shallow waters of lukewarm management commitment.

# Regulation

One of the big concerns about NLP is that becoming fully 'qualified' is usually simply a matter of attending a four-day course. This course will typically be rather evangelical in manner, and its primary objective is that the people attending it leave 'believing' that the techniques work. There are no tests or exams, or even a subjective rating of the extent of your 'believing'. Practitioner certificates are given for attending and will be renewed very much automatically (see Derren Brown's *Tricks of the Mind*). Do not ever forget who invented NLP, and all the reasons why they invented it!

In contrast, in 2013, I gave the keynote Warner Lecture for the 60th Annual UK British Occupational Hygiene Society conference. I assumed they might offer me an honorary membership, or even honorary fellowship as an appreciation. Not a bit of it – apparently, as I'm not remotely qualified, and it never entered their minds. Fair enough, and all power to them! (I did get a nice pen and also a couple of black mugs that turn white and reveal all sorts of interesting things when heated up, which my children love!)

Similarly, being able to call myself a chartered fellow of the Institution of Occupational Safety and Health and a chartered psychologist took, in combination, more than a decade of full-time hard work. This hasn't stopped the following situation arising at least a dozen times at social events:

"Tim, you're a psychologist aren't you? Well, I've sat you next to Eric – you'll have lots to talk about, as he does NLP.", whereupon Eric interjects with "Actually, I'm a *qualified* NLP practitioner."

I was once upbraided by a 'qualified NLP trainer' for using the expression "for what it's worth" several times in a talk. They suggested I was clearly leaking a lack of interest in the subject. Alarmed that this may have been the case and that I was indeed subconsciously low in interest in the topic, I resolved to watch out for it in future and certainly not do it again! Except that the next time I caught myself using the expression twice in a few minutes was when talking about a topic I *knew* I was genuinely passionate about. It's just one of my verbal idiosyncrasies – probably with its root cause in a certain concern that the audience may be asking of my pronouncements "and who died and left this guy in charge exactly?" If you ever saw me on stage waffling on, you'd probably think me the very picture of a self-confident extrovert. But in truth, at heart, like most people, I'm still a little shy and modest, really. My best guess is that this is just one of the ways it leaks. That said, I still try not to use the term if I can avoid it, as, either way, it suggests something negative.

This experience, at least, illustrates my views on the subject of four-day training courses and 'qualified' trainers and consultants. We know from the Pareto or 80:20 principle that a little knowledge can go a long way. On the other hand, it's also true that 'A little knowledge can be a dangerous thing' and the topic of this book literally concerns life and death. Whatever we do we need to be certain that it's the right thing to do and that it's done well. Half-baked gimmicky methodologies marketed for profit, or selected by someone hoping for a magic bullet, can kill people.

# Chapter 8.
# **Safety Leadership**

In this chapter I'd like to flesh out the model of total culture with specific reference to other *leadership* skills. This is because the one way we do most definitely influence what people think – or more specifically how they *act* regardless of what they think – is the way we lead them. Good leadership clearly involves maximising mindfulness around the concepts of 'risk literacy' as described above. To reiterate, a good safety leader:

empathises with their colleagues as much as possible, remembering that the vast majority of unsafe and unhealthy acts are caused primarily by environmental factors and so asks the question "Why?" *curiously*, as a matter of course, if anything untoward is seen, rather than "Why?!" aggressively;

*proactively* asks if there's anything slow, or uncomfortable about doing the task safely? knowing that an answer of yes to this means a systemic problem that needs addressing. (And that the answer "Yes, actually since you ask…" will be frequent);

understands the principles behind Heinrich's Triangle and Reason's Cheese model and that every time we walk past something unsafe, we are increasing the size of the bottom of the triangle, or increasing the size of a hole in the cheese layer. They also understand that just because this issue might not directly cause a problem *today* it will sooner or later;

generally remembers that the upper limit of their effectiveness is set by their ability to be objective, and that objectivity is very difficult to achieve;

understands that lost-time injury figures and pie charts are *necessary* but a long way from *sufficient* and are not necessarily any assurance that someone won't get hurt soon; and

generally understands that addressing the above well means world-class safety standards, and that this inevitably means a world-class organisation that's sustainable, profitable and good to work for.

This is an excellent start, I'd argue. However, it's not yet a **total safety culture** because so much of the 'meat' in a safety culture is in everyday behaviours and communications and the way the employees perceive these. All leaders, formal and informal, are absolutely central to this. Discussing the role of the individual in safety, James Reason quotes Sun Tzu from *The Art of War*, in his summing up of when it is appropriate to undertake violations:

"If fighting is sure to result in victory, then you must fight, even though the ruler forbid it; if the fighting will not result in victory, then you must not fight, even if at the ruler's bidding."

This begs two caveats; The first is what the Geneva Convention might have to say about the former approach but the more practical point Reason stresses is that this excellent guidance stands or falls on the ability of the leaders on the ground to assess the situation accurately and then have the decisiveness to implement appropriate actions.

Working this military theme further Reason gives an example of the German Army in WW2. Despite much derision among the allies portraying the German soldier as a mindless thug the figures suggest that the German soldier was actually hugely efficient, suffering an attrition rate much lower than that of the UK, USA and the Russians. They actually lost only one man to every five the Russians lost and only two for every three the allies lost so they got something right. This, analysts suggest, was in large part because of the way that the fighting units were organised. In particular it is suggested that a key factor was the principle of a 'mission system', where well trained NCOs were able to innovate in the pursuit of tactical goals. It's suggested that this mindset allowed the German army greater ability to react effectively – particularly in difficulty.

There's more than a touch of Spike Milligan about this. "OK stop doing what I've been telling you to do and, on my command … wait for it … on my command! … *wait* for it … right *start innovating now*". It does support the view, however, that many of us have that though senior management commitment is vital nothing has as much direct impact on the day-to-day culture and outcome as the mindset and behaviour of the supervisor.

The best sporting example I can think of is Roy Keane's performance for Manchester United away in Turin in the semi-final of the Champions League in 1999. They came back from 2-0 down to Juventus driven almost entirely by his willpower alone it seemed. (I note that while Reason quotes Sun Tzu's *The Art of War* and military history, I'm quoting Spike Milligan and football. I'll never make professor at this rate!)

In the world of safety, however, many companies seem happy to leave this utterly essential role to a wide variation of people. Some are motivated, experienced and skilled; Most are not. This is vital, as I argue that it's the nuances around front-line manager and supervisor communications that are the very epicentre of a safety culture and one bad experience can undermine a number of positive experiences. This section therefore considers the elements of the original model we've yet to address, particularly from the field of transformational leadership:

> **Leading by example** (last but by no means least);
> **Communicating** a genuine commitment with advanced psychology and nudges and a clear vision;
> **Coaching** not *telling* to develop and empower;
> **Challenging** effectively;
> The use of **Praise** not *criticism*; and
> Maximising **Workforce involvement**.

The UK Health and Safety Laboratory has a simple five-element model of safety leadership suggesting:

> health and safety vision;
> motivating and inspiring;
> showing concern for others;
> being fair; and
> communicating – which, when you look at the specifics more closely, is the above list with elements of Just Culture (fairness) and Bradley Curve interdependence (brother's keeper) included.

There are lots of excellent books – and residential month-long training courses for that matter – that cover these areas in great depth. This overview summary is merely intended to put the application of these skills in context and provide a list of 'They really should know how to do this' techniques for an organisation to ponder and debate. I'll only go into enough detail to illustrate the point and give some examples of their application.

It's worth saying again, though: if your supervisors are weak in any of these areas then your safety culture can be improved with some general training in soft skills, and as *all* of these skills are generally applicable it will benefit the organisation as a whole. (Some influential writers, for example Flin *et al*, have made the conscious decision to refer to such skills as 'non technical' rather than 'soft').

The classic Situational Leadership model (Hersey and Blanchard) suggests that in basic situations and in very complex situations command and control is most appropriate. In between, however, the model suggests a more collaborative approach is required to get the best results. This book isn't addressing the basics or does it any way presume to be directly addressing the more technical and complex aspects of HRO organisations. Nearly everything this book seeks to address falls under 'in between'. That is it seeks to address the day-to-day events within typical organisations: tool box talks, walk and talks, challenging subcontractors or seeking clarification from supervisors who are giving out mixed messages.

Therefore, there's no need to consider whether or not such a prescriptive model is appropriate for a safety culture generally. That said, one element of situational leadership is worth considering which is the two by two matrix that considers motivation and expertise as the two axis. For those low in both a *directive* style is clearly required – though ideally *alongside* training and empowerment programmes. For those with the expertise but not the motivation, then empowerment programmes are appropriate. For those with motivation but not expertise then training only will be required.

For those with both motivation and expertise just light touch coaching and feedback is needed to ensure nothing degrades. A problem that often occurs is where companies convince themselves just a light touch is required when something more fundamental is – most typically when an organisation announces itself bemused by a shortfall in motivation.

Similarly, the UK HSL (one of the most respected safety bodies in the world) uses the COM-B model (from the work of Susan Michie), which ensures the systematic analysis of capability and opportunity before considering motivation to the behaviour in question.

The basic model still holds: we should always seek to maximise analysis, coaching and empowerment – but should tailor our methodologies and resources to best suit the local situation.

# Imparting a Vision

### What's Interesting to You (Boss) is Just Fascinating to Me

An example of this truism comes from a study from the Notre Dame Deloitte Centre for Ethical Leadership which considered how corporate values impact a business culture. Though the majority of organisations considered had safety as a formal value only a quarter of respondents could recall any of the details it actually contained. This isn't so much of a problem though as it's the *symbolism* that's most important. The survey identified that when a value was frequently discussed with one's boss, or when it was included in formal performance evaluations, it tended to have a greater effect. Discussions with peers and subordinates, or more casual discussions of values, didn't have the same impact.

# Case Study

The moral crisis within the world of Formula One racing in 1994 is as famous an example as can be found of everything changing because those at the top decide it be so. At San Marino in 1994, Ayrton Senna, perhaps the world's most talented ever driver, was killed during the race. A fellow driver, Roland Ratzenberger, had been killed just the day before during qualifying, taking the total number of F1 fatalities to 47 in 44 years. The day before Ratzenberger's crash, another driver, Rubens Barrichello, had very nearly been killed in a heavy crash during the final day of practice. The sport was traumatised by this weekend and Max Mosley, head of the FIA, announced publicly that "This must never happen again" and *meant* it. Among many other things teams were forced to share safety data and technology and, specifically, Mosley ensured that the utter commitment to excellence and innovation that the teams applied to speed was applied to safety, too.

Industry expert Mark Gallagher formerly of Cosworth, Jordan and Red Bull racing has commented that: "This was a complete culture change in my industry that rolled out through every driver, engineer, maintenance technician, designer and contractor. Previously, death was part of the culture." Indeed the famous Joss Verstappen pit fire (mentioned previously) that happened just two months later "Actually proved helpful" according to Gallagher. It highlighted the dangers of modifying equipment for speed and the consequences of cutting corners in basic maintenance. It therefore helped F1 embed a complete culture change throughout all of the teams and their contractors.

Though Max Mosley is now rather more famous for his taste in risqué parties it must be said that as at the end of 2013, Ayrton Senna remains the last driver to die in F1.

# Leading by Example

A key thing anyone **must always do** is lead by example and model safety at all times (whether undertaking a safety conversation or not).

A client site had a visit from Gordon Brown just before he became UK prime minister, during which he declined to wear several items of PPE. Local management were concerned that this would play badly with the workforce but let him get away with it, hoping the workforce would understand their difficult position.

But to quote the CEO directly: "Did they hell!"

He still says: "I've paid for that decision every day since. The lads didn't say, as we hoped, 'I'd have done the same if I'd been in Vic's shoes' … they leapt on it with glee and every tool box talk and briefing and *especially* at any disciplinary, we get 'what

**Photo 5. Gordon Brown visitng Glasgow shipyard** Source: Getty Images International

about Gordon Brown!' If I could turn the clock back, I would!"

Similarly, one of our clients had a visit from a senior chap from HQ who flatly refused to don his hard hat during a site visit. Quickly, the local secretaries spoke to their contacts at HQ and found out that it was because he wore a wig and was worried it would come off and embarrass him. As well as causing our PPE enhancement process no end of problems for months, you might be amused to know that even before he'd even left site he was known as the "Tit with the toupee". So as well as everything else the 'maintaining dignity' plan didn't work quite the way he'd intended!

We talked above about peer influence and how it's vital we have compliance over and above a tipping point of around 90 per cent or so, or else new starts and subcontractors will feel they can choose to comply or not, as they won't particularly stand out. With management 90 per cent would be an utter disaster, as just one example of non-compliance will be leapt upon with glee by the workforce as an example of double standards and used as an excuse to act the way that best suits them on the day.

More bad news for organisations is that every one of them is full of leaders. All managers, all supervisors and all safety representatives are leaders, of course. So are the experienced workers and even the inexperienced ones who are admired and/ or charismatic. They're safety leaders too. Indeed unofficial leaders are well worth targeting with invitations to get involved in safety initiatives. (In his million-selling book *The Tipping Point* Malcolm Gladwell discusses the influence these people can have, calls them 'Malverns', and stresses the value of targeting them as part of a change programme. I've already outlined how behaviour can lead to attitude change through cognitive dissonance. In the coaching section next in this chapter we'll talk about 'positive labelling' as an influential tool. Use it on these people important trend setters too!)

Of course modelling safety behaviours is only the start because when we talk about a world class culture this modelling needs to extend to all aspects of the desired culture, for example how we show trust, listen, coach, how we respond to personal challenge and how we react when we get it wrong.

# Communication

The very first thing is to ensure that the colleagues with whom we are seeking to communicate are able to understand the message. This isn't simply about first language issues, which are becoming increasingly important as international migration increases. (The increased and creative use of visual multimedia is very much to be applauded). These issues are readily apparent to most organisations and those that aren't making concerted efforts to address them have work to do in the 'basics' of H&S not addressed in this book.

A basic skill not often addressed is that in giving a presentation. Often the key communication in any given week is a formal or semi formal presentation whether it is brief or a toolbox talk. If the workforce receives a mumbled, embarrassed and badly prepared session it is unlikely to communicate the key issues that need addressing and it is unlikely to communicate the perceived importance of safety either. This may or may not reflect a lack of commitment to safety from senior management. However, it might well if the failure to provide **basic presentation skills** training to those required to present key messages reflects a lack of commitment! Any formal safety presentation should be organised, clear and given by someone confident enough to give it with meaning. If a lack of skills hinders this then training in basic presentation skills is needed.

Specifically, however, many organisations, whilst systematically underestimating the *intelligence* of the workforce, systematically *overestimate* their literacy skills. Indeed, regardless of the first language of the audience, the increased use of visual multimedia should be encouraged whenever possible. For example, a study of US oil refineries by the Larkin communications consultancy found that the typical safety communication was pitched at a level only 4 per cent of the US population could understand.

It would be easy to be cynical and suggest that hardly anyone reads the files full of lengthy documentation. However, struggling badly to understand them even if they take the trouble – or really need to understand the detail – is another matter entirely. We know from ABC analysis that many people will simply give in the face saving temptation not to ask for help.

## Getting People Talking and Listening

Training key personnel in basic interview skills and listening techniques will benefit all safety conversations, as well as incident investigations. It also oils the wheels of any empowerment, or analysis process.

## Building Rapport

Some people like to remain anonymous in the expectation that the person they are talking to will remain more natural and open if they don't know they're the CFO, or some such. Personally, I think this far often leads to anxiety, uncertainty and the view that you lack basic social skills! An example of the latter: I went to a nephew's school concert when he was in his first year and all the parents in the audience were new to the school. At the end, a woman popped up and started to wax lyrical about how wonderful everything had been and how impressed she was personally. A chap who perhaps had a drink too many before arriving mumbled far too loudly "And who the *&^% are you, exactly?" Arguably a bit unnecessary, but he did at least articulate what everyone else was thinking! (She was, of course, the headmistress).

The point is: don't risk the workforce thinking you're playing mind games with them; show some social skills and introduce yourself!

## Actively Building Rapport

People tend to like people with whom they have something in common. They will, for example, be more likely to donate to a disaster fund for a town or country with a similar name. Similarly, we are more inclined to stop and help people in 'our' team's football shirt. Salesmen and conmen use this principle all the time when desperately seeking to find some common ground, or they will just make something up. Be warned: nine times out of ten, if someone says something like:

"You come from Cwmbran? Well I never! My Uncle Ernie came from there… a lovely bloke he is … my favourite uncle actually!"

...they are after your money (See Lieberman).

More positively, you can use this technique to find some common ground on which to build rapport before a safety discussion. Sport is usually a good topic, politics perhaps less so! The important thing is to not take it too far. Just find some common ground, have a brief but positive discussion about it, and then leave it at that. In the above example, the salesman might go on to say:

"He always said anyone from Cwmbran is tough but fair and that they can always spot a bargain!"

And the penny will drop with a loud clang and all rapport will be lost!

Another classic con is to ask for something unreasonable so that the person 'anchors' on this request and subsequent lesser requests are more likely to be given in to: "Can I have the price of a plane ticket to get home to see my sick mum? No? OK, the taxi fare to the airport? No? OK just a couple of pounds to make a phone call?" If this is done with any sort of style and panache: "I'm *so* sorry. Why should you trust me?" the last request is almost impossible to refuse. More seriously, in his book *Inevitable Illusions* Massimo Piatelli-Palmarinin describes how the Bush administration used 'anchoring' shamelessly during the Gulf conflict by quickly putting out outrageously low estimates for civilian casualties.

(Please see the book *Never be Lied to Again* by Daniel Lieberman if you'd like to read up on the psychology of lies and cons. Quiet a few other politicians get a mention.)

## Talking *Safety*

Once they have relaxed a bit, or as time restrictions demand, you'll want to be talking about the topic at hand, not sport, or Uncle Ernie's home town. For example, any safety specific conversation will get off to a decent start through the use of neutral and hypothetical questions. Some hypothetical questions you can ask to get people talking:

If you really had to, how could you work more quickly?

(As mentioned several times above) "What's uncomfortable about working safely?"

"Are there any aspects of working safely that slow down the job?"

"What's inconvenient about working safely?"

"Are there any aspects of working safely that would make you feel silly, or foolish because you'd be in the minority?"

None of these has any element of blame attached to it and all of them either ask about the person's thoughts, or give them an opportunity to boast about their abilities, or ingenuity.

## Active Listening

*Active* listening is an example of a simple thing that we can all dismiss as too obvious to mention. It is really all about paraphrasing and, while there are all sorts of rules about listening skills, the main one, perhaps, is to ensure you've heard the person correctly and you reflect back what they've said. Don't just parrot it back - but put it into your own words and include the **feeling** as well as the literal meaning. It involves effort and can be quite tiring. However, every culture will tell you that the organisation could be much better at it and that any improvement would be very welcome. Again, it is simple to describe but requires thought and effort to embed.

A famous example from the world of theatre illustrates the use of paraphrasing. An actor was visited backstage by the playwright Noel Coward, who was prepared to be nice but not actually lie! Noel flounced in and announced: "Darling, you were sensational … it was quite unforgettable what you did out there!" The actor asked: "Oh, so you liked it, Noel?" to which Noel replied: "Now, darling, I didn't say **that** exactly…"

When seeking clarification a good form of words to use is something like: "So what you're saying to me is …" This is important because many people will use vague language when it suits them to be misunderstood but saying yes to a question like that is a straight lie if it's *not* true. Of course, some people will still wriggle at this point if it suits and not simply reply honestly "Yes, you're correct"; or "No, actually you're not quite correct there." If this happens, you need to turn the paraphrase into a 'yes or no?' question.

The UK TV interviewer Jeremy Paxman demonstrated this listening skill when talking to Michael Howard. Demanding a yes or no answer can be considered the boxing equivalent of cutting the ring down on your opponent. Paxman kept asking the former minister "yes or no? … did he *threaten* to sack a junior civil servant - yes or no?" The scene was replayed to much amusement on the popular satirical TV programme *Have I Got News For You* and after Howard's tenth or eleventh deliberately obtuse answer, they cut back to the show's host who nailed the point that I'm trying to make by observing to much laughter: "I think we can safely take that as a *yes*, then!"

Imagine a manager who insists "No corners can be cut but this needs doing by Friday at the latest!" The person on the end of this might reply: "Well I can try …" At this point, it will suit the boss to walk off, having effectively delegated the problem - and of course leaving themselves all sorts of scope for manoeuvre if things go wrong. A good response from the employee would be to state: "I just can't promise to achieve both, boss." Or, better to ask: "I'd really like to clarify this. I can promise to get it done by Friday but I may have to cut a few corners? Is that acceptable to you? Yes or no?"

At this point, the boss has to commit himself one way or the other - or refuse to answer a direct question. As Michael Howard found, doing so makes you look untrustworthy. (His political career never recovered). If nothing else, being able to quote this conversation word for word at an inquiry following an incident would be damning.

## The 'Two by Two' Empathy Matrix

Perhaps the single best use of the well known 'two by two' management training matrix is that which systematically addresses the strengths and weaknesses of both sides of an argument. This encourages a holistic overview of any issue that encourages empathy and cooperation. Certainly, a good conversation will actively seek to tease out the views the person you're talking to might seek to suppress because they're worried it will be what you don't want to hear.

For example, if we have a room full of naturally risk aware and cautious parents they will be able to quickly point out the benefits of a cautious approach to parenting (greater control and risk reduction!) They will also be easily able to articulate the risks of a laissez-faire 'free range' approach (increased physical risks, less control). On the other hand, if the parents we are discussing child rearing with are 'ageing hippy' types they may well stress that the benefits of their approach are a greater range of experiences and greater independence, and articulate that the risks of the cautious approach are obviously a less rich and stimulating environment and fewer 'street smarts'.

What this technique suggests is that each side on **any** debate must take the time to systematically consider the point of view of the other before debating it. Safety and health is an obvious arena, and a conversation that starts "This is wrong and needs putting right" is a good place to start. We've all seen over the years a variation on:

"This is dangerous, get it fixed!"
"But we can't afford to do that."
"What! You're telling me that you're putting a price on safety!? That's scandalous!"

No empathy, any progress unlikely.

I saw a memorable variation on this at a major UK safety conference some years ago. A senior figure in the UK regulatory body was fielding phone calls from the BBC re: a report that detailed exactly where the cut-off occurred for investing in safety improvements to a specific element of the UK infrastructure, in terms of expense per likely life saved. He explained he'd been 'invited' to appear on the BBC current affairs programme Newsnight to discuss this report with our infamous attack dog of an interviewer, the aforementioned Jeremy Paxman. "Good luck with that!" we all commented, but he explained:

"No need for that - I'm not going on! I know it won't sound good when they say we refused to appear as demanded, but if I do, there will be the mother, partner or child of someone killed at (infamous incident) on with me just so Paxman can look at them when he demands of me 'how can you sit here in their presence and put a price on safety!?' I'm just not putting myself through that."

I must stress again that this man wasn't from a hard-nosed employers' federation, or in any way the 'unacceptable face of capitalism'. He was a highly conscientious and well respected man who had dedicated all his working life to workforce safety and wellbeing. He just didn't have an unlimited budget. Nobody does. The more often we discuss this reality objectively, and from a mindful perspective, the better.

## The Psychology of Communication

This part of the chapter is intended to provide the reader with a user friendly explanation of the latest key psychological theories that can influence the perception, mindset and behaviour of employees from boardroom to shop floor. Few are of much use in the medium to long-term if that genuine commitment to improvement isn't there but *all* will be useful if the commitment is there, but the workforce just haven't caught up yet.

Specifically, I'd like to go into greater depth about how we say what we say is utterly central to the perceptions of what is desired and acceptable. Again, "It ain't what you do, it's the way that you do it … that's what gets *results*." For example, when my partner asks me to take the children somewhere, or accompany her somewhere and I say I'm too busy she'll say: "OK, I'll do it"; on other occasions, however, she'll say something completely different. She'll say: "OK, I'll do it". Every reader will know exactly what I mean! The second version should be written as: 'OK … *I'll* (have to) do it' (myself then) … you miserable sod who clearly doesn't love and value me anymore and who is now in deep trouble!... With this accompanied by an evil and blood-curdling stare.

Studies show that the vast majority of a communication is in the body language

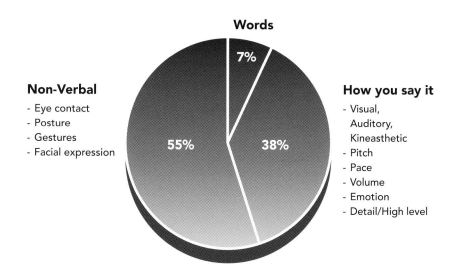

**Figure 22. Elements of Communication** Source: Professor Albert Mehrabian

and voice tone. This means that we can say the words that we have to say and still effectively communicate what we *mean*. What we mean is utterly vital to the people who work for us, as they are motivated to give us what we want. Often textbooks will quote that 7 per cent of a message is in the words spoken, 38 per cent in the tone and a whopping 55 per cent in the body language. Though these figures are oft quoted and widely influential what the pioneer of the research (Professor Albert Mehrabian) actually found was that:

7 per cent of message *pertaining to feelings and attitudes* is in the words that are spoken.

38 per cent of message *pertaining to feelings and attitudes* is paralinguistic (the way that the words are said).

55 per cent of message *pertaining to feelings and attitudes* is in facial expression. And body language.

Now clearly, we can ask a colleague to pass a report across the desk and mean simply that you'd like them to pass the report. Frequently, however, communications about safety are loaded with meaning and politics and it is these that the famous ratios apply. This will include everything from the aforementioned CEO who asks aggressively "Any problems with that?" (meaning 'There had better not be') through the apathetic presentation of a safety brief (meaning 'I just need to tick this box') to the delegate at that brief who asks "How long will this take?" meaning 'This is a waste of time').

Worse is that even if we make a conscious attempt to say things with apparent conviction we can 'leak', subconsciously, through the order of the words spoken.

## The Vital Importance of the Word 'But'

As briefly mentioned under 'optimising violations' above if you've ever been told by a partner or prospective partner: "You're a really nice person and I really like you *but* …" you don't need them to finish the sentence. You *know* you need to fetch your coat. No exceptions. This is because we always put the important part of the sentence after the 'but', and anything before that 'but' will be seen as waffle and disregarded. Therefore, as briefly mentioned in the Just Culture section "Do this job safely, *but* make sure you do it by Friday" will mean something very different to "Do it by Friday *but* make sure you do it safely". Afterwards, at the investigation it will be very deniable, as in "I explicitly said to do it safely". However, we will have communicated what we really wanted, and we most usually get what we communicate what we really want. This takes us back to genuine management commitment. We will get what we really want and that will leak and be communicated in a 1001 different ways.

The night before I wrote this chapter I was reading an interesting book by a famous British newspaper editor (Piers Morgan), and who has often been accused of being a bit on the 'manipulative' side. He described a call with a reporter who was in Baghdad when the second Gulf War started who was a bit worried about his safety. Our man Morgan describes saying to this chap "Well, if you want to come home just do it, of course … *but* …you're doing some fantastic journalism out there" (He stayed).

## Switch 'But' with 'And'

Communications experts (too numerous to know who suggested it first) point out that when there are two issues we want to discuss we can simply make sure that we finish with the positive. For example: "You're very clever but not trying hard enough" to a student from a teacher would be better phrased as: "You're not trying anywhere near hard enough but you're very clever". The latter clearly sets the tone for a constructive conversation about what can be done about the issue not what the fault is.

In similar vein, simply substituting the word 'and' for the word 'but' in a sentence sets up the conversation to be a discussion. "I need this doing by Friday and I need it doing safely" has no hidden meaning.

## Positive Thinking and the 'Balancing But'

Positive Thinking gurus use a variety of techniques to encourage a more positive mindset. One of the most frequent is to practise picking out the positive words from a sea of positive, negative and neutral words – so that 'spotting the positive' becomes more instinctive. (*Horizon*, BBC July 2013)

I haven't seen anyone refer to the 'balancing but' yet but someone must have by now. This technique, which I must have read about but forgot the source, is simply to always finish any cognition with a 'but positive'. Hence: "I really don't want to drive all the way to Bristol tonight **but** I can listen to that new Killers album on the way down and drop in on my aunt on the way back so I'm not obligated to do that at Christmas". Of course, it can be applied to more important issues like health and family, or to safety culture. Indeed, a Buddhist would suggest it should be applied to all important issues several times a day!

(If this is by some fluke original thinking it's certainly the closest I'll ever come to a 'top tip for a happy life!' Even if it is original, nothing will ever make me try and trademark the term 'balancing but'!)

## Even Basic Audits aren't just Learning Events – They throw an important shadow

To return to that very antithesis of a 'mindful' culture, BP in the time of Texas City, we can see that though audits were undertaken, little was learned from them. This wasn't because of a lack of technical knowledge, it was because of the *way* the audits were undertaken.

One way of overcoming the problems associated with a defensive mindset is simply to phrase the question, or research orientation correctly. Asking an audit team: "Anything *wrong?*" automatically sets up a blame mentality. It's also risking a simple: "No everything's fine" response. Sadly, there are many high profile catastrophic events that followed 'clean bill of health' audits. Piper Alpha is perhaps the most well known in the UK.

This makes no sense if we have any sort of learning mentality. If we send an employee to an expensive development centre we would not be at all happy to have them return and announce: "Apparently, I'm perfect … here's the bill". It's a simple mindset shift; the organisation can't possibly be perfect, so an audit's primary process has to be to identify where we can improve.

## A Good Walk (Not Spoiled)

A leader should be briefed before setting out on a 'walk and talk' so that they have a broad understanding of how a procedure should work. A 'mindful' leader will also ask to be walked through a process from beginning to end with the fundamental risk assessment questions in mind. "Explain to me what you're worried might happen, why it might happen, what will result if does so, therefore, and allowing for the likelihood of it happening, what you have decided to do - or not do." With 90 per cent of the causes of problems environmental, then by logic, 90 per cent of the conversation should be about the organisational environment.

This should be the starting place for a healthy scepticism, not an easy way around a potentially awkward conversation. For example, do not ask "And you always read the hot-work risk assessment before signing off the permit …?" because that's really setting up an "Of course" response. A better way of asking is: "What do you feel are the primary weaknesses in the risk assessment, or permit sign-off process?" Other good questions to ask are: "What most needs addressing?" or "If we can only address a handful of items what should they be?" or even: "What should we address if we had unlimited time and funds?" It's just applying a basic, analysis-driven SWOT approach, as you would with an individual appraisal, so it's nothing to be defensive about.

Again, to minimise defensiveness when talking to *individuals* about risk to themselves we must ask: "What risks to yourself are you most concerned about?" not the blame alluding: "How could you get it wrong and hurt yourself?"

That said, in my experience, many conversations aren't even that personal but will be a variation on a macho theme of: "You OK?"; "Yeah, no worries!"; "Good man! Crack on, then."

## Near-Miss Reporting

This is also a fruitful area to focus on during a walk and talk. Once we've identified a near miss we can dig into it by asking: What was learned? What actions were suggested as a consequence? Who followed up to ensure those actions were closed out? Who followed that up to ensure those changes delivered the improvement in performance we planned?

Having to answer these will keep any local manager responsible for the near-miss process on his or her toes. A mindful leader will find the following type of answer concerning:

'The cause of this incident is that there should have been more care taken and we've asked, through toolbox talks, for all workers to take more care in future…'

They don't need technical knowledge to understand that this is just hopeless - they just need some basic risk literacy.

As well as missing out on a learning opportunity this vagueness and simplicity also sends out a hugely powerful symbolic message. It's said that: "Those things of interest to my boss absolutely fascinate me!" A leader who lets a worker get away with a vaguely positive response to any of the questions above is sending the clear message that they're not all that bothered really, and a bit of waffle will suffice.

You could sum up the whole process by suggesting that the key to successful safety leadership is to transfer scepticism (of management's commitment to deal with issues) from the shop floor to the management themselves. The scepticism should rest with management regarding the practicability and effectiveness of the systems that look so good in the files.

# Nudge Theory

Perhaps the most interesting theory to have emerged in recent years is nudge theory. Originally deriving from a branch of economics described as the 'Chicago School' and as a response to the flaws in rational choice theory the concept was most famously described in the book *Nudge*, by Thaler and Sunstein.  It became very popular with the UK government, which had its own 'Nudge Tsar' and which set up a nudge department in the Health and Safety Laboratory in Buxton, UK.

An early experiment involved giving a subject £100 and telling them they can keep it but they must give some to a stranger. However, if the stranger rejects the offer both get nothing. Rational choice theory would suggest the stranger will accept any amount offered but the results showed the subject holding the money offered surprisingly large amounts (not wanting to appear greedy, even to strangers) and that these strangers often rejected 'insultingly' small amounts, motivated more strongly by the concept of *fairness* than by monetary gain. This is '*behavioural economics*', which spawned such fascinating books as *Freakonomics*. (I'll be very surprised if, based on workplace experience, the expressions "Right, where are those injury claim forms?" and "Now look what you made me do!" aren't in the minds of most of you as you read this).

If you've already heard of nudge theory you'll know that the most famous example is the well placed painted ceramic fly on the Amsterdam toilet bowl that most men can't help but aim at! This reduces splashing by a full 80 per cent apparently, with associated savings in cleaning costs and the environmental impact of cleaning chemicals. Seriously, imagine trying to match that improvement with a new rule, training or supervision! In Amsterdam once I realised I was actually using one of these fabled urinals and seizing my chance to take a picture that I could show at conferences whipped out my camera ... (I'd forgotten in my enthusiasm that I was in a public toilet in Amsterdam. This could have ended badly).

Of course, the concept of 'nudging' isn't new. If you've ever used paint to mark a floor or a wall to make clear where something goes - or doesn't go - you've arguably used the nudge concept. Having jaunty, upbeat music playing in shops where the basic items are frequently moved around so you can't just walk straight in and straight out again is nudge theory in action, so is describing mass redundancies as 'rightsizing', or invasions as 'conflicts'. Though I may be in danger of trampling over academic definitions, in essence I think of a 'nudge' as **any** small and/or simple thing that can have a big influence on people's behaviour. (Rather illustrating the 'nothing new under the sun' concept Thaler and Sunsein credit an Aad Kieboom as the originator of the 'fly' but he himself says the original idea came from a colleague, Jos van Bedaf, manager of the cleaning department. Van Bedaf himself says he got the idea from his time in the army in the 1960s, where he first came across small targets placed in the urinals ... (See https://worksthatwork.com/1/urinal-fly).

Indeed, there is an interesting academic controversy as to whether 'nudge' by flying under a 'behavioural economics' flag is just the rebranding of old psychology with a snazzy title. Thaler, wondering how ideal it is that these (financial) economists and lawyers have a monopoly on giving advice to governments has wryly observed that the impact of a snazzy title rather proves the point! A whole series of presentations by Thaler and others given for the British Academy in 2012 are available online.

A fascinating example: studies show people rate others far more positively if they share some of their name – even if they don't consciously notice this. For example, Malcolm Gladwell quotes research that found that someone called Dennis is almost twice as likely to end up a dentist as someone called George. Of course, if you found a dentist called Dennis and asked him if he'd been influenced in his choice of career by his name he'd say no and consider you deranged - but something is going on! The statistics are incredible. There should be about 260 dentists in the US called Dennis but there are around 480 – with this name deliberately chosen as 'class neutral' in the USA. This is an example of 'nominative determinism' or 'name-driven outcome' as seen with the classic paper on painful urination in the British Journal of Urology (vol 49, pp 173-176, 1977) by A. J. Splatt and D. Weedon. Usain ('Lightning')

Bolt often gets a mention around now.

Another example would be that, faced with a number of strangers' pictures, again all selected as attractiveness neutral, we go for the one with our own initials, though couldn't afterwards say why. (Though this might not be the only reason I'd consider Tony Manero a better John Travolta screen persona than Danny Zuko). A study of charity donations following hurricanes in the USA found that after Katrina people whose names began with K contributed a full 10 per cent to the appeal with this a full 150 per cent up on their average 4 per cent contribution to other, similar, appeals. You'll see stage 'mentalist' mind readers use this effect quite frequently.

**Photo 6. The Schipol Urinal Fly** Source: Schipol Airport

For example, the UK magician Derren Brown has a trick where he leaves a full wallet in the middle of a busy pavement but inside a red painted circle – then saunters back to pick it up untouched an hour later. This is because people will not reach across the red line.

Linking to Kahneman's *Thinking, fast and slow* the influence of the fly is that, often, men don't consciously point at the fly - they just *instinctively* do! You might think of this in terms of Homer Simpson, and Mr Spock from Star Trek. Faced with a target, Spock might consciously try and aim at the fly, monitor his performance and evaluate his accuracy. Homer would just … well, you get the idea.

UK government inspired examples include empty police vans parked near potential trouble spots; tax forms asking "Are you sure you haven't forgotten anything" and motorway signs saying "Don't litter - other people don't", which is a nudge with reference to social norms. They do work. Early data suggest that a large percentage of respondents who are ordinarily quite happy to 'accidentally' omit detail from their tax return balk at having to sign that commitment and so go back and amend their response.

## Two famous mainstream examples of small nudges that have a big impact:

In the UK in September 2012, a senior government politician had an argument with a policeman, during which he was alleged to call the policeman a 'pleb' (it's not a swear word but is a highly derogatory term for a person perceived to be of lower social class being short for plebeian: common or lower class). Just one word, not even a swear word, but it generated a huge amount of negative feeling and reaction. His entire political party dropped several points in the opinion polls. Interestingly, a policeman has since been successfully prosecuted for inventing details about this incident and the politicians protestations of innocence are receiving a far more favourable hearing although he remains demoted as I write.

In contrast, around the same time, the transcript of the argument between the Premiership footballers John Terry and Anton Ferdinand contained frequent and aggressive uses of every base sexual insult known to man. None of which was considered at all noteworthy, or offensive, either at the time or later. (Nothing offensive, that is, except for the use of the word 'black' because of the racial connotations and about which the arguments raged).

### Critical Incidents

This introduces us to the concept of the 'critical incident' first studied systemically by a Col. John Flanagan of the US Air Force which tells us that often *little* things can mean, and teach us, a *lot*. These aren't necessarily 'nudges', as defined by the textbooks but I'd like to include them, as the important point is that they may not look important at a glance but their impact is substantial. ('Minor behaviours, comments or incidents that punch above their weight and have a big impact on behaviour' simply isn't a very snappy title, is it?)

### Organisations and Societies

The briefly discussed term in the culture chapter above the expression 'Black

Swan' was coined by Nassim Taleb when discussing the disproportionate role of high-profile, hard-to-predict, and rare events. Taleb suggests that individually and collectively we can be unaware of the massive role of the rare event in historical affairs. For example, around as many people were killed on the roads of the world on the same day as the attack on the Twin Towers in New York on the 11th of September 2001. '9/11' will without doubt resonate as one of the single most important dates in terms of changing history on a global scale. Similarly, in many organisations everyone is only too well aware of the impact a single fatality can have.

## The Individual

There's a saying that "You never really know a person until you attend the reading of a will with them" but you can tell a lot about a person from more subtle interactions.

I'd like to use a personal example as an excuse to mention one of the world's most famous people and add a bit of glitz to proceedings. Some years ago (around 1996) I was shopping in Manchester and thought I recognised one of my young students. I said: "Hi, are you OK? Studying hard? Nice to see you" and walked on my way. Confronted by a confident older man when shopping with his dad my student smiled and nodded and looked a little shy, of course, but as I walked away I noticed a gently amused expression playing around his eyes as he caught his father's eye. I pondered why the young student should have found my "Hello" amusing and looked back. Then I groaned. It wasn't one of my students - it was David Beckham.

From this two second interaction I thought I could tell that David Beckham is a little shy but has a good and gentle sense of humour. In the 15 or more years since I haven't seen any evidence I was wrong, despite the fame and lunacy he's had to endure and the vast wealth he's accrued. He could have found the incident annoying and scowled, or he could have laughed at me with a sneer, but he didn't.

Nearly all footballers swear at each other, like Terry and Ferdinand did – it merely tells us something about the general culture of football, not about the *individual* men involved. However, the politician simply couldn't have blurted out the word 'pleb' without holding an underlying sense of social superiority. The fact that the word was alleged to have popped out *under stress* made it even more damning. (By the time you read this he may have been cleared and this incident merely a good example of using 'nudge' theory as a tool of political assassination).

Similarly, the jeweller Gerald Ratner described his own jewellery as "crap" in a talk to businessmen, which was reported by the press. His customers already knew this, of course, but this indignity nudged huge numbers of them over a line that made buying anything else from him totally unpalatable. The company share price dropped to £0.02p and he was sacked by his own company and went bankrupt. (Incidentally, I shared a conference stage with him once. He was extremely funny about the events that he brought on himself rolling out liners like "so I ended up owing the banks a total of one *billion* pounds … (pause for effect) … which back in those days, of course, was *a lot* of money!")

## Critical Incidents, Nudges and Safety

As discussed above, managers who ever fail to follow their own safety rules throw a big negative nudge, as it's often said that the worst level you set as a leader is the highest level you can expect from your those people reporting to you. Other examples might include starting a meeting by saying: "'elf and safety first, of course", clearly meaning "Let's get it out of the way before we can address the *important* issues …" or the order of words before and after the word 'but' in the middle of a sentence. There are many other examples that impact on safety perception as previously cited. The whole nudge concept really does explain how easy it is for a company to undermine the safety message. We don't hear what you say, we hear what you *mean*.

Going back to the previously mentioned four VIP visitors to Macondo the day before the explosion, they actively praised lost-time injury rates and management's recent decisive action regarding a harness/fall issue. What they didn't do was dig into process safety issues, as they didn't want to imply a lack of trust and also didn't want to disrupt the process unless they had good reason. (With personal safety issues a good reason is far easier to *see*).

As we've seen, this mindset leads directly to asking leading and semi-pointless questions like: "Everything now OK with that issue (with readings) we saw earlier?" It also, I'd argue, gives local management a big nudge regarding what's really important.

## Using Nudges to Positive Effect

With the benefit of hindsight it's easy to say that, before the Macondo visit, had BP and Transocean cascaded the learning from the near blow-out in the North Sea and planned to observe the process and ask digging questions of the testing they would have noticed something was wrong and been able to stop it. From a nudge perspective, however, it's worth remembering that these visits hardly ever occur before something goes wrong. What they can always do, however, is, during a visit, nudge the regular employees towards a more analytical approach to process safety on a day-to-day basis.

For example, Shell Scandinavia has stopped asking the question: "Why did you choose to shut down?" and started to ask instead: "Why did you think it safe to start back up?" You'll note that the technical information in the reports will be the same. "This happened and we thought this was the cause… so we thought …" but the shadow it throws is entirely different. I stress again that this systemic and deliberate use of positive rather than negative 'shadows' is at the very leading edge of safety management.

In Europe, there have been a lot of experiments with road junctions where removing traffic lights has encouraged greater thinking. This, it has been found, is particularly so if a small (almost 'token') roundabout is put in place. Circumventing it physically doesn't take much effort at all but it 'nudges' the person to think about the junction. In Kahneman terms, this is simply a nudge into thinking *slowly* (who has the right of way?) and away from thinking quickly. The pro-social helping experiment I recounted in the introduction would be another nudge - as was the short skirt that also featured which clearly led many men to move from an instinctive "No chance I'm busy" to "Well, perhaps I could spare ten minutes…"

## How to 'Nudge' a Thoughtful Assessment of Risk

Another use of a nudge might be where we find our risk assessment process has become a paper driven bureaucratic exercise where no one reads them and no one writing them expects anyone to read them. (A cynic might say that's nearly all of them, then!). However, if we stop asking for 'risk assessments', which nearly always triggers thoughts of clipboards and a paper trail, and instead stress the importance of 'assessing the risk', then thinking and analysis are suggested. For example, every time I cross a busy road or leave my (central Manchester) house late at night I 'assess the risk' and, I like to think very thoroughly, too. I wouldn't last long if I didn't. I've never considered that I've done a formal 'risk assessment', though. Supervisors would be well advised, therefore, to ask: "Have you assessed the risk?" or better even, "What did you find when you assessed the risk?"

## The 'Positive Labelling' Nudge

A variation on the use of praise is when labelling a person. Studies have shown that people respond to positive labels well. An example quoted by Malcolm Gladwell would be where someone is interviewed about whether they are going to vote in an upcoming election and asked to pick a favourite colour, or some such. They are told: "It's interesting, but people who pick that colour (regardless of what they said!) are far more likely to make use of their vote in an election …" and it is found that this positive label does indeed make the person more likely to do so. Imagine a football coach talking to a striker who has missed a few chances recently. They can see he is on the cusp of losing confidence because, in the last match, he passed a few when really he should have shot. They might say something like this:

"Do you know, one of the things I like about you is that you never lose confidence when you miss a few … you keep going … I can almost see you thinking 'the law of averages must kick in soon … I just need to keep going and keep my head up…' Do you know it's a great example to set to the younger players of how to deal with missing a few chances."

We can obviously use this in the world of safety by saying something like: "It's a good job you always wear X, or don't take Y shortcut because, with your level of experience people around here will look to you for their lead … and will follow your good example."

### Nudge – Conclusion

This book is, therefore, hopefully full of suggested 'nudges' and ways to use them. Echoing ABC theory Thaler himself frequently repeats 'make it easy' as a mantra. (A good quality 'walk and talk' is the perfect vehicle to nudge colleagues in the right direction). In short, if the commitment to excellence isn't there then the workforce will know. If it is, we should actively find ways of communicating that.

## Coaching and Positive Feedback

A good safety conversation "Can be difficult" notes Professor Andrew Hopkins. Not only will most workers not appreciate being interrupted and be sceptical as to the aim of the conversation the manager may themselves be wary of approaching a worker on their home ground. Hopkins therefore suggests that since these "interactions are potentially awkward for both parties" then leaders "may benefit from being coached or in engaging in role play before going out".

I find Professor Hopkins' books hugely persuasive and insightful, but I'd like to suggest that these comments are understatements of huge proportions. My experience is that most employees would derive a *lot* of benefit from some training in this area, and I will make three claims to illustrate this:

1) Any gap analysis is likely to find that supervisors' limited soft skills are one of the major problems the organisation is facing - full stop! Training supervisors in these soft skills without even mentioning safety may be the single best thing an organisation can do to develop its safety culture or its culture *generally*.

2) In my experience most supervisors are happy to acknowledge this and will

eagerly soak up any training they can get in this area like a sponge. (Though they will, of course, be full of bullish dismissiveness about this 'tree hugging nonsense' at the start of the course).

3 Any individuals who worry they might not do something *well*, let alone worry they'll do it badly and make a fool of themselves - will take every opportunity possible to avoid doing it at all. (See under "Training is Only Half the Story" in chapter 3). This has huge implications for a 'walk and talk' approach, and setting one up without helping prepare the individuals who'll have to run it with some training and role-play opportunities is asking for trouble.

## Coaching

This short section seeks to boil down the key principles from the many books and DVDs about coaching that are on the market.

In the UK, many supervisors need to be taught techniques for coaching at all naturally but if you understand the principle of the 'feedback fish' you'll understand the basics of coaching. Imagine your five-year-old has brought you a picture of a fish and its pretty rubbish – just a rough outline, with no detail. You wouldn't say: "That's crap that! Go away and come back when you can show me something that doesn't look more like a bloody biscuit!" You'd first compliment its brilliance and then hint about things that would improve it by asking "Let me think – how do fish see?" and your five-year-old will shout: "An eye … they have eyes!" and draw one in. Similar hints will lead to gills and fins and soon we have a recognisable picture of a fish!

Though the fish picture is a simple, even childish, example the analogy is actually a strong one. Studies show that for ownership to kick in, the key thing seems to be that the person being coached is the one that *says the answer first out loud*, even if both people talking know full well that the 'coach' knew the answer and led them to it with questions. (Writers such as Hallinan and Kahneman have written at length about our instant ability to see ourselves in a good light and being able to articulate an answer is all the 'proof ' we need that we knew it all along and would, of course, have acted on it).

For example, we have an exercise we use in team building sessions, which can only be solved by a pulley system that needs to be set up by someone throwing a ball wrapped in string around the leg of a table and bouncing it off a wall. We want our teams to succeed and we want them to go home roughly on time, so if the brainstorming element of the exercise is going badly we often cue them in by bouncing a ball off a wall in a bored 'waiting for them to sort themselves out' manner. (Think 'cooler king', as played by Steve McQueen in *The Great Escape*).

What's key is that this isn't at all subtle if you know what's happening, and there will always be a knowing smile from someone when the solution is suggested. What's interesting, however, is that in the debrief of the exercise nine times out of ten the group will have rationalised these events and will comment "it just came to me" or "I got the hint but it was on the tip of my tongue anyway … and anyway it was the only rational solution." Hardly ever do they say "We all know you effectively told us the solution so it spoilt the whole thing!"

The reason for this is that what is key is that they say the answer out loud first. This gives them ownership of it, and ownership is king. It's coaching from you but it feels like discovered learning to them. In a trivia quiz we run on courses I recently asked what was the name of the cooler king in *The Great Escape* (as above) and someone said "Oh I know this … it's er … Steve McQueen played him… and he was wonderful in it … jumped the motorbike over the fence and did the stunt himself … oh what is it now?" and I hinted "ironic really as it sounds a bit like Hitler himself" I got "Hiltz! It's *Hiltz* … of course it is. *See, I told you I knew it!*"

The worker who comments "I see what you're hinting at and I agree. We *do* need a banksman allocated to this operation" is experiencing a very similar mental process. The key thing is that when they say it first, they are much more likely to be resourcing a banksman as you drive away from site.

### When to Coach and When to be Directive?

When should you coach and when should you be directive? The simple answer is to coach wherever and whenever you can, so that you rise up on the shoulder of others. Indeed, some behavioural safety consultancies actually use safety coaching as their sole methodology and often very successfully too, so it's clearly a hugely important tool in the bag. It's probably easier to list the times when coaching *isn't* appropriate:

When someone is clearly a risk to themselves or to others you need to be directive and the simple request "Stop now" will be appropriate. Someone working at height from a wobbly ladder, perhaps?

When one or both of you haven't the time and or it's a simple behaviour and or it has been discussed before and a simple reminder is appropriate. "Hold the banister!" to your children using stairs while engrossed with their phones, or "Hard hat?" to someone who's jumped down from a cab and forgot to put it on.

Finally, when it has been discussed recently and a simple reminder will suffice. In which case a friendly "Lewis!" (to my son) or an eyebrow raised in the general direction of the top of your head.

## Praise

It is suggested that praise is something like 10 times more effective in changing a person's behaviour than criticism. (Figures vary of course and I can't find a definitive meta analysis study but the very title of books such as Aubrey Daniels' *Bringing Out the Best in People: How to apply the astonishing power of positive reinforcement* illustrate the point). This is because (as in the section on individual drivers) we are all hotwired to be optimistic, overconfident and to learn from positive experiences. Basically, the parts of our brain that deal with positive experiences are far more sensitive and powerful than those that deal with the negative.

One of the best selling management text books of all time, *The One Minute Manager* includes the key slogan "Catch a person doing something *right*". Indeed, it's a key element of all 'how to maximise potential' texts, including the *Seven Habits of Highly Effective People*. Imagine being told a month prior to an appraisal: "Those two areas of weakness we discussed last year? I've noticed a significant improvement over the last 11 months and am looking forward to giving you that feedback formally next month." What ratio of criticism would match the increase in motivation? Would it even be possible if you were followed around the workplace with a gun?

In order for **criticism** to resonate and not be seen as yet another nag it needs to have been preceded by four praises, ideally. This 4:1 ratio is quoted on just about every management course. An interesting spot-check is to ask a workforce how many instances of praise they get relative to criticism. It rarely ever 1 to 4, that's for sure! Indeed, when doing our culture surveys we have a scale that ranges from 'derisory laughter' all the way through to "No, that's not true - *never* isn't fair - I was praised once last year, I think!" (I exaggerate, but not by much).

Developmental studies by researchers such as Wang and Kenny are often quoted in newspapers as showing that shouting at stroppy 13 year olds does not actually make them better behaved 15 year olds and often quite the reverse. Worse, as well as resentful and badly behaved they are more likely to be depressed too. In his book *Other People's Habits* Aubrey Daniels explains how he was influenced initially by teaching and parenting best practice.

What this means in practice is that managers need to have a default setting as an encouraging and praising coach, not as a nag. That way, when they *do* need to give some negative feedback it is far more likely to be listened to, and impactful. It's very difficult to feel that you've let someone down when their default setting is to criticise.

A word of warning is required here. Many training materials and techniques that work in one culture may well backfire in another. Foe example, some cultures find giving praise harder than others and several US 'how to praise' videos really don't travel very well, especially to countries where a significant minority of the workforce can balance a healthy scepticism with an *unhealthily* negative and cynical approach. In the UK, even a straight "I noticed that you did that safely – well done" will make most supervisors uncomfortable. The one in ten technique described just below, on the other hand, is one that most are perfectly comfortable with.

This, I think, is a good example of the overall model I am trying to introduce for general use here. Whatever we try to do to impact on workers' behaviour we must understand the huge importance of **local** and **national** norms. Anything that doesn't allow for them will be very difficult, if not impossible to implement effectively.

### The 'One in Ten' Coaching Technique that Builds in Praise Automatically

One really useful coaching technique is 'One in Ten' and it is stolen from the world of educational psychology – original source unknown. (The people at Milliken would approve).

It involves asking someone to rate themselves on a task from one (poor) to ten (good) then when they respond with seven perhaps we don't ask "why only a seven!?" but instead "Excellent, but can I ask why aren't you a nought? What do you do well?"

When they explain why they justify a seven you listen, nod, smile, murmur and maybe even risk a "sounds more like an eight to me!" When you have built some rapport and offered some praise naturally for what they actually do well, you switch to *coaching* mode by asking:

"But you know I'm a safety coach and my job is to halve accidents around here. So if I can get you up from that 7 to an 8.5, that's my job done – well, for now at least. How do you think we could do that?"

I'm sure you can imagine the two people are now well primed to have a productive and constructive chat – particularly as this approach nearly always leads naturally to 'curious why?' questions and the other objective-analysis techniques that we keep stressing as vital. In any number of major incidents poor communication has proved to be a key element, so here's a proactive way of using the technique that would have been really useful in most, if not all, of these cases.

"How would you rate the shift handover communications on a *typical* day 1 to 10?"

Followed by:

"How would you rate the shift handover communications on a *bad* day 1 to 10?"

As so often in this book, I'm going to suggest strongly that this simple discussion, used systemically, with the learning that it generates followed up, would have saved any number of fatalities and financial loss over the years.

# Case Study

There is a manufacturer of submarine parts in the south of the UK that picked up on this technique from one of our DVDs and whose safety representatives would tour the site asking 'one in ten' questions as they did so. When they approached me at an exposition some years ago and told me about this, I asked: "but what about all the other techniques in the DVDs? What about 'five whys' and ABC analysis for example" and they said: "oh, all of that flows naturally from a good one in ten!"

They'd won a prestigious in-house award with their approach so I can honestly boast here I have given an organisation an award winning behavioural safety approach in one simple question!

# Data and Illustration

It is said that the best way to change a person's behaviour is through the use of data and illustration. For example, regardless of all the process safety issues on a drilling platform as so clearly illustrated by Piper Alpha and Macondo annually around 65% of lost time incidents will be caused by simple slips, trips, falls and struck by falling objects. In the North Sea Oil Industry this will run to a cost in the tens of millions annually. For example, when discussing something as simple as holding the handrail we might try:

"Do you know I've just been on a course. 65 per cent of lost time incidents are caused by simple slips, trips and 'struck bys' and the cost runs to tens of millions when you multiply it all out. We simply can't get anywhere near zero harm unless we address simple behaviours like holding the handrail."

Pause…

"only I noticed you weren't holding the handrail just then."

Even moving away from industries where a simple broken leg can cost millions in disrupted production and to a simple family farm data can also be powerful.

At the Healthy Workplaces Summit 2013 in Bilbao, Spain, farmers from the West Offaly Dairy Farmers group of Ireland presented on their reasons for embarking on an effective risk management programme. They described how they had a meeting with 'safety' a long way down the agenda (far behind such as 'yield per cow' they confessed!) until they came to a set of statistics showing that they were three times at risk as any other occupation in Ireland. They had of course grown used to this risk as 'normal', indeed many had *grown up* with these risks and it was this 'family' issue that made them pause. On many farms the whole family will help out, and from a very young age in some cases too, so that not only were they at risk so were their partners and their children.

The data, along with a few case studies, made them question whether they were comfortable continuing on as normal and they decided that, actually, they *weren't*. One of the farmers, John Hickey, confessed candidly "to be sure, there are short cuts I would simply never take now that I would have taken a few years ago without a second thought". Faced with an international audience of safety experts he didn't go into any further detail!

**Data Driven Risk Literacy 'Micromorts'**

A 'Micromort' (a term coined by Ronald Howard) is basically a one in one million chance of dying in an accident. For example, it's said to be about every 6,000 miles in a train, 230 miles on a road, 6 on a motorbike; 180 yards on a motorbike if over the drink limit! Although I'm not sure about the exact veracity of these Wikipedia resourced figures and the research behind them, as with Heinrich and his increasingly infamous triangle, it's the principle that's most useful.

For example, the micromort figure for miles *flown* is said to be 1000 miles but that must be misleading. For a start 99% of the risk is in the take off and landing but American airspace alone sees more than 815 million passengers per year (travelling *billions* of miles) but aviation saw only 306 fatalities worldwide. That said the fact that the quoted micromort rating for increased risk of cancer due to greater radiation exposure (6000 miles) is exactly the same it is for terrorism is interesting. (As a scientifically ignorant psychologist I find myself asking: "*What* radiation risk?").

In a previous book I discussed an example where I elected to travel by train when tired rather than drive as I realised that the combination of fatigue and the notoriously dangerous roads at the end the long journey would significantly reduce that 230 even further away from the 6000 for the train. I'm sure that was a sensible (risk literate) decision and it was the data that helped me make it.

# Challenging Unsafe Acts or Conditions Effectively and Overcoming Inhibition

A simple truism known by everyone in safety is:

"If you walk past an unsafe act or condition you leave the risk present on the day itself and worse than that you **condone** it for the future. The highest standard you can **expect** is the lowest standard that you will **tolerate**".

It has been said so often and by so many people I'm not sure who to credit with saying it first.

I attended a talk once by a construction worker, who described how he noticed a badly-guarded hole when making his way to the canteen "for a quick brew". He noted that a dip in the ground made it quite difficult to see and thought to stop and discuss it with the workmen nearby, who seemed to have moved on to another task, but then he thought he'd address it on his way back as, frankly, he was "desperate for a hot drink". He never finished his coffee because of the commotion that erupted outside. He said he wasn't exaggerating for effect and that the man who died that day really was his best friend.

Why do we walk past something in situations like these? It's very simple: Sometimes, it's because we are not risk literate enough. We don't know about Heinrich and his triangle and the incident numbers associated with gravity, and so simply don't appreciate the risk. Or, perhaps, we have a blame mentality and are happy to leave it to the individual to take their chances. If they're not paying attention, then it's just natural selection at work isn't it? Sometimes, of course, it's simply because we don't appreciate our basic legal obligations.

More often, in organisations that already have half-decent cultures and standards, it's because we are busy and tempted to 'leave it for later'; or because we are slightly uncomfortable at the prospect of saying something (as ABC analysis describes so well Discomfort always means potential trouble). We are all hot-wired to leave it for others while rationalising that if it were really important, we'd say or do something. (The underpinning psychology is covered under the notes on cognitive dissonance above). We can help minimise this rationalisation if we remember the case study of Kitty Genovese.

## Kitty Genovese

Kitty Genovese was a New Yorker who was infamously murdered in 1964 in an attack at the back of the apartment block in which she lived. What was notable about this murder is that dozens of people heard the attack and several switched on lights and/or opened windows to see what the shouts and screams were about. The murderer was scared off by this but returned a little while later to enjoy the sight of the crime scene, as these psychopathic people are apt to do. There wasn't a crime scene, however, as not one of the people who'd heard the attack had rung the Police. They'd all left it to someone else. So, finding her where he'd left her, he took the opportunity to attack her a second time and, this time, killed her.

As you can imagine, this caused a lot of heartfelt introspection in America and many comments about the loss of simple humanity because of the 'urban jungle'. It did at least inspire some groundbreaking research into the bystander effect. (See Darley and Latane 1968 for example). The basic experiment was to show a subject a control bar next to three other bars of similar length and ask the subject which one matched. (It was a difficult visual task but one that could be done 999 times out of 1000). However, the trick was to have a group of people who were all in on the experiment lie and choose the wrong bar, with the unsuspecting subject one of the last to be asked. What the experimenters found was that 9 out of 10 denied the evidence of their own eyes, lied, and choose the same bar as the confederates of the experimenter. On the other hand, when they re-ran the experiment and had just one subject call the right bar, then 90 per cent of the time the subject would say something like: "I don't know what the rest of you are seeing but I agree with X - I think it's (the right one)."

There are two incredibly important learning points from this experiment. The first is that we hate to put our heads above the parapet and be the first to dissent, (we've discussed this already when talking about the power of peer influence). The second is that, as in the Hillsborough case, if just one person takes a deep breath and speaks up, then it can make all the difference in the world.

The good news is that simply by spending the last minute reading about this you are now significantly less likely to suffer from the bystander effect in the near future, as, next time you find yourself asking "Why isn't anyone saying something", you'll know one of the possible answers!

## Using This Principle During Training Or Briefings

Many a trainer or presenter has asked "any questions or challenges?" at the end of a session to be met with total silence from the audience. Afterwards any number of delegates will explain why what was presented won't work. However, if just one person speaks up others will often say: "I'm so glad you asked / challenged that that because I was thinking that too". Invariably, a productive debate will then ensue. A trainer can help facilitate this by asking questions such as: "Who is going to ask the first question?" or "How else could we address this?"

## Individual Passions

Everyone we work with has something they're passionate about. For many of us, it's our children. For others, it's a sport or a hobby. It's obviously a good idea to also talk about these during a conversation about risk to raise the issue of *loss*. Research by Cialdini and others has shown that the potential loss of something we have is hugely motivating. For example, imagine yourself looking at an out-of-style shirt or blouse in a charity shop. It's nice, not at all expensive but you know you'd be very unlikely to wear it. Walking away is very easy, isn't it? Now imagine the exact same shirt or blouse but this time pulled from the back of a wardrobe by your partner with the comment "You never wear this – I'll throw it out". Would you not instinctively respond with "No, don't you dare, it used to be one of my favourites!" The same principle applies to rather more important issues such as eyesight and the ability to play with children and grandchildren.

You don't have to be so direct as to say something like "How would your son feel if you fell from here and paralysed yourself!?" Instead you can simply ask something like "So you enjoy a kick about with your son?" in the middle of a chat about football and let them join the dots. In the US, you'll often see a sign near some road works that says: "Please slow down, my daddy works here".

## Personal Integrity – 'My Word Is My Bond'

When we seek to make a challenge personal it is the case that the eyes (and 'I's') have it. For example, imagine you're on a beach and someone asks you if you'll keep an eye on their bags while they take a quick dip. If you look them in the eye and say that you will, how long will you make an effort? Can I suggest a long time, and, if they never come back some of us will have bundled the bags up, handed them in to a local shop and left a note under a rock. On the other hand, if you asked someone the same question and they looked at the sand and mumbled: "Ok … yeah" would you trust them? Can I assume not?

Similarly, imagine you're booking a table at a nice restaurant. Consider these two typical conversations:

The person booking the table: "A table for two, Saturday at 8pm please."

Reservations: "That's all booked for you … please ring if you can't make it."

Diner: "Yes, OK."

Now replay with a slightly different wording:

"A table for two Saturday, at 8pm please."

"That's all booked for you … can I ask will you please ring and let us know if you can't make it?"

"Yes OK I will."

You may be surprised to know people are only a third as likely to fail to show up without ringing when asked the second way. It's because of the "will **you**" and "yes **I** will" in the conversation. Though similar words are used, it's much more **personal**. Issues of personal integrity and trust are activated by the eye contact and use of the 'I' word and, effectively, we've made the grown-up version of a 'pinky promise', as a child would have it. These subtle, subconscious references to societal norms are the most important elements of any conversation.

In this case, behaviour is held to be impacted by a factor of *three*. (Even the much desired and publicized 'step change' of a 50% reduction in accidents as in the North Sea Oil Industry is only a factor of two). Therefore, when you've made a challenge: look people in the eye, mean what you say, and ask "will you"? Then make sure they *look you in the eye back* and give a personal commitment to act.

Of course, it helps if you're naturally assertive or have been taught assertion.

# Assertion and Negative Feedback

Psychologically speaking, being assertive doesn't mean 'asserting oneself' like on a sports field. It means not backing down but without getting aggressive. Of course, not being aggressive comes easily if you're *analysing*, not blaming, in the first place and we'll discuss the practicalities of that presently. However, there will be times when you'll be tempted to walk away to avoid a fuss, even though it's your job, or best practice not to do so.

The following notes just cover the very basics. That said, the '80:20 principle' applies as ever, and not ever breaking any of the simple rules briefly covered here would make you one of the most assertive people in the country!

### When You *Are* In The Wrong – 'Regret, Reason, Remedy'

One of the key elements of being assertive is to speak honestly. If you're fudging and twisting, or have a reputation for it, you'll more than likely provoke similar communications. When you're in the wrong you could try waffling your way out if it which always works doesn't it? No one ever notices that's what you're doing, bites their tongue but then leaves thinking less of you!? That never happens!

Or, you can try 'regret, reason, remedy'. Basically, you say: "I'm sorry, this is what happened; this is why; and this is what I'm going to do about it". (See McFarlan and others)

It isn't great to have to use it, of course, but it minimises the negative impact. Indeed, sometimes you can even *improve* things with it. There is a famous marketing fable about the pizza company that developed a great reputation by spending a month withholding every 50th pizza until one minute after the 'if it's not there within 30 minutes it's free' promise. The delivery people were asked to wait until the 31st minute, knock on the door and say:

"We're really sorry this is late! The new chef set the ovens just a bit too high and burnt your first one a little … not too bad but we didn't want to take the risk" (or some such). "So this one's free … enjoy!"

Following this rule makes you look more in control and credible than a typical waffle, the *intended* message of which is "so as you can see, basically, this wasn't my fault" but gives out the *unintended* one, which is that "unlike the wise man who learns from the mistakes of others I don't even learn from my own mistakes". It also follows one of the key principles of Buddhism that negative things will happen and, once they have, all we can do is choose how we respond to them. If we respond well, then we minimise the damage and may well turn that negative into a positive by influencing someone else who sees your response. For example, when a borderline call about stopping the job elicits the response "Damn, that's really inconvenient but we need to stop the job and think about this" it will travel around the organisation in minutes.

When I was on the Cullen panel looking into the Ladbroke Grove train crash a senior railwayman sitting next to me was tapped on the shoulder, gathered his papers and quickly left, looking alarmed. I saw him on the TV later that night using the '3 Rs' technique provisionally about a derailment. He was saying: "We're horrified at events, not sure yet what caused the derailment, but we are investigating and I'll be back here at 10 to update you personally even if it's to say I know nothing more yet". As it transpired his company was blameless but another company that provided a terse "no comment" suffered very badly in commercial terms especially when it turned out they were culpable. They made themselves looked shifty and defensive, as well as incompetent.

A utility client in the UK once had a storm knock out some very important electricity pylons on Christmas Eve. The head of emergency response (Jon) had very sore ears initially but made a media announcement to say: "We are working 24 hours a day because of course we know you need your power back as soon as possible. We've brought in every spare man in the company and you should know that several van loads have volunteered to drive up to help out because they're totally committed to their work and are mortified to think we can't supply power at Christmas. They're all sleeping on the floors of church halls and away from their families … we really do all want this fixed as soon as humanly possible".

The criticism stopped, cooked turkeys were dropped off at church halls, and horns were beeped and cheers given as people drove past the workers. That simple communication brought into play issues of empathy, fairness and reciprocity and, again, illustrates that these psycho-social issues (and good communication) can make all the difference in the world.

## Don't Personalise and Don't Generalise

Again, we want to avoid provoking aggressive or defensive responses when giving negative feedback to others so it is important to keep all language objective and impersonal – especially when you have to criticise someone. Never personalise or generalise but stick objectively to facts about specific behaviour. You can *describe* emotion but you can't *show it*. Using words like 'always' and 'never' will hardly ever be applicable. When we're feeling defensive the slightest inaccuracy in a person's accusation can make us angry.

Imagine you see a worker not wearing their hard hat. Obviously, shouting: "Oi, crap-for-brains. Get your bloody hard hat on NOW. You're just useless, you are" is both personalising it and generalising it!

Instead, you should say something like: "Excuse me, but I really need to talk to you about your lack of PPE. It's a risk in this location and, frankly, I'm really not at all happy to see this. You've had a toolbox talk about it just recently". In the first case, the person on the receiving end isn't going to be thinking about their risk - they're going to be thinking about *you* and they'll be *talking about you* over coffee later, as you've given them a perfect excuse not to focus on the risk they were running. In the second case, they can try to criticise you to their colleagues but they are far more likely to get the response "Well you could have just worn the hat!" rather than the sympathy they're seeking.

So, it's acceptable to articulate and describe anger but not to show it. Which reminds me of the football joke about the referee who gives a bad decision and is approached by a player clearly about to abuse him. The player checks himself and says: "If I call you an idiot will you send me off?" The referee replies "Of course" so the player asks "But what if I only *think* you're an idiot". The referee comments "You can *think* what you like…" so the player says "OK, then I *think* you're an idiot!" (Sorry).

## Criticism in Private

I remember a delegate once being unnecessarily rude to a waitress on a training course in front of his training manager. After a couple of minutes had passed his manager politely and calmly asked him if could have a quiet word outside. There was no shouting but they came back in a few minutes later with the young trainee looking rather white and very chastened. The manager had ensured he achieved the maximum impact on the trainee and, as a side effect, maximum impact on us too.

Giving someone a telling off in front of others may well increase its impact on the day but it will cause resentment, and the best outcome you'll get is compliance through fear. Always criticise people in private. The acronym 'RIP PIP' is a good guide: reprimand in *private*, praise in *public*. That said there are times when 'praise in public' can be embarrassing for the person on the receiving end. Getting to know the local culture and individual people's preferences is so important. It's not much use if the (unintended) consequence is that the person avoids acting that way again to avoid the embarrassment of being praised for it in front of their sniggering peers!

## Saying Yes and No

In his excellent book *Drop the Pink Elephant* Bill McFarlan tells the story of buying a coffee in the US somewhere and being offered a piece of pie by the waitress "It's delicious, I baked it myself just this very morning etc." He didn't like to say no and ten minutes later, he and his colleague found themselves down $10 and about a thousand calories worse off, as they saw another diner come in and be given the same 'irresistible' sales pitch. His response: "No thanks, just the coffee is fine".

So, say yes when you mean yes, and no when you mean no.

## Broken Record

Broken Record technique was also used by interviewer Jeremy Paxman with Michael Howard (mentioned above) with him asking the same question again and again and refusing to move on until the question was answered. Clever people will, of course, try to drag you onto a new subject but you just hold your ground. And repeat … and repeat. In this case, Paxman needed a simple yes or no answer to the question as to whether this politician knew an event was about to occur, even though he personally didn't order it. The politician kept responding with: "the important thing is Jeremy …". Paxman just kept asking: "Yes or no? It's a simple question".

In the world of safety conversations you may well find yourself requesting a specific behaviour quite reasonably but get in response a passionate diatribe about something else entirely. (Something else entirely except in the mind of the angry person you're talking to, that is. They may well see you as the very personification of the organisation that has upset them). For example, *you* want them to get back into their cab and put their hard hat and high-visibility vest on before you'll look at their paper work. *They* want to discuss the queue to get into the site, or some other genuine annoyance.

However, no matter what they say you always respond with a Paxman-like: "I'm happy to discuss that with you but not until you get back in your cab and put your hat and vest on …" followed in due course by a polite and calm escalation if required. "If you continue to refuse to comply with site regulations I'm going to have to ask you to leave the site … and I don't want that to happen as it'll be inconvenient for both of us". Adding: "but it's your choice" makes it clear you will not be backing down and it will be one or the other, but allows them a degree of autonomy, which helps their pride.

## Challenging Waffle with Paraphrasing

You may just meet people on your travels who waffle and use vague language. Expressions like 'hopefully!' and 'as soon as I can' will be as bountiful as their smiles and good humour. You may find they smile less when you ask: "Can you be more specific please?" (I've noticed this as a trait of certain nationalities where boundless bonhomie, smiles and positive words can change to annoyance very quickly when you seek clarification. This is definitely a local cultural issue. I won't mention who I mean but I will say that their footballers are rather more impressive than their politicians).

Try asking a taxi controller: "By 'just a minute or two', do you mean literally between 60 and 120 seconds; some time in the next 5 to 10 minutes, depending on traffic but no later than 10 because the job *is* genuinely booked and someone is on their way or does it mean you're doing you're very best but, in truth, haven't a clue how long I'll be waiting?" You'll be amazed how often they respond honestly!

Being asked to do two or more things that are mutually difficult is a classic example of the need to paraphrase. The amusing expression: "quick; quality; cheap – please pick any two" exemplifies how clarification question is required when we're asked for all three. (The response is: "You can have quick, cheap and poor quality, you can have quick and good quality but it won't be cheap. What's your choice?" Another example would be when we are faced with a diatribe of general abuse. If you paraphrase their angry words with: "So you're saying that you fear this will prove another example of management promising and then not delivering" both confirms you're listening and saves your ears.

## 'Bubbles' – An Overview Model of Assertion

The 'bubbles' concept summarises the whole approach and takes advantage of the fact that we can't think and react instinctively at the same time. It has its basis in work in Transactional Analysis Interpersonal theory, which came out of California in the

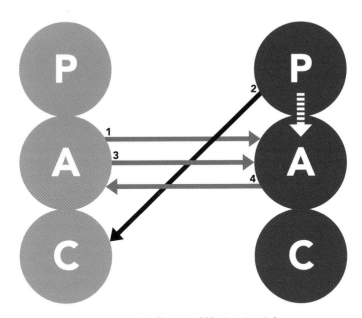

**Figure 23. Repeated Assertive Transactions leading to 'Bubble' (Ego State) change**

1960s. The basic model is like a snowman with three bubbles on top of each other. The lower bubble represents passive, sulking behaviour, 'child', in TA terms. The top bubble represents aggressive, authoritarian or patronising behaviour, 'parent'. The middle bubble, however, is where you ought to be - firm, fair, analytical and reasonable behaviours: 'adult'.

You'll find that when you stop, step back and analyse yourself you'll be amazed how often you *don't* qualify for middle-bubble status. Some examples:

Consider first the manager who closes a meeting with a challenging "So, we're all agreed? (with *rhetorical* body language and voice tone!) Any one got a problem with that? No? Good!" We all know that when things go wrong this person **isn't** going to say: "Well, it was all my decision, given my voice tone and body language I effectively made it impossible for anyone to object, didn't I?" Instead just as with BP and Texas City and NASA and Challenger they'll claim: "But no one told us anything was wrong". In the film *Challenger*, a line that always makes delegates gasp and hiss is when Larry Malloy testifies at the enquiry: "We discussed the temperature issue with the engineers at Thiokol and all agreed there were no issues…".

The theory also talks of the 'Nurturing Parent'. This is still 'top bubble' but without the aggression. The trouble is, the side effects are that your paternal attitude may be seen as patronising (because it is – you're talking down to people). This mindset will also inhibit other people's development and growth, and will get in the way of your listening and communication skills, as you're assuming you know best and we've already seen that a strong culture is based on listening and learning.

If you've ever said to someone "Can I give you some *advice*?" you won't often have had the response: "Yes please!" More likely you will often have had an aggressive response in return. Or they might listen, but look upset. This illustrates the principle that a communication from the 'top bubble' nearly always generates a 'top bubble' or 'bottom bubble' response. Similarly a middle bubble communication usually results in a 'middle bubble' response as 'behaviour breeds behaviour'. For example, when you've been arguing with your partner and jibe has followed sulk and a sulk has provoked a snipe then one of you says: "Oh, I can't even remember how this started and you're going in for that scan next week. Let's stop this. Would you like a nice cup of tea?" it usually works. (I know, I know. Sometimes this offer is seen a sign of weakness and they go for the kill - but not often!)

The real problem is that not being in the middle bubble *always* leads to problems later. Being passive means you avoid confrontation but also means people will take advantage, you'll lose respect and you'll be unlikely to like the view in the mirror at the end of the day. Being aggressive means you might get what you want in the short-term but people will resent you and get you back in some way later.

I ran a course in Romania for a shipping company once, when we discussed how this 'getting you back later' might work in reality and the flipchart filled up with such comments as "withholding information", "not helping new starts", "boycotting social events", "working slowly or to rule", "looking to leave the company", "criticising the company in the pub", and so on. Then, one young female pointed to a scar on her ear and said: "Or losing your head … and I mean that *literally*!"

Her story was that, a few months before, she'd been on a vessel examining a valve that had blown off and nearly taken her head with it (actually cutting her ear) because someone they never were able to identify had sabotaged it. It turned out there was a lot of bad feeling on board the vessel because of an 'over-the-top' verbal criticism that had been given to the whole crew a few days before the incident.

When discussing my holistic model a weakness in this fourth factor usually manifests itself as withholding such as citizenship behaviour. This isn't the only example of it manifesting itself in something more sinister and proactive.

### Why 'Bubbles' Works

To summarise, there are two key factors: First, thinking and reacting are mutually exclusive, so if you can train yourself to stop and think which bubble you are in you'll be halfway there already. The second thing is to remember that behaviour breeds behaviour, so if you're in your middle bubble other people will tend to match that. Sometimes, it takes a little while of course but it will happen more often than not. On the flip side, if you're not in your middle bubble it's really not very easy for people around you to be in theirs, because *behaviour breeds behaviour* - aggressive responses generate aggression or sulking, but pleasant objective responses usually generate similar ones. To quote either Albert Einstein, or Isaac Newton: "For every action there is a reaction". (Science was never a strong point).

There is a wonderful YouTube clip in which a US State Trooper who has clearly swallowed a book on assertion shows the patience of a saint with a motorist who screams and shouts at him through his driver window and even rips up the ticket he's just been given and throws it at the trooper. Without showing the slightest annoyance, the trooper, writing up a replacement ticket, comments: "Sir, I need you to pick that up or I'll have to write you a second ticket for littering …". The man does as requested and the trooper returns to the car and chuckles: "Some people!" clearly not the slightest bit stressed by the exchange. Though he used several of the techniques described above what was most important was that he never even came close to leaving his middle bubble.

## Maximising Workforce Empowerment and Involvement

As stated in the introduction to this section on leadership, the ability to empower the workforce is last in this section but by no means least. It is, perhaps, the greatest skill of all as it is the only one that can directly impact on the very essence of a person.

Reflecting this, the workforce empowerment champion Nigel Bryson often quotes Dale Carnegie's classic book *How to win friends and influence people* as saying that "The deepest principle in human nature is to be appreciated". In similar vein, the American safety doyen Aubrey Daniels suggests: "A manager should only insist on their own idea if it's three times better than their workers, as the worker will work twice as hard at their own idea". I'm not sure those figures have been scientifically validated but we all know exactly what he means.

There isn't a business guru on the planet who doesn't stress the principle that empowerment is a powerful tool of success and the academic studies back this up. However, it simply isn't as widespread as the win: win logic would dictate.

For example, in an article in SHP (Feb 2013), Nigel Bryson references several case studies, pilot programmes and HSE initiatives that stress clearly both the efficacy of workforce involvement and high level support for it. Similarly, UK HSE chair Judith Hackitt identifies it as one of her top three priorities - along with leadership and competence - in a 2009 strategy launch. The HSE review of the success of the massive Olympic build programme in London also identified workforce involvement as "central to the success of the project" and this was the first Olympic build in history where no one was killed.

In the UK, it is a legal requirement for an organisation to either consult the workforce representatives (if unionised), or the workforce themselves in good time on a whole range of matters, including:

The introduction of any measure or new technologies at the workplace that may substantially affect the health and safety of the employees covered;

The arrangements for appointing and nominating competent persons, as required by the Management of Health and Safety at Work Regulations;

The planning and organising of any health and safety training the employer is required to provide for the employees under the relevant statutory provisions.

However, Bryson quotes HSE figures that show up to 40 per cent of organisations fall well short of achieving this. He finds that the follow-up by the UK HSE of this lack of compliance is "lukewarm" and that, effectively, there is no enforcement. Rather, organisations are *encouraged* to comply. The official justification for this is that in order for this cooperation to work well, there needs to be trust between all parties and trust cannot be stimulated through compulsion by a third party.

Workforce involvement in safety is an all-round excellent thing and a legal requirement but it is not even as widespread as it should be by law, and this book is aiming far higher than mere legal compliance!

It's easy to agree, I think, that what's holding us back is unlikely to be malice but a combination of fear of handing over power, short-term views driven by time poverty and a lack of vision. Combine these with some good old-fashioned laziness, some residual snobbery and a lack of genuine leadership from the very top and you have the situation that Nigel describes.

### Some Simple Case Studies to Illustrate The Psychology of Workforce Involvement

Imagine you're crossing a train station concourse when someone with a clipboard approaches. Typically, we try to get around them if we can - but if we do stop and talk, we often find ourselves saying things like "and another thing!" or "Write this down, too!" and *they* are the ones trying to get away. (Or is that just me?)

The two truths that explain this are that no one likes to be interrupted and one of the few things we like more than we dislike being interrupted is being asked what we think.

### *Timing* Empowerment and Ownership

It's well worth reflecting on where in classic models of improvement we involve the workforce. A classic model of general improvement, the DMAIC model, is:

Define
Measure
Analyse
Improve
Control

If we involve our workers only at the improve level we have already defined the issue and are merely involving the workforce in rectifying that. The cognition is "We have decided what's wrong – help us put it right". That's fine as far as it goes but ideally the workforce will be involved from the very start by being asked at the outset: "What is the problem?"

### The *Two* Lessons from the TV Show *Undercover Boss*

I taped the latest series of this TV programme so that I could undertake a highly scientific study of its results. (Just in case you are one of the few people who hasn't seen a version of this programme it's where a boss so senior that no-one on the shop floor would recognise them puts on a hat and overalls and pretends to be a new start being filmed for a documentary about new starts).

As with every previous series, in all eight episodes the boss later announced that they had learned huge amounts from the experience. Of course, there might be some self-selecting sample issues here. If there was an episode where they didn't, it wouldn't have made a good programme and would have been dropped! (I'm sure that hardly ever happens). It's not a scientific study, though, so I'll move on to the point I'm trying to make and illustrate with a true anecdote.

At the denouement of each episode the key workers are called in and told how much has been learnt and that, more often than not, they are to be promoted to a head office function looking at some of the key issues raised by the programme. They all beam with joy and look as if they can't wait to ring the partner, or children to boast: "You'll never guess … I've just had a pay rise". What I noticed, though, was that when, inevitably, the 'uncovered boss' goes on to praise the person with comments such as: "Because you're great you are. I'm just really thrilled to have people like you working for the company", around 50 per cent well up. This praise and personal validation is clearly reaching them at a deeper level than a pay rise can.

Maslow's famous hierarchy of needs suggests that the need to be a valued team member and to develop yourself to your maximum potential exceed material comfort (once material comfort has been achieved, of course). We all know this to be true, and writers like Dale Carnegie articulated this many years ago.

I'd like to share an anecdote that features an even smaller sample but one which illustrates my point and will always stay with me. I was sitting at the side of a stage on a safety day for a large utility company, waiting for my speaking slot. Before I got up the compere announced unexpectedly that four people in the audience were to be given awards for safety excellence. The names were read out and the four surprised people made their way to the stage to accept their certificates and vouchers. Once on stage, they were lavishly praised for their efforts, and details were given regarding just how much benefit to the company they had been. There was much warm applause, some good-natured catcalling and bashful smiling. Then the senior manager lavishly praised their characters and mentioned how humbled he was to have people like this working for him. As if I'd scripted it two of the four very visibly welled up. A personal validation gets to you somewhere very deep and meaningful. Carnegie, Maslow (and Nigel) know what they're talking about!

## A More Practical Example

I was on an oil platform some years ago and watched a 'suit' from the 'beach' introduce a housekeeping initiative to a group of drill-floor workers that had just come off shift. He showed some example pictures and explained how this open door on the edge of a walkway could be blown by the wind, and also a puddle that could ice over. It's fair to say that their body language conveyed that they weren't entirely engaged. Though I can't know exactly what they were thinking, it's probably fair to say it wouldn't be printable if I did.

In the next session, I suggested he introduce the slides with some hard data about injuries caused by poor housekeeping. Then ask an open-ended question about what they thought about an illustrative photograph he thought to be a clear-cut 'fail'. Even after the data, the first comment was: "Oh, ***&&^ hell, come on I could get my *&^%$ car past that …" followed by the challenge: "Have you seen where we work?!".

However, once they'd got that off their chest, a sensible debate broke out and the genuine risks associated with spontaneously swinging doors and slippery floors were discussed and the group agreed that the photo in question would work quite well as an example of an 'unsafe' for the purposes of a behavioural checklist.

Two incredibly important mindsets flow directly from the discussion I have described. The first is that the workers involved were now far more likely to 'own' the standard and, when coming across such situations, close the door and clear the blockage causing the puddle. The second response was rather more subtle but just as important. When we asked if anyone was interested in volunteering to be involved in a workforce analysis committee, we got a better response. In this case, some good-natured jeering followed by some vague but genuine promises to 'think about it' that later turned into two excellent volunteers. The response from the shift from the previous session was almost complete silence. No good natured responses. I think I'm on safe ground to say that no one was even slightly tempted to volunteer.

### Empowerment – Summary

I think it is almost impossible to overstate the benefits of ownership and empowerment. Not only do we get the practical benefits of the knowledge of our front-line experts, we also increase the ownership of the solutions in the population that will have to implement them. This is, of course, utterly central to them being undertaken as we'd hope them to be when we aren't there to watch.

Even more than that, however, we set a tone of respect and trust that is good for the organisation as a whole - and even society in general. Leaving aside the various health benefits, do we not want to send our workforce back to their families and wider society feeling respected and valued, rather than frustrated, belittled and bitter? After all, leaving aside moral arguments, our children go to the same schools and we drink in the same bars.

# A Step to the Side – The 'Stress' Issue

This is not a book about stress, but stress management is a very important aspect of the 'elephant in the room' that is the cost of ill health. Everything recommended in this book would be stress reducing I'd argue but in particular enhanced empowerment and job satisfaction mean less stress, less ill health and less absenteeism. (See Warr). That translates into less turnover and fewer spurious claims. In terms of hard cash this might actually be the most important paragraph in the book.

# Case Study

I'd like to give a business example to illustrate this small but important aside. I gave a board presentation to a rail company which went well and at the end the CEO (who had built up the company personally and who held great power) asked the others in the room to comment. In particular he picked out the woman in charge of occupational health. He commented: "A lot of these recommendations sound like the initiatives you've been suggesting we implement to address the so called stress issue". She agreed. He then challenged me: "You don't buy into this 'stress' crap, do you?". I asked him if he considered himself a hard headed business man. He nodded. I suggested that it didn't matter what either of us thought about the concept but encouraged him to sit down with his hardest headed accountant and look closely at the figures. When he said he would the occupational health woman shouted: "Yes!" and punched the air!

# Chapter 9.
# **The Management 'Walk and Talk'**

DuPont (and many other companies now) call this 'Visible Felt Leadership'. It's the most obvious proactive and structured way of applying the principles discussed above to the workforce. Not everyone is convinced, however. I once worked with the board of a worldwide company whose director of safety told me they had read Geller and warned me in advance that he "Didn't want a walk and talk" because:

"I agree with Geller that safety needs to be part of the very DNA of the company and if that's so, then we don't need a dedicated walk and talk – it'll flow naturally".

I showed him the 'Spot the gorilla' DVD (as explained in Chapter 3), and challenged him that while what he had said was true to an extent, it was irrelevant, as safety wasn't even close to being fully embedded in the DNA of the company; - How was he going to get it there?

With reference to Dekker's *Drift into Failure* and DuPont's most important core value (that if we are not actively pushing forward then we are most certainly drifting backwards) how was he going to *keep it there,* if he achieved it?

In other words, I argued that the fact that he'd convinced himself he didn't need a 'walk and talk' was a false economy. I thought it was a compelling argument but *he* didn't! He showed me the door and went for a 'if everybody just paid more attention' face valid approach instead. It didn't work and, as it happened, his number two (who was also in the meeting, observing quietly) contacted me several years later …

In a similar vein, I had a conversation with safety expert Professor Peter McKie, where he clarified an anecdote I'd heard about him. He confirmed that he had indeed told John Harvey-Jones and the rest of the CBI (Confederation of British Industry) board back in the 1970s that a manager who genuinely valued safety on a par with productivity would spend an hour a day walking the site looking at safely issues only.

Peter's challenge on the day to this group of individuals – who, at that time, were some distance from fully understanding safety culture, was to ask them to consider what they actually did on any given day. What they actually focused and checked on - this *last* week for example. (Here's a psychologist's tip – never ask about *typical* if you can avoid it. Asking about last week, or yesterday, you'll nearly always get 'well X – but I must stress that that's not typical' and it's nearly always 'not typical' in favour of the socially acceptable!)

Then, he indeed asked them to contrast these answers with their boast that that they "Gave safety and productivity equal weight". The challenge was how could that statement possibly hold up in the light of what they actually did? Of course, several had conceded that they could go weeks without thinking of safety and health *at all*.

As you can imagine, in many respects DuPont (for whom Peter worked) were in many respects the trailblazer for the 'walk and talk' approach and its STOP™ programme is near ubiquitous in some industries. What it thinks a line manager should look out for when undertaking such a site visit was effectively detailed in Chapter 1 in the section on the '10 core values'.

# Why 'Walk and Talks' Are So Important

Obviously, when we undertake a walk and talk we get the chance to learn directly from the horse's mouth. Again, NASA gives us a good example**.** At the inquiry into the Columbia disaster, the chairwoman of the mission management team was asked what she did about dissenting opinions and she replied that when they heard about them, she took them on board etc, etc, and so on. Then she was asked: "But sometimes of course there are problems out there and you *don't* get to hear about them. What do you do to go out and *find them*?"...

(A now infamous) silence …

Indeed, a good walk and talk fits squarely in the toolkit of *any* leader under any circumstances. The classic work of Komaki demonstrates how leaders that use a range of monitoring techniques to review performance are more effective. She highlights four approaches. Work sample (observation of behaviour and performance), product sample (review of output, materials, workplace), self report (ask and listen to performer) and secondary source (ask other people around, colleagues, customers, visitors – sometimes known as 360 degree feedback). This evidence, she says, must then be used by to deliver appropriate and timely consequences. (Komaki, 1998)

The basic safety 'walk and talk' model of contradicts nothing recommended in Komaki's classic book. (It's important to talk to workers of course as well as watch them in case the observed behaviour is 'best foot forward' when someone with a clipboard is around).

When conducting these dedicated talks we also get the chance to actively coach, praise and lead by example. That much is obvious, but there's something almost as important that, again, lies squarely in the unspoken, subconscious grey area that this book has sought to address. It's because, as previously discussed, in relation to Rosa Parks, it turns strangers into casual acquaintances, and the culture between acquaintances is much stronger than that between strangers.

A warning, however: Every single communication no matter how 'unimportant' and brief impacts on the safety culture. Turning a stranger into an acquaintance is usually a very good thing. *Confirming* that safety isn't important is probably worse than the previous silent assumption that this is so!

After a quick overview of the walk and talk approach I'd like to summarise two well-known approaches as a SWOT analysis. First, a classic nine step model that has been used (often successfully) by many companies, and then my own five-step model.  The reader can choose which one they like the sound of best, or can invent an amalgam third model, of course! The comments as I work through are intended to work as a 'taking all this out on site and using it in practice' - focused summary of the whole book.

Then, as a summary to this section, I'd like to walk through the four main problems we see when we are asked to undertake a SWOT analysis of an existing walk-and-talk approach.

## A Step-by-Step SWOT Analysis of a Basic 9-Step SUSA™

SUSA™ stands for *Safe And Unsafe Acts* and is an approach championed by the consultant John Ormond, formally of ICI. His nine step model is summarised in the Outtakes film *Safety Watch*, which also featured a young Welsh psychologist popping up now and again to say: "I really can't stress how important this analysis section is!" and, frankly, rather spoiling the flow of the whole piece. As well as the DVD I've seen John and his colleagues and ex colleagues present on this material several times, and the following notes are based on that. I've also undertaken a lot of SWOT analysis of previous behavioural and culture-change programmes that have been based on STOP™, SUSA™ or an in-house version of them.

I must stress that I've chosen this approach to SWOT because of its success and, in particular, its *thoroughness*. Genuinely making this approach more user-friendly and efficacious would definitely be a good thing!

The nine step model:

1. Stop and observe people.
2. Put the people you're talking to at their ease.
3. Explain what you're doing and why.
4. Ask about the job – what are you doing and what are the stages?
5. Praise an aspect of safe behaviour.
6. Ask "What's the worst that could happen and how?"
7. Question "Why?" to any unsafe behaviour.
8. Ask what corrective action is required.
9. Achieve a commitment to act.

This is clearly a very thorough approach. Indeed, the first thing I'd like to argue is that although there's a lot of really good material in there, it's rather *too* thorough. I'd also argue that it can prove a bit too top-down from a Just Culture or union 'don't blame the worker' viewpoint in *practice,* at least, if the user isn't careful. I'll try to justify the above by addressing the logic and practicality of each point as we walk through.

## 1. Stop and Observe People

This element stresses that observation must be active and will require concentration, hard work and effort, and some dedicated time. The analogy is with 'active listening', which, done properly, is rather hard work. Again, the famous 'spot the gorilla' ice-breaking exercise also applies. Managers observing their own work area as part of a training course often comment: "I've never seen that before" concerning something they've walked past for weeks, months or. . .

## 2. Put People at their Ease

Introduce yourself and explain who you are, what you're doing and why so that you come across as friendly, concerned and constructive. You should establish that you're there because you care.

This is my first area of concern. The list above can't be faulted at face value but this is the first hint of '*paternal* parent' in assertion terminology. Done badly, I feel this could come across as a little ominous (OK, this is for my own good but there's a 'but' coming up here), or even a little patronising. "I want you to know I'm here for you" is fine in a Hollywood film if you have lots of takes to play with, but it's a difficult line to deliver cold on a North Sea oil rig.

I've previously suggested putting people at ease by talking to them as an adult – quite possibly about sport.

## 3. Explain What You are Doing and Why

This step is self explanatory but there is a point I'd like to make that I think very important and this is as good a place to make it as any.

It's said that the average person can only handle seven cognitive items at any one time – plus or minus two (For many of us, the spread of 'plus or minus 2' means five or six and I much prefer a triptych of 3 if possible please!) For example you might note that no element of a telephone number is ever longer than 6 digits.

Following from this it can be argued that no list of this sort should ever be longer than seven and this third element is for me the first one that needs amalgamating. After all, is it not merely the non-controversial element of item two?

## 4. Ask about The Job – What are You Doing and What are The Stages?

Here, it's stressed that questions should be open-ended rather than closed. We want the individual to talk in depth and openly, not retreat behind closed answers. For example: "Are there any safety aspects of this task that concern you?" is likely to get a "No" from someone wary, or under time pressure. It's suggested that "What are the safety implications of doing this task?" is a better question. It certainly is! It's also an excellent way of breaking the ice and starting on some analysis.

## 5. Praise Aspects of Safe Behaviour

Again, absolutely! However, this is another area where the question "How skilfully?" is raised. For example, in the *Safety Watch* DVD John Ormond himself stresses the importance of not being phoney and/or stiff and formal, but then gives the example: "I noticed you were lifting safely there, it won't be you going home tonight with a bad back". Someone as passionate and charming as John himself will get this right but it is, I'd argue, uncomfortably close to the "Way to go Joe!" US approach that so often goes down so badly outside of America.

Many 'hairy-backed' supervisors around the world will struggle to use this technique and, because they feel uncomfortable, will avoid it entirely. Or, they will try their best but get it wrong.

I'd suggest the process incorporates some praising techniques that are best suited to the local culture and, importantly, that this *follows* analysis and comes towards the end of the session, so that rapport is more likely to have been built.

## 6. Ask "What's the Worst that Could Happen and How?"

As John himself says, "This is a really interesting bit". This is dynamic risk assessment in action, of course, and also looks to encourage discovered learning: the very best form of learning as thinking of something and articulating it is an *active* process.

In the DVD John gives an example of discussing carrying a container, as the observer was concerned that any cracks could lead to a leak of the corrosive material in it - or that dropping it would fracture the container and cause corrosive splashing. This was intended as a lead in to a discussion of the need for suitable PPE and the option of using carrying devices. Except that the answer was that: "If I drop it, it may well *explode*". And a discussion that was apparently about PPE and manual handling became a process safety discussion.

## 7. Question "Why?" to Any Unsafe Behaviour

Clearly, as a passionate believer in the Just Culture perspective, I'd consider this element utterly vital and non-controversial. (Except that it shouldn't be just **one** thing in a list of **nine** of course!)

## 8. Ask "What Corrective Action is Required?"

Again, coaching and discovered learning skills are central to this element. Getting the individual to articulate what needs to be done is active for them. There is a loop back here to analysis, and the DVD stresses that the observer might get an answer they weren't expecting. In particular, that they might well get a better answer than they themselves could have come up with. Again, I'm wary that the underlying tone is one of paternal expert pleasantly surprised by a worker's thought and knowledge, and again, I'm more comfortable working from the assumption they are thoughtful and knowledgeable unless they prove conclusively otherwise. And they certainly know more about the day-to-day realities of the job than we ever will.

Specifically, it is suggested in the DVD that "a training need might be identified". This doffs a cap at 'no blame' but is the nub of my concern about the approach. A training need is a *person*-focused response. Coming at this from a Just Culture perspective the most obvious output from a discussion is: "I need you to sort this out for me, please".

This is a minefield of nuance. At a glance, a person-centred approach here will sound sensible and plausible to many companies and managers, but **not** if you are genuinely coming to a discussion with Dekker's 'new view' squarely in mind.

**9. Finally, Achieve A Commitment To Act …**

This very explicitly means from the person **being observed**. Because, after all, that is clearly the obvious close-out to a conversation of this type, Isn't it? That's what we were building to all along, and this is really the clinching piece of evidence here. From a paternal perspective, this makes total sense. People are acting unsafely and they need to commit to stopping that but this is squarely in 'We need to talk about your behaviour' territory. This will sometimes be appropriate, of course, but under the Just Culture section we stressed that 90 per cent of the causes of unsafe behaviour are *environmental*. Therefore, wouldn't simple logic dictate that 90 per cent of these close-out commitments to act come from the **observer**?

**9-Step Model - Conclusion**

SUSA™ style methodologies continue to be used successfully by a variety of organisations all over the world. John and the other users will I imagine stress that of course the training given to support the approach addresses the points I've made. With reference to the classic model of assertion I'd argue that that's 'top bubble' but done with the best of intentions and a good heart. I'd stress 'middle bubble' *always*.

Remember that the vast majority of these audits are undertaken months after the training course by front-line supervisors, and the more opportunity there is for the wrong tone to be struck, or the wrong emphasis given, the more often it will happen. In the heat of battle, people will nearly always boil it down to a triptych and focus on the elements they're most comfortable with. If this is occurring in an organisation that is pathologically compliance-focused and with limited soft-skills training then that's asking for trouble. Consequently, because I think this model is too complicated and too person-focused I'd argue it gives too much scope for an authoritarian, or patronising, approach to come across and cause a real issue. I'd like to suggest instead a five stage model, as detailed in my earlier book *Talking Safety*.

# Recommended 'Walk and Talk' 5-Stage Model

It's worth going back to basics and recalling why we have been given this valuable organisational time to undertake a walk and talk at all. It is never to try to catch someone out, it is:

> to learn something about the way the organisation actually works through the eyes of the people who work there. In particular to understand the unspoken, by vital *nuances*;

> to **model** the behaviours and mindset on which we want the organisation to be

built on; and

(specifically) to coach, empower, facilitate and even inspire your colleagues;

finally, very occasionally…

to insist on an improvement in existing standards of behaviour and/or approach.

In short, that's basically learn, coach, learn, coach, inspire and (sometimes) seek a commitment to act differently.

Of course, there are several variations on the walk and talk as well as the standard 'at least a half an hour a week walking the site'. There might be a particular issue that needs 'drilling into' which may or may not involve observing a task for a while. There might be something untoward seen or raised that needs discussing. It might be a one off site visit by a high level group.

Depending on the circumstances different elements should be given different emphasis as appropriate. Regardless, the basic approach of treating people like adults, seeking to learn, seeking to coach and only then (if appropriate) seeking a commitment to act should be followed.

## 1. Introduce Yourself and Set the Tone

You're interested in them and their work and not trying to impress them with your knowledge so you'll ask questions and listen to the answers. You'll ask about their home life, the task they are undertaking, and about process as well as personal safety issues. You should try to draw them out with the 'what if?' question which shows curiosity, commitment and 'mindfulness'; it is not an attempt to catch them out.

You simply talk to them on the assumption that they are intelligent, committed and knowledgeable - until they prove conclusively otherwise!

## 2. Analysis

If you have seen anything worrying you ask why – but you ask it *curiously*, knowing that, 90 per cent of the time, you'll get something interesting back that is about the organisation and environment, not about the individual.

You can proactively start this discussion, even if you've seen nothing, by asking: "Anything slow, uncomfortable or inconvenient about doing this job safely?" They will nearly always have something to say here and, if they trust you, then they'll tell you (so a good rapport is important). The conversation never has to move from the hypothetical and anonymous, so is just as useful with peripatetic workers. The *learning*, however, isn't hypothetical.

## 3. Coaching

You're already fully in coaching mode and modelling the mindset required. If there is some specific learning you want to actively impart, however, you simply need to use the questioning technique of drawing the answer from the person in their own words to maximise discovered learning. More often, you'll just want to be using coaching techniques to lead them through a chain of thought. Following the three golden rules, as illustrated by the feedback fish described in the section on coaching earlier in this chapter, means you can't go far wrong:

> You ask questions (The 'rate yourself 1 to 10', perhaps);
> They say it first (thus proving they knew it & therefore maximising ownership of it);
> You maximise the praise opportunities that flow from this.

## 4. Promises

If you've done the first three properly, then any promises required will be likely to have been made *internally* already. This is vital, as it means they are far more likely to be kept when you're not around. There are times, however, when we need a promise to be made genuinely. In which case, they need to look you in the eye and use the 'I' word.

## 5. Close Out and Follow Up

Thank them sincerely for their time and insight. Turn anything that needs doing into a SMART goal and then follow up and close out – or if it was delegated follow it up to ensure it was closed out. As well as whatever specific benefits this brings it also shows our genuine commitment.

# Practical Problems with any 'Walk and Talk'

Clearly, I feel that the analysis-focused 5 point plan helps design problems out at source so, as well as acting as a summary to this section, this overview is put forward as evidence to support the views above! There are five main *practical* problems with a walk and talk. The main symbolic one, as I've outlined above, is that it can set the wrong tone - one aligned with 'über-compliance', not with learning and coaching.

## 1. A Lack of Planning

As the old saying goes, "*if you fail to plan, you plan to fail*" and that's true of nearly all situations. So, what planning is required for a walk and talk? First, we should check any 'walk and talk' data base, or review previous safety contacts and consider:

who went on site last and what did they target?
what did they find?
what actions resulted?
And of course follow up on any actions. How are things progressing?

Also

a basic consideration of which jobs are being undertaken and when …

This will help ensure you don't turn up looking to target the same things as the last person. So, for example, you might note that no one has targeted working at height for a while so you could focus on that.

You could find yourself waiting forever for it to be totally convenient to undertake a safety contact audit, so don't be too timid. However, please do show some discretion. If it's obvious the people you need to talk to are *absolutely* flat out, or if interrupting them could actually be dangerous, then give them some space and look at something else for a while. While you must, of course, make it clear you're not going to be totally fobbed off and leave, please *do* empathise and put yourself in their shoes. Simply ask yourself what would be reasonable if they were making a suitable effort.

## 2. A Lack of Depth

The techniques mentioned briefly here are covered in detail in the chapter on root cause analysis and much of the rest of the book. This summary overview is designed for those readers who have (quite reasonably, in many respects!) skipped straight to the most practical section …

One of the biggest problems we see with systems like safety contact is that analysis lacks depth. We often get asked: "How is it that things aren't getting any better, despite the fact that we've put right 1001 things highlighted over the past year?" The answer is that, often, auditors will list any number of problems but simply generate what's known as a 'crap list' of items that will recur.

James Reason uses a mosquito analogy. He suggests that if you have a problem with mosquitoes then a short-term solution is to buy nets, repellent and swatters … **but** a better solution is to find the swamp they come from and *drain it at source*.

One of the specific causes of these 'crap lists' is that people are often wary of approaching someone they don't know and this is especially so if they're uncertain of the technicalities of the job. So, they avoid talking to them at all and just pick on something visible and easy, like housekeeping, then pop an action point down around that. (You'll recall that, to an extent, the VIP visit to the Macondo well the day before the explosion was accused of this). A hazard may well be removed as a consequence, and that's always a good thing, but it's not necessarily the best use of time. The questions suggested above should generate a suitably in-depth discussion every time.

Typically, as well as noticing the immediate risk, once you've used your 'five whys' analysis as above you may well find yourself considering things like:-

- risk assessments
- barriers
- signage
- supervision
- suitability of PPE
- training
- inductions
- selection and monitoring of contractors
- behaviours that are typical and not remarked on

Working through any of these issues *systematically* and analytically and formulating an action plan is a long way from a basic hazard spot but doing this systematically will nearly always require an in-depth conversation with the person doing the job.

## 3. Too Narrow A Focus – Don't Forget the Elephants!

Best practice from one field should always be proactively applied to others, so an excellent walk-and-talk set up to look for personal safety issues should also look for the two thumping great elephants in the room: process safety and health. Andrew Hopkins says this well:

"The behavioural approach is just as applicable to process safety as it is to personnel safety, and auditing and monitoring activities should cover both. One of the criticisms that has been levelled at behavioural safety generally is that it ignores process safety. It is vital that behavioural safety programmes face this challenge!"

Absolutely! And when we consider the numbers, everything that applies to process safety applies 100 fold to health issues. On 'walk and talks' we should, of course, talk about obvious risks, such as falling down the stairs, but we should also talk about unlikely but catastrophic containment risks and delayed but personally catastrophic risks relating to long-term health.

We must be led by the data, not by the easily visible, or our areas of expertise or comfort.

## 4. Poor Feedback and Close-Out

This little section could be included anywhere in this book but is probably most applicable following a one-to-one walk and talk, where something useful has been raised.

We know that capital projects can be frustrating and time consuming to set up, and that we can all get so focused on the day-to-day realities that we're tempted to put the long-term issues on the back burner. The psychology of giving in to that temptation and to fudge and bluster was explained in the section on ABC analysis. Basically, in the short-term, it's a relief.

It might be that a problem with a root cause or contractor seems too big to tackle at a site level, and that a local SMART resolution isn't really possible. In this case, you may well need to make formal contact with more senior management to articulate your concerns and observations. For those of you who **are** senior managers please ensure you follow the same principles if someone comes to you with a concern – especially if you delegate the issue to someone else. It really won't be very encouraging for the auditor if your response to a follow-up call is: "I asked Bob to look at it weeks ago … but I've heard nothing back yet". We all know they'll assume the worst, and trust will decrease and cynicism will increase and, in this way, the culture is undermined.

It's vital that we don't file it in the back of the cabinet but actually stick to the SMART timetable, then return to the person involved and update them on progress. (Or send them a message – or ask someone to talk to them). Of course, if you do ask someone to talk to them don't cross it off the to-do list until you double-check that they actually did!

## 5. Quantity Not Quality

A final problem is where people feel they have to spend a certain amount of time doing a safety contact. But it is *quality* we are after, not just going through the motions, so the good news is, when it's finished, ***it's finished*** and there's no need to drag it out. If that's quicker than expected, that's fine - everyone will be happy.

Alternatively, in order to hit a quota safety contacts will be knocked off, or even made up towards the end of the month. The figure just below is an amalgam of several clients' data, which were all remarkably similar. You can see clearly that the number of walk and talks increased just before the quota deadline. It's an assumption that many of these 'late' observations were rushed and/or made up, but the qualitative research that we undertook suggested that was exactly the case. More than that, the accident rate had flat-lined and I'd argue strongly that the numbers had become an end in

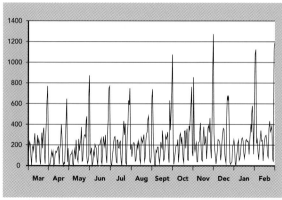

**Figure 24. Daily Observations graph revisted**

themselves.

What we need to do here is to cross-reference quantity with **quality**. We know exactly what we want from these conversations: analysis, challenging, coaching, praise, leading by example and empowerment behaviours. We don't want blame, blind-eye syndrome, preaching, criticising, hypocrisy and learned helplessness. It's easy to write some tailored appraisal items that address this, but, as ever, things are best seen from at least two angles, and I'd strongly recommend some 360-degree feedback items that can be applied to the workforce, tailored and adjusted to discriminate, depending on the current state of the culture. For example:

How often does your supervisor lead by example? (for a currently **weak** culture):

    5 Nearly always
    4
    3 Usually
    2
    1 Sometimes

Or

How often does your supervisor lead by example? (for a **strong** culture):

    5 Always
    4
    3 Nearly always
    2
    1 Usually

Note that a rating of 'nearly always' in a *weak* culture will almost certainly reflect a high level of *individual* effort and integrity. Conversely, a rating of 'usually' in a *strong* culture would nearly always indicate an individual who has yet to 'get with the programme'.

This, for me, is the very core of any culture improvement programme. We've identified a need to improve, and senior management have bought in. We've rolled out good-quality training to all supervisors, which included some photos of Gordon Brown at which we all laughed and everyone left the room promising never to fail to lead by example. How systematically and thoroughly we follow this up, praising individuals when we find people behaving as promised, and coaching (and sometimes punishing) those that aren't will represent 80 per cent of the efficacy of our process in the medium to long-term.

## Walk and Talk - Conclusion

Setting up work-force behavioural analysis teams is my favourite approach to cultural improvement. They are at the very core of analysis and empowerment and are great for public relations, too, as they look fantastic in front of visiting insurance companies and clients.

But even they are not as important as this basic follow-up work, though.

Done well, a good walk and talk will deliver savings through:

less time and effort spent enforcing rules and regulations that are impractical or contradictory;

a reduction in 'crap lists' that although they are diligently circulated and rectified simply recur, time after time;

less admonishment of employees who are honestly trying their best, (and who subsequently very much resent being 'unfairly told off').

The way a supervisor talks to an employee about safety is I argue the very epicentre of safety culture. Once a compliance-based approach has reached the law of diminishing returns it's all about learning and coaching, not just challenging. Setting up a robust user-friendly approach that minimises the likelihood of drift back to the historical comfort zone of a simple person focus is utterly vital. My previous book *Talking Safety* had the bullish strap line "If you do just one thing, do this and do it this way". Please shout if you think that's *bullish* in more ways than one. I'd be an appalling hypocrite if I weren't very open to learning!

# Chapter 10.
# Applying these Principles via a Robust Methodological Framework

I have tried to describe the theory behind a world class safety culture and why an organisation would want one. I've also sought to describe the sort of day-to-day behaviours and cognitions that comprise it and why they might or might *not* occur and I used an overview of the 'walk and talk' as a summary of how that might be typically used as a day to day methodology. This final section is intended to offer readers a simple framework that can be used in practice to apply the principles within an organisation. I'll try and apply the 80:20 or Pareto principle whenever possible and avoid a detailed description of the pros and cons of variations on a theme.

## Some (Final) Case Studies

This section will broadly follow the classic 'plan, do, review, enhance' model, which is, of course, perfectly adequate for pretty much *any* endeavour. (Again, if it's done *correctly*) …

### The 2012 Olympic Build

Few people are unaware that the Olympic build for the 2012 London Games was a great success: Excellent buildings, delivered on time by an enthusiastic and motivated workforce. Accident rates were very low and especially so for the industry, and it was the first Olympic build in history during which no one was killed. (In contrast it's known that at least 8 workers were killed building the 'Bird's Nest' Beijing Stadium alone and as I write this there's worldwide disgust at the obscene mortality figures being quoted for the Qatar World Cup build). The Health and Safety Laboratory reported that the scores for its Safety Climate Tool were, across all companies involved in the build, the highest they'd recorded for *any* companies, which, they admitted, "Wasn't what you'd expect from a construction project".

Team GB won dozens of medals across all disciplines, Danny Boyle's opening ceremony was utterly spellbinding, and London was a friendly and efficient place when I went with my children (as we got tickets to watch Brazil in the football as well as the 1,500 metres! and all was well with the world. (Well, at least: '… just for one day' as the classic David Bowie song they used as one of the anthems for the games has it).

The initiative to make porridge available to workers to help with energy levels first thing in the morning is, perhaps, the practical example most often quoted but what is the secret of such excellent safety performance?

I'd argue that there isn't one. Building on the desire to put best foot forward and show the world what the UK could do, Lawrence Waterman and his safety team just *did it right*. They had strong leadership based on a clearly communicated vision combined with high levels of workforce involvement and engagement based on Just Culture principles. I must have listened to a dozen presentations from various members of the team about what they did, and there was honestly nothing new to note and 'borrow' as a consultant. Everybody involved had been on lots of projects before. They didn't necessarily learn anything new, (we all already knew that porridge is good for energy!), they just applied it better. Lawrence simply knew exactly what was required and he and his team delivered that. We all just need to follow the template!

## A Transport Company

To again illustrate the point of just doing it right I'd like to quote the UK bus company National Express. In a case study published in *HSW* magazine in September 2013, it reported an 80 per cent fall in lost time injuries and a lost time injury free month for the first time in its history. Again it's a case study in 'doing it right'. They had strong leadership from the very top, they engaged front-line staff and managers and provided them with excellent leadership training (written and delivered in house), which formed the basis of a Visible Felt Leadership process that was rolled out nationwide. They also rejigged the incident-reporting system, so that it was much more user-friendly and the MD showed his commitment by obtaining a NEBOSH certificate. Previously some 1,600 vehicles generated just 50 'near miss' reports a year but as communication improved and became easier, drivers started reporting issues such as poor parking at stops, or poorly located stops, that meant passengers had to alight in the road, not at the stop, and management acted on these observations and insights.

This is a company hugely more risk literate top to bottom than it was three years ago, and one with only a fifth as many injuries. And all achieved in-house. (I have presented to senior people from this company at transport conferences several times over the years, so am hopeful I might qualify for a small 'nudge' credit!).

I wonder just how utterly vital the 'MD himself did a NEBOSH' element of the above case study is. It certainly suggests genuine high level commitment from the most important employee of all. I've no idea what triggered this but the impact of this commitment is, I'd argue, clearly similar to the previously mentioned situation where a CEO returns from an employee's funeral wholly committed. Another way of reading this book is as a description of what goes wrong when the senior management are really *quite* committed but not *wholly* committed.

This is not a book on project management, or on the mechanics of SMART goals, or presentation skills training. Consequently, I've only stopped to address issues where I feel I have something *specifically* useful to say, based on experience – perhaps an example of best practice that feels worth passing on. Basic senior management commitment is more important than detail. However,  knowing what to look for to assess this commitment and knowing how to communicate a genuine commitment remains worthwhile.

# Planning

### Having a Vision

Clearly, the first thing we need to do is to assure ourselves that the senior management especially the CEO and the CFO are fully and genuinely committed to the vision because they genuinely value it. It doesn't much matter what combination of moral or business drivers achieve this - just so long as they really want it. Benchmarking against other companies may be helpful but it's vital that the senior management have a very clear idea of what success will look like and how they'll know that it's been achieved.

We need to make sure that plans to validate this simple vision are airtight, though – collecting qualitative data that ensures the quantitative data is accurate. (For example, a halving of the accident rate ***and*** a doubling of 360 degree feedback scores re the use of praise, coaching and analysis techniques that confirm that apparent improvement is genuine and not just 'the numbers wanted').

Obviously, the vision should be communicated as clearly, concisely, passionately and innovatively as possible, directly to all employees from the MD from a soap box in the canteen for example. Many organisations I've worked with have captured the CEO on a DVD made specially.

### Communicating That Vision

Next, we'll want to make sure that everyone who is going to be affected by this push has this explained clearly to them, in a forum where they can comment and contribute. For example, as above, we're going to need some new appraisal items for managers that measure the *quality* of safety communications, not just the quantity, so we need to work with HR on a plan for including them, following them up and embedding them.

## Aligning With Existing Process

Inevitably, there are already a lot of people doing a lot of good work in the organisation which overlaps with what we are proposing. Employees responsible for driver safety and health may well have thriving processes or, at the very least plans and campaigns into which considerable effort has been invested. The incident investigation procedures and near-miss reporting process will also need aligning, if only in terms of the language used. There may also be in-house trainers with excellent presentation skills, or assertion-skills modules already tailored to suit the organisation.

Whatever we find, we need to align with them in as 'joined-up' a way as we can, to ensure that previous work isn't seen as wasted but as a valuable foundation that can be built on, incorporated or even *stolen* with pride. (Indeed, embracing the concept of 'stealing with pride' as advocated strongly by the Milliken organisation introduced in Chapter 1, for example, is a useful approach to embrace in itself, especially if 'not invented here' syndrome is rife!)

## Design

Perhaps the best way of ensuring a strong safety performance is, as detailed in an earlier chapter, to design tasks with high levels of end-user participation in the first place! As already stated, it's very much easier to do this at the planning stage than to have to retro-fit at a later date. I know that although it's an important point, it's from the school of the bloody obvious - but it still begs the question why so many organisations get this badly wrong?

## Communicating The Vision – To Brand Or Not?

One decision to be taken at the design level is whether or not to **brand** the culture-change process.

I once presented a paper at a conference in Barcelona and was approached by a large multinational company that already had a brand for their big safety push - they just didn't yet have a methodology. "We think you might be of some use", they suggested and explained that the whole company knew that this programme called 'Heartbeat' was coming but that, as yet, the heartbeat team hadn't decided what the methodologies would actually be.

To date they'd used some 'vision' consultants, who had suggested all sorts of innovative ways of communicating said vision with colourful and 'sticky' ways of painting pictures of what the company will be like in five years. They even circulated a 'letter' (dated five years hence) that detailed the success achieved and articulating praise for all the hard work undertaken.

As it was a multinational organisation with numerous languages spoken it was heavily based on a 'train the trainer' approach, where teams were set up in each country (or region) to cascade the training and to follow up the SMART goals. All of which was done under the in-house brand, which they feel was a key step in the process.

The positives are obvious and the one downside I would warn against is the brand being too closely associated with the safety department. As ever, line ownership is everything so make sure the local champions are not simply the local safety department. An organisation will automatically turn to them first for train-the-trainer volunteers but it's absolutely vital that some line management be involved in the team, too.

A second problem is that the volunteers *we* want are wanted by everyone. The ones that line management might want to push forward (as they are considered expendable) would not be our first choices. Again, there's a direct link here to senior management's genuine desire to do it and do it *well*. If they do want safety improvement as much as they want productivity, then *good* people will be freed up.

## Politics and Co-Ordination

We're going to change the culture of the whole organisation? Obviously, we'll need a suitably detailed SMART plan (or plans) and someone senior enough to make sure we stick to it/ them. In a small organisation, a champion will do. In a large organisation, probably a steering team will be required. In a huge organisation, a steering team per country and/or per division. Again, we'll need a clear definition in advance of what success looks like.

Ideally, we'll be politically adept here and target key individuals who can help us. Genuine volunteers are best but induce them on-board, if necessary! If there's someone who is always going to be a blockage no matter how much coaching and positive labelling we give them, then we need to move them out of the way, if at all possible.

# Implementation

I'd like to suggest a basic framework and then describe the key methodological steps in a little more detail – describing some specific best practice that I've seen over the years.

(As above) Communicating the vision to all employees and contractors

(As above) Communicating the action plan to all required

Considering the feedback that generates (as above) and refining the original plan if appropriate.

Train all management and (any) safety representatives

Following that training up to ensure all behaviours requested occur more frequently/ undesirable behaviours less frequently.

Set up workforce empowerment teams

- As limited time duration *projects*

- (Possibly) as on-going *processes*

Up-skill the *entire* workforce to include anyone who has not yet been involved in risk literacy either through a full involvement process. (For example, a walk-and-talk process that everyone is required to do) or through cascaded workshops.

All we need to do then is follow all of these up to ensure that outputs are as desired, praising all individual input, and maximising any PR opportunities that flow from their success.

### Checklists and 'Golden Rules'

After a while, the risks associated with a task become so well understood that a set of rules can be generated as 'golden', but most workforces instinctively hate golden rules. For example, there was huge resistance in the medical profession when it was suggested that a checklist be introduced to help avoid leaving instruments inside a patient after an operation. How patronising to a person of such training and experience that they drop the 'Dr' and go back to being 'Mr' or 'Ms' again, so that people in the medical professions who understand these things know just how senior they are! After all, they argued, the medical profession has been getting on without simple checklists for hundreds of years. (See *The Checklist Manifesto* by Atul Gawande which argues that modern life is so complex, error of one sort or another is almost inevitable).

Except, these checklists work well, and there has been a significant percentage reduction in iatrogenesis complications. It was indeed, hundreds of years in, an excellent simplistic innovation that directly addressed human error.

Incidentally, it's not as if the profession wasn't aware that innovation can be good. For example, the single biggest advance in medicine came when Lister suggested that doctors always wash their hands before going near a patient - especially if they were going to operate on them. Hundreds of millions of lives have since been saved by this simple innovation that wasn't possible until we knew about microscopic germs.

My experience is that a set of golden rules can be particularly useful in two ways: first, when we want to roll out internationally and want to detail what's *non-negotiable* and what can be tailored locally; secondly, when trying to balance local autonomy with common practice. For example, I've seen the military use 'holding the handrail' as a golden rule even in the *active* theatre. The rationale is: "There are thousands of men out there actively trying to kill you. Having you out there in the field being shot at is one thing. I have *planned* for that! It's my job. But I don't want you laid up with a broken leg and no bloody use to me because you fell down the stairs of the canteen after a beer too many!"

## Safety Leadership Training

With a walk-and-talk, a specific outcome has been covered in great depth above. Just to reiterate:

In nearly all organisations safety leadership training is utterly essential;

Don't forget that the soft (or non-technical) skills are just as important (if not more so) as the technical skills;

But it won't deliver much benefit in the medium to long-term if the behaviours requested are not followed up and embedded.

## Behavioural Root Cause Analysis (BRCA) *Project* Teams

Being on the end of an excellent walk and talk is all well and good but it's passive. We need to come at the culture problem from two angles and we need an approach that fits into the 'bottom up too' camp. Even when applying the 80:20 principle at the very least we need to set up a **BRCA project team,** or teams.

This methodology is simply to elicit some volunteers from the shop floor to be given a couple of days training in the basics of behavioural root-cause analysis. They should leave the course with a good, robust working knowledge of:

The Safety Hierarchy;
Heinrich's principle;
An Impact Matrix;
ABC analysis;
'Five whys' analysis; and
Just Culture and the basic causes of Human Error

In other words they need a working understanding of the appropriate elements of 'risk literacy'. Some organisations also cover creative problem-solving, or 'brainstorming' and problem-solving in teams which is often very helpful. However, all we really need is a mechanism for the team to be able to clearly articulate *what they already know*.

Once trained, their job is to select a handful of key items they know to be sub-optimal in reality and to give them the time to analyse and report back. Anything in the 'high impact / low cost' box should be addressed immediately and all public relations opportunities that flow from that maximised. Anything 'high impact: high cost' and often it's 'welcome to the world of management'! Although, if this is the case, then feedback must be given so that those involved know what's happening or why it isn't. (Sometimes, of course, management will know that X can't realistically happen now because there's a good chance that Y won't be there at all in a few years, and that possibility can't be communicated until a final decision is made.)

More typically, "We simply haven't the budget for that at this time" *can* be communicated – though if it's because "First and foremost the board need their bonuses" then it might not go down very well. Every option has its strengths and weaknesses, of course, and treating people like mushrooms ("Keep them in the dark and pour crap on them from time to time") does have its advantages if you're in charge. I simply think that the downside far outweighs the upside of information control but, at this point, it does get complicated and political, if not philosophical, and I know it's very easy for me to throw a "good luck with the exact details of that!" over my shoulder as I drive off in a taxi.

Leaving the complications of more open communication to one side the good news is that these teams *always* come up with some high-impact, low-cost solutions. Absolutely always! As the walk and talk is the one thing management really should do, then participating in analysis teams is the one thing a workforce should always be given the chance to do. (It's also a reminder that a walk and talk should be *analysis*-based not compliance-based. There's so much to learn). We just need to set up as many teams as required to cover the whole organisation. That might be one, or fifty.

**Awareness-Raising Sessions for All**

The final of the three key methodologies is to take two or three of the most suitable employees from the **workforce project team** and then help them design a two-hour to half-day awareness session for *all* of their colleagues. This is simply the best way to cascade risk literacy to the whole workforce, and in accord with the findings of Scott Geller and others, who stress that a key way of developing a true safety champion is to give individuals the chance to train others in the techniques and principles.

People like me can give these presentations of course, and the credibility an expert outsider brings is useful but I do think, on balance, it's better to have some employees do it in their own words, with their own passion and with their own examples. Before a presentation, these volunteers may be very nervous. However, after they have stood up and articulated their thoughts to all their colleagues they will be impassioned in-house champions with cognitive dissonance effects kicking in, in our favour for once! (You mean it even more after you've said it in public – I believe a well-known partner pairing ceremony is based on the same principle!) Quite simple the more they own the hands on methodology the more it embeds in their DNA.

A secondary benefit of this approach is that (if appropriate) asking for volunteers at the end of these sessions will usually generate a large number, who can be trained as behavioural observers, should a behavioural-safety process be planned.

I'd advise giving these volunteer individuals a little training (i.e. a day) in presentation skills, then have someone spend a day helping the team write the session around key themes. This can be a consultant, or someone suitable in-house, but usually they'll need a coach in their corner to help them prepare. The support these teams typically then request is:

> running the first session or two *with* the coach;
> the coach watching a session and feeding back afterwards; and
> leaving them to get on with it!

# Case Study

Some years ago, I worked with a chemical company in South Wales that wanted to push on from a standard observation and feedback based behavioural approach that had only been moderately successful, and which had come to the end of its natural life. From a workforce of 500 they had only two volunteers for training for a 'new wave'. We recommended a much more bottom-up approach as above, ensured the previously sceptical unions got involved in the project teams (which went very well, as always,) and had a say in the final design of the awareness session. (We didn't feel it right, for local political reasons that they actually run them and, as it happened, everyone was happy, as they had no desire to!)

One of the presenters was a local man who was well respected for his toughness and integrity (he had part of an ear bitten off in a rugby game – did I mention this was South Wales?) We got more than 200 volunteers representing more than 40 per cent of those in the audience.

These two men were called Martyn and Peter, and every organisation has people like this working for them and who are underutilised – they just need to find them, train them and empower them, and they, too, can go from 2 to 200 volunteers. Then, if you have that many genuine shop-floor volunteers, you can certainly think about shop floor based *processes*.

# Optional Methodologies

A Behavioural-Safety *Process*?

At this point, the benefits of the '80:20 principle' are pretty much exhausted and the next step (if considered appropriate) is to commence and commit to an ongoing *process*. The company can then make an informed choice to set up a tailored behavioural process that is based on:

> peer-to-peer observations, challenge, discussion and some form of lead measurement;

> peer-to-peer observations with challenge and discussion only; and

> peer-to-peer observations with discussion only.

I've tried to make it clear above that, for me, leadership training for supervisors that leads to them behaving in a way that cues safer behaviour *is behavioural safety*. Setting up root-cause analysis teams that lead to impactful suggestions *is behavioural safety*. Training the CFO in risk literacy that leads to more mindful strategy-level decisions *is also behavioural safety*. Anything that leads to a positive change of behaviour and a smaller Heinrich's Triangle is behavioural safety!

That said, this section brings us to the type of behavioural safety that might be called 'classic' behavioural safety, as derived from the work of Deming and other quality gurus. It was their work that the USA's Tom Krause and others looked at in the 1980s and said: "I can apply this to safety" then did so very successfully. Today it can also be seen in approaches such as Six Sigma with the emphasis on measurement and workforce involvement also evident. (Deming's work and its huge international influence are covered well by Rafael Aguayo).

If lead measures are collected, then the excellent benefits of feedback charts and goal-setting sessions are possible, though the level of paperwork increases and the 'behavioural safety is too bureaucratic' criticisms can become valid. The controlling committee simply needs to ensure that the data are genuinely useful and not simply an end in themselves. An MD, walking past a chart recently updated with encouraging data, needs to mindfully ask him or herself if they are validated accurate data from a suitable-sized sample, or something knocked-up from one or two half interested survivor volunteers. As above, not only are the data important, the process of collecting them (as in "What gets measured gets done") has positive effects, too.

## An All-Encompassing Case Study

One of my very first clients was a pallet repair company and it elected to go for the 'full' approach, following a fatality at one of its factories in the south west of England.

The methodology was to ask for volunteers to set up a steering committee to select 24 items to measure, as well as a name for the approach and a logo. (The winning logo entry won a night out in town for two). We prepared robust, replicable measures as described in the section on lead measures above and put the new name and logo on all booklets and measures. We then trained some further volunteers as observers in the use of the measures, and the Steering Committee in data validation techniques.

We used random number tables to decide at what time and in which direction observers would tour the factory, and collected baseline figures for a number of categories, including: housekeeping, manual handling, PPE and the interaction of plant and machinery. We trained our committee in the techniques of facilitating not leading a goal-setting session (for example: Never, *ever* suggest a target number first … the audience will be tempted to say "OK then if you say so"!) Then we got the whole factory to assemble in the canteen and fed back the baseline figures and asked: 'What can we get to over the next few months?  and: "What are the obstacles to getting there?" With these figures and observations collected, we placed huge feedback charts in strategic locations and updated them weekly, with brightly coloured tape.

An example of how powerful this can be came straight away, when someone opined:

"We can get from 40 per cent to 90 per cent overnight on man-machine interaction if you can get a couple of extra keys cut so we don't have to override the lock outs, and if someone opens that side door before lunchtime so we don't **have to** use the fork lift truck entrance before then."

They didn't **have to** 'override' or 'nip through' anything, of course – technically, they should have crossed the site and found the keyholder and exited the long way around. But they were paid for pallets completed, so no one did, and I stressed the 'have to' deliberately to make a point about their perfectly reasonable mindset. It also illustrates the huge step up in trust required to give people keys (which was near zero when we started) and a mindset from: "I'm busy and I'll open that door when I come over later – in the meantime go the long way around!"

Several of the (12) site managers kicked back against this drastic culture change but the management commitment was rock solid, and things were explained to them in simple terms by the two men that had attended the funeral. Consequently, despite the fact that it was arguably overly ambitious and naïve of us to go for a full behavioural approach from the off, the project was very successful, and it was used as an exemplar case study in several IOSH publications. We also saw a reduction in accidents over the following three years to less than a tenth of historical levels.

The learning points from this case study are threefold. The first is what a classic version of a full behavioural safety process looks like. The second is that I was naïve back then and would, today, try hard to talk the management into a more 'build up to that' approach so that the launch was less bloody. The third, however, is perhaps the most important one in the book and one that has been said by 1001 different observers in 1001 different ways:

If you have the right levels of management commitment you can drive through any methodology you want because in the end you get exactly the levels of safety you're prepared to accept. Though huge credit must go to the two men who drove this through (Neil and Vince) you will note that this is another example of a fatality being the game changer.

My simple passion is that we can be more proactive than that, because, to get from good to world-class, necessarily means running an organisation in a way that is the very definition of win:win.

# Driving Safety, Home Safety, Health & Wellbeing

Several times in this book we've discussed how driving to work is nearly always more dangerous than being there and that there are more accidents in the home than in work. Clearly, an organisation driven by data will look to address these issues as part of a holistic package. It has been intended as a generic book as applicable to occupational health as to occupational safety. It goes without saying that we recommend defensive driving training for anyone important (that's everyone). Best practise is to support this will telemetric feedback checking for smooth ('green') driving with bonuses ands rewards for 'green champions'. Green driving saves a fortune not just on accidents and petrol but also on servicing as brakes, shock absorbers and tyres need changing far less often. (Companies such as Wincanton have claimed to have saved millions this way). In addition green driving is driving less stressed. All told then a very good idea.

In addition, many organisations give out DVD take homes to remind employees that stairs cause more accidents than anything else on the planet (even cars) and that unguarded trampolines cause more life changing injuries and misery than blast furnaces.

Please refer again to the health figures in the introduction. It really is the elephant in the room that we seem to be bizarrely fatalistic about. Proactive health screening and early intervention programmes involving employee assistance and support always prove to be an investment with a spectacular return on capital. As with 'green driving' initiatives I simply do not understand why any profit driven organisations wouldn't employ them.

Again, I'm in danger of going off on a tangent. I'll stop there!

# Conclusion

If we do not hold 'zero harm' as a cherished ideal, if we allow the knot in the rope to be pulled inch by inch, if we ask fatalistically "What can you do?", then we have little chance of performing those behaviours – especially in times of stress – that pull us back to genuine balance. And when we overstretch, then people will get hurt and get sick and we will be asking ourselves: "What could we have done?" and the answer will always be: "Well, we could have done many things". Show me someone being a little defensive following an incident and I guarantee another incident is likely to come soon.

Safety and health is incredibly simple – we just need to go and actually *do* the things described proactively not muse on them reactively with the benefit of hindsight. Often, we'll watch people announce, as the blood runs around there feet and another occupational health 'epidemic' fills the hospitals: "At least we'll learn from this and make sure it doesn't happen again". Sometimes we do, but it's hardly the best way to learn. More often, we *don't* learn because we simply don't have the right mindset at all to see what's all around us. Asbestosis followed Pneumoconiosis (Miner's Lung), Columbia followed Challenger, as Macondo (Deepwater Horizon) followed Texas City.

More positively many organisations and even entire countries buck this trend of repetition. I hope wherever you are is one of them. As Elvis so eloquently put it: "A little less conversation a little more *action*" because, as ever, rude Nike rules apply.

# References

Agnew J and Daniels, A (2010) *Safe by Accident?,* Performance Management Publications.

Aguayo, R. (1991). Dr. Deming: *The American Who Taught the Japanese about Quality*, Fireside.

Ajzen, I. (1 December 1991). *The theory of planned behavior*, Organizational Behavior and Human Decision Processes 50 (2): 179–211.

Alloy, L.B., & Abramson, L.Y. (1979). *Judgment of contingency in depressed and non-depressed students: Sadder but wiser?*, Journal of Experimental Psychology: General 108: 441–485

Alter, A (2013) *Drunk Tank Pink*, One world.

Appleby, M. *Differences of Opinion*, SHP Jan 2013

Baltimore, John Hopkins University Press.Berlinger, N. (2005). *After harm: Medical error and the ethics of forgiveness.*

Blanchard, K. (1982). *The One Minute Manager,* William Morrow and Co.

Braunig, D and Kohstall, T (2012). *Calculating the international return on prevention for companies: Costs and benefits of investments in occupational safety and health*, International Social Security Association.

Bryson, N. (2011). *Zero Harm. Worker Involvement – the missing piece*, Bryson Consulting.

Bryson, N (2103) *Full Esteem Ahead.,*SHP Feb.

Cavendish, C. (2013). *Cavendish Review: Healthcare assistants and support workers in NHS and social care*, UK Department of Health.

Cavendish, C. (2013). *I saw what needs to be fixed in the NHS*, Sunday Times, 17th November.

Cialdidni, R,B., Reno, R.R., and Kallgren, C.A. (1990). *A focus theory of normative conduct. Recycling the theory of norms to reduce littering in public places*, Journal of

Personality and Social Psychology, 58, 1015-1026.

Clarke, S. (2102) *Safety leadership: A meta-analytic review of transformational and transactional leadership styles as antecedents of safety behaviours,* Journal of Occupational and Organizational Psychology 83, no. 1

Clarke, S and Robertson, I (2005): *A meta-analytic review of the big five personality factors and accident involvement in occupational and non-occupational settings,* Journal of Occupational and Organizational Psychology.

Coates, J. (2012) *The Hour Between Dog and Wolf,* Fourth Estate

Collins, A. & Keeley, D. (2003). *Analysis of onshore dangerous occurrence and injury data leading to a loss of containment,* HSL seminar paper, May 2003

Colten HR and Altevogt BM, eds. (2006) *Sleep Disorders and Sleep Deprivation: An Unmet Public Health Problem,* Board on Health Sciences Policy. National Academies Press.

Cooper, D. (2009). *Behavioural Safety: A Framework for Success,* BSMS

Conlon, E (2013) *Do Corporate Issues Make A Difference?,* http://ethicalleadership. nd.edu/ethics-resources/write-ups/do-corporate-values-matter

Daniel, A. (2007). Other People's Habits: *How to use positive reinforcement to bring out the best in people around you,* Atlanta: Performance Management Publications

Darley, J. M. & Latané, B. (1968). *Bystander intervention in emergencies: Diffusion of responsibility,* Journal of Personality and Social Psychology 8: 377–383

Dawkins, R., (2006) *The God Delusion,* Black Swan.

Dekker, S. (2013). *Just Culture: 'Evidence', power and algorithms,* Journal of Hospital Administration. Volume 2, No 3.

Dekker S A *Just Culture after Mid-Staffordshire,* Draft paper submitted to BMJ shared with author

Dekker, S (2006). *The Field Guide to Understanding Human Error,* Ashgate

Dekker, S (2007). *Just Culture,* Ashgate

Deutschman, A (2007) *Change or Die: The Three Keys to Change at Work and in Life,* Regan (Harper Collins)

Dorell, J (2013) *Sweet Simplicity,* Health and Safety at Work. (Feb Issue).

Dorell, J (2013) *National Express: Driving Down LTIs,* Health and Safety at Work, Sept Issue.

Dunlop, L. (2013). *Beyond the safety triangle,* SHP. Oct Issue.

Festinger, L., & Carlsmith, J.M. (1959). *Cognitive consequences of forced compliance*, Journal of Abnormal and Social Psychology, 58(2), 203–210.

Festinger, L. Rieken H and Schachter S (1956). *When Prophecy Fails: A Social and Psychological Study of A Modern Group that Predicted the Destruction of the World*, by Leon Festinger, Henry Riecken, and Stanley Schachter. Harper-Torchbooks.

Flanagan, J.C. (1954) *Critical incidents*, Psychological Bulletin, Vol. 51, No. 4.

Flin, R., O'Connor, P. & Crichton, M. (2008). *Safety at the Sharp End*, (Ashgate)

Flynn, F. (2005). Identity and Emergency Intervention. *How Social Group Membership and Inclusiveness of Group Boundaries Shape helping Behaviour*, Personal and Social Psychology Bulletin.

Fointiat, V. (2004). *I know what I have to do, but… When hypocrisy leads to behavioral change*, Social Behavior and Personality, 32, 741-746.

Gawande, A (2009). *The Checklist Manifesto: How to Get Things Right*, Metropolitan Books

Geller, E.S. (2001). *The Psychology of Safety Handbook*, Lewis Publishers.

Gladwell, M *Blink*, Penguin, (2005)

Gladwell, M *The Tipping Point*, Penguin, (20??)

Glendon, A.I. Clarke S and McKenna, E (2004). *Human Safety and Risk Management*, Taylor Francis

Goldacre, B. (2008). *Bad Science*, Fourth Estate.

Goldstein, N.J., Martin, S.J., and Cialdini, R.B. (2007). *Yes! 50 secrets from the science of persuasion*, Profile books.

Haddon-Cave, C. (2009) *The Nimrod Review: an independent review into the broader issues surrounding the loss of the RAF Nimrod MR2 aircraft XV230 in Afghanistan in 2006 report*, The Stationery Office.

Haidt, J (2012) *The Righteous Mind*, Allen Lane,

Hare, R. D. (1996). *Psychopathy and Antisocial Personality Disorder: A Case of Diagnostic Confusion*, Psychiatric Times 13 (2).

Harrison, E. (2001) *The view from the dugout*, Parrs Wood Press.

Hershfield, H., Wimmer, G. E., & Knutson, B. (2009). *Neural evidence for self-continuity in temporal discounting*, Social Cognitive and Affective Neuroscience, 4(1), 85-92.

Hersey, P. and Blanchard, K. H. (1969). *Life cycle theory of leadership*, Training and Development Journal, 23 (5), 26–34.

HSE (1999). *The costs to Britain of workplace accidents and work-related ill health in 1995/96*, HSE Books.

Hopkins, A. (2008). *Failure to Learn*, CCH Australia.

Hopkins, A. (2012). *Disastrous Decisions*, CCH Australia.

Horizon, *Out of Control*, BBC, March (2012)

Hornstein, H; Fisch, E. & Holmes, M. (1968) *Models of behaviour … relevance as a comparison other on observers' helping behaviour*, Journal of Personality and Social Psychology, Vol 10(3)

Howard, R.A. (1984). *On Fates Comparable to Death*, Management Science 30 (4): 407–422

Hudson, P. Vuijk, M and Bryden, R. (2008). *Meeting Expectations: A New Model for a Just and Fair Culture*, Paper prepared for International SPE conference, Nice France. Society of Petroleum Engineers (SPE) 111977.

Hudson, P. (2010). *Integrating Organisational Culture into Incident Analyses: Extending the Bow Tie Model*, SPE 127180-PP

HSE (1997) *Major incident, minor incident ratio triangle in Successful Health & Safety Management*, HS(G)65, HSE Books.

Huff, D. (1954) *How to lie with statistics*, Norton and Co.

Johnson, R.,W., (2013). *Zuma and his men drain the magic from Nelson's fairyland*, Sunday Times, 15th December.

Jones, E.E. and Harris, V. A. (1967). *The attribution of attitudes*, Journal of Experimental Social Psychology.

Johns, G. (2010): *Presenteeism in the Workplace: A review and research agenda*, Journal of Organizational Behavior, 31, 519-542.

Kaplan R S and Norton D P (1992) *The Balanced Scorecard: measures that drive performance*, Harvard Business Review Jan – Feb pp. 71–80.

Knox, R. E., & Inkster, J. A. (1968). *Post decision dissonance at post time*, Journal of Personality and Social Psychology, 8(4), 319-323

Komaki, J., Heinzmann, A.T.; Lawson, L., (1980) *Effect of training and feedback: Component analysis of a behavioral safety program*, Journal of Applied Psychology, Vol 65(3), Jun 1980, 261-270

Komaki, J.L. (1998) *Leadership from an Operant Perspective*, (People and Organizations). Routledge.

Krause, T.R. Hindley, J.H. and Hodson, S.J (1990). *The Behaviour Based Safety Pro-*

*cess*, Van Nostrad Reinhold.

Larkin T.,J & Larkin, S. (1994) *Communicating Change*, McGraw-Hill.

Lawton, G, *So Did Nudging Work?*, New Scientist, June 2013.

Lofsted R.E. (2011) *Reclaiming health and safety for all*, (Lofsted Report). Work and Pensions.

Lieberman, D.J. (1998) *Never be Lied to Again*, St Martin's Griffin.

Lin, M-L (2012). *Behavioural safety – tales of the unexpected*, Safety and Health Practitioner, May.

Lombardo, Michael M; Eichinger, Robert W (1996). *The Career Architect Development Planner*, (1st ed.). Minneapolis: Lominger.

Mandela, N. (1994). *Long Walk to Freedom*, London. Abacus.

Marsh, T. (2013) *Talking Safety*, Gower.

Marsh, T. (2104). *In Defense of Heinrich*, SHP. Feb.

Maslow, A., H., (1943) *A Theory of Human Motivation*, Psychological Review, 50, 370-396.

McCormick IA, Walkey FH, Green DE. (1986) *Comparative perceptions of driver ability--a confirmation and expansion*, Accid Anal Prev.  Jun;18(3):205-8.

McDonald, A.J and Hansen, J.R. (2009) *Truth, Lies and O-Rings: Inside the Space Shuttle "Challenger Disaster*, University Press of Florida.

McFarlan, B. (2003) *Drop the Pink Elephant – 15 ways to say what you mean and mean what you say*, Capstone.

McGregor, D (1960) *The Human Side of Enterprise*, New York, McGrawHill.

Mehrabian, Albert (1971). *Silent Messages*, Belmont, CA: Wadsworth

Michie, S., Stralen, M.,M., and West, R (2011) *The behaviour change wheel: A new method for characterising and designing behaviour change interventions*, Implementation Science.

North Sea Offshore Injury Statistics are downloadable at http://www.hse.gov.uk/offshore/statistics.htm

Organ, D. W. (1988). *Organizational Citizenship Behavior: The good soldier syndrome*, Lexington, MA: Lexington Books.

Ornish D. (2002) *Intensive Lifestyle Changes in Management of Coronary Heart Disease*, In: Braunwald E. Harrison's Advances in Cardiology. New York: McGraw Hill.

Parfit, D. (1986) *Reasons and Persons*, Oxford University Press.

Piaget, J. (1954). *The construction of reality in the child*, New York: Basic Books.

Piattelli-Palmarini, M. (1994) *Inevitable Illusions – How Mistakes of Reason Rule Our Minds*, Wiley.

Reason, J. (1997) *Managing the Risks of Organisational Accidents*, Ashgate.

Reason, J. (2008) *The Human Contribution*, Ashgate

Reason, J. (2013) *Doctor Tell Me the Truth: Improving patient safety by doctors admitting mistakes*, BBC Radio 4.

Rosenthal, R and Rosnow, R.L. (1991) *Essentials of Behavioural Research*, 2nd Edition. McGraw-Hill

Ross, L. (1977). *The intuitive psychologist and his shortcomings: Distortions in the attribution process.*

Ross, L; Lepper, M R. and Hubbard, M (1975) *Perseverance in self-perception and social perception: Biased attributional processes in the debriefing paradigm*, Journal of Personality and Social Psychology (American Psychological Association) 32 (5): 880–892

Rousseau, D. M. (1995) *Psychological Contracts in Organizations: Understanding Written and Unwritten Agreements*, Thousand Oaks, CA: Sage.

Salas, E (2102). *So Much Training, So Little to Show for It*, Wall St Journal, 26th Oct,

Simons, D.J. & Chabris C.F. (1999) *Gorillas in our midst: sustained inattentional blindness for dynamic events*, Perception, vol 28, pages 1059-1074

Seligman, M. E. P. (1972). *Learned helplessness*, Annual Review of Medicine, 23 (1), 407-412.

Sell, A., Bryant, G., Cosmides, L.,Tooby, J., Sznycer, D., von Rueden, C., Krauss, A. & M. Gurven. (2010). *Adaptations in humans for assessing physical strength and fighting ability from the voice*, Proceedings of the Royal Society B, 277, 3509-18

Skinner, B.F. (1974) *About Behaviorism*, Knopf.

Skinner, B.F. (1974) *Science and human behaviour*, The Free Press: McMillan.

Stone, J., Aronson, E., Crain, A. L., Winslow, M. P., & Fried, C. B. (1994). *Inducing hypocrisy as a means for encouraging young adults to use condoms*, Personality and Social Psychology Bulletin, 20, 116-128.

Stowell, R. (2103). *All eyes on the horizon*, SHP. Sept Issue.

Syed, M. *The idea of natural talent sells hard work short*, The Times, 4th Sept 2013

Taleb, N (2010) *The Black Swan: The Impact of the Highly Improbable*, New York: Random House

Thaler et al British Academy (2012). *Nudge and Beyond: Behavioural Science, Policy and Knowing What Works*, http://www.britac.ac.uk/policy/Nudge-and-beyond.cfm

Thaler, R.,H., & Sunstein, C., S., (2008). *Nudge. Improving decisions about health, wealth and happiness*, Penguin.

Tversky, A & Kahneman, D (1973). *Availability: A heuristic for judging frequency and probability*, Cognitive Psychology 5 (1): 207-233

Irving Wallace I, Wallechinsky, D and Wallace, A *The Book of Lists*, (1977) Bantam.

Vroom, V (1966): *Organisation choice*, in Organisation Behaviour and Human Performance

Warr, PB (1987): *Psychology at Work*, Penguin

Williamson A & Feyer A. (2000) *Moderate Sleep Deprivation Produces Impairments in Cognitive and Motor Performance Equivalent to Legally Prescribed Levels of Alcohol Intoxication*, Occup Environ Med. October; 57(10): 649–655.

Wang M-T and Kenny, S (2013) *Longitudinal Links Between Fathers' and Mothers' Harsh Verbal Discipline and Adolescents' Conduct Problems and Depressive Symptoms*, Journal of Child Development.

Weber, T. (2012) *Hitler's First War*. Oxford University Press.

Wheen, F., (2004). *How Mumbo Jumbo Conquered the World*, Harper Perennial.

Whyte, W. H., Jr. (1952). *Groupthink*, Fortune Magazine. March.

Wilson, J.Q., and Kelling, G.L. (1982). *Broken windows*, Atlantic Monthly. (Available online at www.the atlantic.com/magazine/archive/1982/03/broken-windows/4465/.).

Yerkes R.M, Dodson JD (1908). *The relation of strength of stimulus to rapidity of habit-formation*, Journal of Comparative Neurology and Psychology 18: 459–482

Zak P *The Moral Molecule*, Bantam Press, (2012)

Zohar, D., & Luria, G., (2003) *The use of supervisory practices as leverage to improve safety behaviour: a cross-level intervention model*, Journal of Safety Research, 34. 657-577.